Not **THIS** Bear!

Story and pictures by
BERNICE MYERS

SCHOLASTIC INC.
New York Toronto London Auckland Sydney

ISBN 0-590-01556-7

26 25 24 23 22 21 20 19   8 9/8 0 1 2 3/9

Printed in the U.S.A.   23

For Marc and Danny

Little Herman
went to visit his
Aunt Gert.
He got off the bus at the
last stop.
But he still had
a short walk
to her house.

It was
very very
cold.

And to keep warm,
Herman pulled himself
deeper
inside his
long furry coat.

And he pulled
his big furry hat
down
down
over his face.

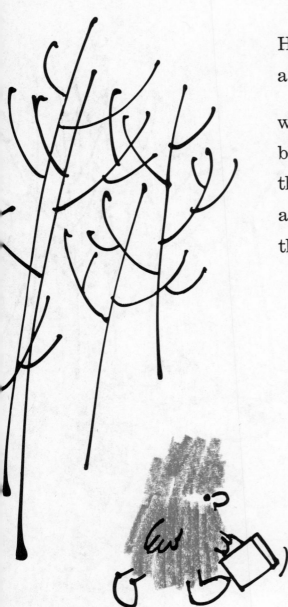

He looked just like
a bear —

which is funny,
because
that is exactly what
a passing bear
thought he looked like.

"You must be
my Cousin Julius!"
said the bear.

Grabbing Herman
by the hand,
the bear ran with him
to his cave.

"Look who I found
at the edge of the woods!" he shouted.

All the bears ran over
and kissed Herman
hard and wet.
"Cousin Julius, Cousin Julius!"
they shouted.

"My name is Herman,"
said Herman.
But no one even heard.
They were so excited.

"I'm not a bear...,"
Herman said.

"Dinner is ready,"
Mama Bear called.
"Take your places.
Cousin Julius,
you sit
here."

When Mama Bear
served the soup,
all the bears lapped it up
with their tongues.

But not Herman.
He ate politely
with a spoon
that he happened to have
in his pocket.

And when the vegetables
were served,
Herman ate with a fork
that he happened to have
in his pocket.

The bears were
amazed.
"My, my!" Big Brown Bear
stared at Herman.
"How smart
you are
to learn a trick
like that."

And all the bears
clapped,
as if they were watching
a circus act.

Poor Herman.

He wasn't a bear.

He was a little boy.

He was sure of it.

But the bears

were just as sure that Herman

was their Cousin Julius.

"So," thought Herman,

"I'll just prove

I'm really

a boy!"

He began to sing
        and dance

    and whistle;
    tie his shoelace
    and

        stand on his
        head —

—all the things a boy
knows how
to do.

But whatever he did,
the bears still thought
Herman
was a bear.
And they clapped even harder
at his tricks.

"See what happens," said Papa,
"when a bear has a chance
to go to the big city
and learn a trade."

"What a clever cousin
we have," said Big Brown Bear.
And he yawned
and went outside.

Big Brown Bear
looked at the sky
and announced the time
of year — winter.

"After Mama's big meal
we won't have to eat again
until spring," he said.
And all the bears
got ready
to sleep.

"Remember, we sleep
for at least
two months,"
said Big Brown Bear.

"Two months!" said Herman.
"I only sleep one night
at a time.
During the day I go out
and play.
I'm not sleeping through the winter!"

"But all bears do,"
said a baby bear.

"Not THIS bear," answered Herman.
"I like winter," he said.

"He likes winter," said the bears, astonished.

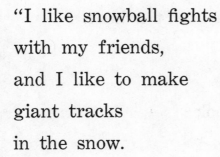

"Yes. I like winter.
I like to go sledding
and to skate.
I like to make
snow men and
drink hot cocoa with whipped cream.

"I like snowball fights
with my friends,
and I like to make
giant tracks
in the snow.

"And besides,
I have to go to school."

When Herman finished speaking,
there was a
long
silence.

Then Big Brown Bear
spoke.
"Perhaps you aren't a bear
after all.
In fact,
now that I look
closer,
you don't even have
a nose
like a bear."

"Look!" shouted a bear,
removing Herman's
furry hat and
coat.
"He's not a bear at all."

And
there,
shivering in the cave,
stood little Herman.

"See, I *am* a boy,"
he said.

Papa Bear
roared
with laughter.
"That's the best trick
of all.
And the trick
was on us."

Herman put on his
furry hat and coat again.
He said good-bye
to all
the bears.

"Come and visit us in spring,"
they yawned after him.

"I will," he answered,
just to be polite.

And Herman began to walk
toward Aunt Gert's house.

He was almost out
of the woods when
a big black burly
bear
jumped out from behind a tree.

Running toward Herman, the bear shouted,
"Cousin Bernard, Cousin Bernard..."

But Herman ran
just as fast as he could
out of the woods.

Herman was glad when he finally
reached
Aunt Gert's porch.

And Aunt Gert
was very glad
to see Herman.

IN PURSUIT OF
THE TRUE
CHURCH

THE ATTRACTION OF RESTORATIONISM ON
THE NINETEENTH CENTURY AMERICAN
FRONTIER: SIDNEY RIGDON, THE DISCIPLES
OF CHRIST, AND THE MORMONS

Lloyd Alan Knowles

Linus
Publications, Inc.

Published by Linus Publications, Inc.

Deer Park, NY 11729

ISBN 1-934188-35-2

Printed in the United States of America.

10 9 8 7 6 5 4 3 2 1

About the Author

Dr. Lloyd Knowles [Ph.D. from Michigan State University -- 2000] has been a Professor of History at Great Lakes Christian College in Lansing, Michigan, since 1970. He was born in Cleveland, Ohio, in 1946 and was "nurtured" in the Miles Avenue Church of Christ there. After growing up in Northfield, Ohio, he obtained degrees from Milligan College in east Tennessee [B.A.,1968], the Emmanuel School of Religion seminary [M.R.E.,1971], and Michigan State University [M.A.,1976] before getting his Ph.D. in American (religious) History. He has had numerous articles published and has served as an interim minister in various Christian Churches since 1990.

Abstract

Back in 1950 Whitney Cross wrote a work entitled <u>The Burned-over District</u>, in which he described the cultural effect on western New York state of the multifarious religious movements that happened there in the first half of the nineteenth century. But there is an important sequel involving religion on the nineteenth-century American *frontier* during these developing years which must be known by all American social historians. It involves a movement known as "restorationism," and the two largest Christian denominations indigenous to America today—the Disciples of Christ (including the Christian Church and Church of Christ) and the Mormons—both grew up on that frontier and both still claim that appellation today.

Many pioneers of the period had become frustrated with all the babel of truth claims being advocated by the various competitive denominations, and were seeking a simple and syncretistic panacea. Others were also troubled with the inflexible Calvinistic theology that threatened impending doom for them unless they were given a supernatural sign of their election to salvation. Into this context a philosophy of religion called restorationism insinuated itself, issuing a plea for a return to the doctrine and forms of the "original New Testament Church." For the Stone-Campbell Movement (the Disciples of Christ) restorationism was regarded as the means to unify and bring order to a divided Christendom, by emphasizing the basic beliefs which virtually all "the sects" had in common, while also calling for the elimination of all creeds and structures that tended to promote factionalism.

But as the two restoration movements developed, each one found it necessary to define what in fact the New Testament Church was, and further, to delineate the "essentials" which needed to be restored in "the true church." Therefore, instead of any significant ecumenicity resulting among the major denominations of America, the course of time simply revealed the addition of two more sects to the rest.

This work traces the impetus for, and idealistic hopes of, restorationism on the early nineteenth-century frontier of western Pennsylvania, western Virginia, Ohio, Kentucky, and Tennessee—with a special focus on the Western Reserve area of Ohio where both movements coalesced. It then describes the decline of restorationist influence, and attempts to explain the reasons for it. This is done in two parallel ways: first, through an overview and analysis of the two movements in general; and second, through a biographical portrayal of the life of **Sidney Rigdon**, the most influential restorationist adherent common to both movements.

Acknowledgments

A work of this magnitude always involves the efforts and sacrifices of many people, and the following scant recognitions are certainly inadequate to express the debt I owe them.

First of all, I would like to express my eternal love and gratitude to my parents, Mr. and Mrs. Lorence Knowles, who gave me life and made life meaningful and happy in the context of a Christian family. They taught me the personal disciplines needed for success in life, just as my teachers in the Nordonia (Ohio) school system and at Milligan College (Tennessee) competently imparted the academic skills necessary.

Second, I want to recognize the significant personal and/or literary influences of Dr. Henry Webb (of Milligan College); Dr. Dean Walker (of the Emmanuel School of Religion); and Dr. Leroy Garrett, Dr. Richard Hughes, and Dr. Leonard Allen (through their written works) for the way they have all provoked my interest and impacted my depth of thought on the topic at hand.

Third, I wish to express special affection for my own nuclear family—my wife Debi, and my boys Derek and Cody—for making the constant sacrifice of sharing my time with this relentlessly demanding project. While I had pre-determined never to sacrifice any important family event to it, nonetheless there still were hundreds of evenings they endured with "Dad" at the office working until the wee hours of the morning.

Fourth, I am indebted to the personnel at Great Lakes Christian College for lightening my load in so many ways: to head librarian Arthur Grove and assistant librarian Joyce Dannemiller for their unselfish help in procuring many materials for me; to academic dean James Estep, presidents Jerry Paul and Larry Carter, and business managers Harry Richards and Bill Brossmann, for their many acts of understanding and generosity towards me—each one with his own special and personal contributions on my behalf; to admissions director Mike Klauka for reproducing the photo pages included in this work; to Becky Anderson for typing a few chapters of my rough draft; and *especially* to faculty secretary Carrie Leazenby, who certainly labored much beyond the call of duty as my constant partner in this project, patiently maintaining a pleasant demeanor while thrust into a cauldron of working with a perfectionist.

Fifth, I am very grateful to the four members of my doctoral committee at Michigan State University: to chairman Dr. David Bailey, who took a personal interest in my project, and shared his expertise and excitement with me on many occasions; to Dr. Eleanor Huzar, who was always my encourager in "the down times" and who I am honored to call a good friend; and to Dr. Robert Anderson and Dr. Sam Thomas who were kind enough to serve on my committee while enduring busy schedules themselves. It is noteworthy that Dr. Huzar and Dr. Anderson both retired during the duration of my research and writing, but both unselfishly remained on my committee to see the process through.

And finally, I would like to thank the following people for their help along the way: Ann Sindelar and the staff of the Western Reserve Historical Society in Cleveland; David McWhirter at the Disciples of Christ Historical Society in Nashville; archivist R. Jean Cobb of the Bethany College library; the staff of Regenstein Library at the University of Chicago; religion specialist Gary Gillum and Larry Draper of the Lee Library at Brigham Young University in Provo, Utah; photo archivist Bill Slaughter of the Latter-day Saints archives in Salt Lake City; librarian Tom Stokes at the Emmanuel School of Religion in Johnson City, Tennessee; John Hagan at the University of West Virginia library; Sandra Tanner of the Utah Lighthouse Ministries (Salt Lake City); Jean Winfield, secretary of the Mentor (Ohio) Christian Church; Georgia Rayburn, secretary of the Warren (Ohio) Central Christian Church; Sheila Harris of the Houghton-Mifflin Company; and Karen Tomlinson, curator of collections at the Lake County Historical Society.

A note of appreciation is also extended to Dr. William Baker, editor of The Stone-Campbell Journal, for earlier including a condensed and revised portion of this author's doctoral dissertation as an article in the Spring, 2003 (volume 6, number 1) issue of that publication. It was entitled Sidney Rigdon: The Benedict Arnold of The Restoration Movement?, and was read by this author at the following Stone-Campbell Conference as a workshop paper.

I ask forgiveness if my human fallibilities have caused me to inadvertently omit anyone else worthy of recognition here.

Preface

For almost three decades I have been teaching a course called Restoration History at a college affiliated with and supported by the Christian Churches and Churches of Christ. These churches belong to an effort in American history known as The Restoration Movement, which has advocated the reunification of a divided Church through the abandonment of denominational structures and creeds, and the reconstruction of the Church on the pattern of the New Testament model and what are perceived to be its few, clear, basic, *essential* doctrines. A more elaborate definition of restorationism will be given in the introduction.

The foremost progenitors of this movement on the American frontier in the early nineteenth century were Barton W. Stone, Thomas Campbell, Alexander Campbell (Thomas' son), and Walter Scott. These men, and many like them, became enamored with the potential of this concept to reunite a divided Christendom, and poured their lifelong energies into this endeavor. The movement multiplied rapidly throughout the nineteenth century and evolved to become the largest religious denomination indigenous to the United States.[1] Yet the church remains divided today.

Each year's Candide-like advocacy that restorationism was the panacea for division presented me with a dilemma. If the claims of such a movement were valid, then why has the Stone-Campbell Movement (as it came to be known) not achieved its goal in almost two centuries? Furthermore, why and how did it, instead, wind up becoming just *another* denomination itself, and worse yet, with three main subdivisions as well?

I thought that perhaps an in-depth examination of the precepts and process of the movement might yield a "fatal flaw" somewhere that could be identified and corrected. Certainly the human foibles involved in institution-building ought to be exposed for what they are, at least. But I expected that further scrutiny would reveal to us an underestimation or oversimplification of the problems involved and the solution proposed. I also hoped to discover a pattern of development that might explain how a movement that began with such impressive success lost its evangelistic momentum and degenerated into introverted controversies.

---

1   See claims made by Winfred E. Garrison, <u>Religion Follows The Frontier</u> (New York: Harper & Bros., 1931), p. xii; Alfred T. DeGroot, <u>The Restoration Principle</u> (St. Louis: Bethany Press, 1960), p. 134; and Richard M. Tristano, <u>The Origins of The Restoration Movement</u> (Atlanta: Glenmary Research Center, 1988), pp. 4-5. For corroboration and fairly current statistics see Martin B. Bradley, et. al., <u>Churches And Church Membership In The United States - 1990</u> (Atlanta: Glenmary Research Center, 1992), p. 1. *Note: In 1990 the aggregate numbers of the three Stone-Campbell derivative churches was approximately 3.9 million adherents, whereas the combined L.D.S. and R.L.D.S. (the latter unlisted, but around 160,000 domestically) totaled about 3.7 million. With Mormonism's accelerated growth rate in the next decade, the religious census of the year 2000 revealed the Mormons on top with a total of 4,224,026 "adherents" compared to the Stone-Campbell derivative churches with and aggregate of 4,102,621 "adherents". [See <u>Religious Congregations and Membership in the US-2000</u>, (Nashville: Glemary Research Center, 2002), pp. 1-2]

Dr. Leroy Garrett, a Harvard Ph.D. and restorationist professor whose textbook I have used in my class in recent years, contends that restorationism is, by its very nature, not unitive but divisive. He may or may not be right, but his thesis must at least be examined seriously. Therefore I decided to enter a Ph.D. program at Michigan State University and, in a dissertation, investigate the phenomena of America's two largest indigenous restoration movements—the Disciples of Christ (The Stone-Campbell Movement) and Mormonism—in order to determine the validity of his thesis.

While remaining a full-time professor, part-time weekend minister, and over-time father of two very active boys, I took the academic plunge once again in 1992. In my first doctoral class with Dr. David Bailey, who was the chairman of my committee, I became intrigued with the life of a colorful man named Sidney Rigdon, a throughly-committed restorationist who was undoubtedly the most influential leader common to both movements in the early nineteenth century. I began to notice that much of his *personal* spiritual journey and many of his frustrations seemed to mirror those of the two restoration efforts in America.

So in 1996 I submitted a proposal to do a biography on him, believing that only one recent work had been done, and that back in 1971 by F. Mark McKiernan, a member of the Reorganized Latter-day Saints church. I soon discovered, however—to my chagrin at first—that a new and scholarly work had been published in 1994 by Richard S. Van Wagoner, who is, by his own description, "a fifth-generation Mormon and a rock-ribbed skeptic."[2]

Nonetheless, rather than abandon my plans to do further work on a man Van Wagoner legitimately calls "a biographer's dream," I saw the opportunity to expand our perception of Rigdon in at least two other directions: (1) Sidney Rigdon from the Stone-Campbell movement perspective, a movement in which the author is personally involved; (2) Sidney Rigdon and his desire for, involvement in, and contributions to, the two major religious restoration movements of nineteenth century America—The Disciples of Christ and the Mormons. As such my work is partially a biography, but even more so an intellectual history involving the flow and fruition of an idea, or an impulse, that was prominent especially on the nineteenth century frontier. The development of this idea will be examined macrocosmically through the course of the two largest religious groups indigenous to American history, and microcosmically as restorationism played out in the life of one of its staunchest adherents. **In a very real sense, therefore, I am trying to weave a tapestry of two topics—restorationism as a dynamic nineteenth-century frontier movement, and Rigdon as a reflection of that effort—into one narrative.**

Much has been said about Sidney Rigdon as a leader and an apostate of both the Disciples of Christ and the Mormons. But little has been written about him as a contributor to, and representative of, restorationism. F. Mark McKiernan, in his bibliographical essay laments:

---

2   Richard S. Van Wagoner, <u>Sidney Rigdon: A Portrait of Religious Excess</u> (Salt Lake City: Signature Books, 1994), p. X.

Rigdon always lived in the shadows of other men, such as Adamson Bentley, Alexander Campbell, and especially Joseph Smith. As a result, although he appears in a great many primary materials concerning both the Mormons and the Disciples of Christ, secondary religious writers have tended to minimize his influence because he apostacized from their churches.[3]

Mormon works have written a significant amount about Sidney Rigdon as a Mormon. But Campbellite sources have largely ignored him in his relationship with the Disciples of Christ on the Western Reserve. Daryl Chase, in his Master's thesis for the University of Chicago, observed:

> It is difficult to rescue Rigdon's early work in the "Campbellite" movement and give him the credit for that which he justly deserves. Before historians began to write books on the early leaders of the "restoration," Rigdon had apostacized. Those who knew him best either ignored his contribution because of their hostility toward him or they credited it to his early associates who "endured until the end."[4]

Yet even contemporary Campbellite historians begrudgingly grant him only a few pages of passing notice. He is regarded as a sort of Benedict Arnold to the true faith, and hence they have written more about Rigdon's activities during and after 1830, when he defected from the movement, than before, even though he was a vital contributor in the development of Campbell's restoration movement on the frontier.

Biographers have scrutinized Rigdon as a troubled "seeker," a dynamic leader, a colleague of Joseph Smith, a religious fanatic, and a man with occasional mental problems. But to more completely understand this complex man, one must first realize what most Americans of the nineteenth century believed it meant to be a Christian, and further, comprehend what restorationism was. This is vital because it was precisely this Christian principle and movement to which he was completely dedicated all of his life.

> Sidney Rigdon was a man with a vision, a quest and a mission. His entire life, from 1793 to 1876, was a constant search for the so-called "fullness of the gospel," which Rigdon believed he was called by God to expound to the world. The restoration of Christ's true religion as revealed in the New Testament became a compulsive, consuming passion, ... [5]

It is not my intention to give a detailed life history of Sidney Rigdon, because Mr. Van Wagoner has done an admirable job of that, and my purpose is to discuss Rigdon as he relates to and reflects the ideal of restorationism in his life. It is also not my desire to give an ecclesiastical history of either restoration movement in its entirety. That has also been done well by others. My interest focuses on the origin and course of restorationism on the American frontier of the last century, primarily through the lens of the life of one of its most avid proponents.

---

3   F. Mark McKiernan, The Voice of One Crying In The Wilderness: Sidney Rigdon, Religious Reformer, 1793-1876 (Lawrence, Kansas: Coronado Press, 1971), p. 171.

4   Daryl Chase, Sidney Rigdon—Early Mormon (Master's thesis, University of Chicago, 1931), p. 27.

5   McKiernan, p. 11.

The geographical concentration of this work will be on the Western Reserve area of Ohio, but this author is quick to acknowledge that the appetite for restorationism at this time was not confined to that area alone. In order to tell the story of restorationism and Sidney Rigdon fully, I must include some discussion of other parts of the nineteenth century American frontier, such as western Pennsylvania, western Virginia, eastern Ohio, Kentucky, Tennessee, and the Missouri-Illinois territory. But I have chosen to focus this study on the Western Reserve area for two reasons: (1) It was the early converging point of the Stone-Campbell movement, as well as Mormonism; (2) It was the primary location of Rigdon's activities from 1820 to 1838, when he had his greatest influence on both movements.

Rigdon was intimately involved most of his life with this philosophy of religion known as restorationism (also called Christian Primitivism). It should be noted that this ideal has not been confined to any specific time or place in history, but as Nathan Hatch has asserted, "Christian restorationism has been a recurring phenomena [sic] in the history of the Church."[6]

Today, evidences of the revival of restorationism can be seen throughout our society. Jerry Falwell heads the National Committee for the Restoration of the Judeo-Christian Ethic. His television ministry is called "The Old-Time Gospel Hour." Donald Wildmon, president of the American Family Association, states "It is far more important to preserve the integrity of the Church than to preserve the existence of the denomination in its present state."[7] A bulletin from the First Church of Christ in Coldwater, Michigan, carries weekly on its front page the statement: "Our aim: To restore Christianity as it is revealed in the New Testament: To build the Church of Christ without denominational name, man-written Creed or any other barrier to Christian unity;. . . ." And in a 1992 Christianity Today article entitled "The Restoration Movement," Garry D. Nation proclaims, "The influence of restorationism is growing among evangelicals—perhaps more than they realize."[8]

Restorationism may also be evidenced today in such movements as The Promise Keepers, among whose leaders has been Bill McCartney, the ex-head football coach at the University of Colorado. The Promise Keepers organization, which claims that 2.6 million men have attended its regional rallies, descended on Washington, D.C. on October 5, 1997, "by the hundred's of thousands."[9] For weeks before the event, the media questioned and probed McCartney on various theological, moral, and social positions which the Promise Keepers might advocate. McCartney doggedly refused to enter any of those

6   Nathan O. Hatch, The Democratization of American Christianity (New Haven: Yale University Press, 1989), p. 169.

7   Donald E. Wildmon, "Christ's Church Will Survive Our Church," The American Family Association Journal (Tupelo, Mississippi: The American Family Association), September, 1998, p. 2.

8   Garry D. Nation, "The Restoration Movement," Christianity Today (Carol Stream, Illinois: Christianity Today, Inc.) May 18, 1992, p. 27.

9   Ellis Cose, "Promise Keepers: Here to Pray for the Nation," Newsweek, October 13, 1997, p. 30.

arenas, constantly reasserting that the Promise Keepers organization has the sole objective of getting men back to being faithful to what God's Word would have them do as Christians, husbands, and fathers. Whether or not McCartney would cognizantly identify himself as a restorationist, his approach is essentially the same.

The course of such movements may be predicted from what is to follow in this work. Just as the "Jesus Movement" of the 1960's and 70's soon dissolved or mutated into other more acceptable categories of religious and social organization, the Promise Keepers may eventually find internal disagreement over doctrine, feel the need to define what are correct and incorrect beliefs, and as a result, divide and subdivide (or disperse) over these issues. For the time being, however, this organization is pressing a real "hot button" in contemporary American culture.

This author believes that there is a psychological thirst today, in a world growing ever more and more complex, to simplify matters, to boil them down to their basic "essentials," and to coalesce rather than to fragment. Frustration with multiple "truth claims" and all the paraphernalia of denominational systematic theology have led to a loss of interest in complicated doctrines and to a societal desire to syncretize Christianity in this country. In January of 1997, <u>USA Today</u> revealed that, in contrast to about 40,000 Southern Baptist churches and 20,000 Roman Catholic parishes, there are between 75,000 and 100,000 "unaffiliated" congregations, making them the most common type of church in the U.S.A. today. "These Churches are part of one of the biggest trends in American religion today: they are all non-denominational, independent of any religious hierarchy or bureaucracy," states the article. One parishioner testified, "I consider myself a Christian more than I'm a Methodist or a Presbyterian."[10] Those are restorationist sentiments, whether the speaker recognized them as such or not.

Henry Webb, postulating that "We are currently in the midst of a very significant cultural change," acknowledges the extent to which the anti-sectarian plea of restorationism has captured our era by dubbing it "The Post-denominational Age." He perceptively identifies the tenor of people's religious preferences when he recognizes that "Religious affiliation in today's world has much more to do with music and worship style than it has to do with denominational beliefs or dogma;. . . ." The typical contemporary Protestant sermon in most denominational pulpits today, he observes, "has a remarkable uniformity about it that transcends and obliterates doctrinal differences." My experiences and observations concur with Webb's. There is now a rather free evangelical flow of church-goers from one denomination to another. Webb concludes that, "The doctrinal and theological distinctions that once stood at the very heart of denominational identity have largely disappeared from almost every denomination."[11]

And so I pursue my dual topics of Rigdon and Restorationism. My curiosity has been piqued by the following questions regarding this study: Why do restoration movements

---

10 Lori Sharn, "Churches Offering Worship Without Labels," <u>USA Today</u>, January 27, 1997, p. 4A.

11 Henry E. Webb, "Writing Denominational History," <u>Discipliana</u> (Nashville: The Disciples of Christ Historic Society), Spring, 1998, pp. 9 & 3.

almost inevitably fail as unity efforts? Why can't simple back-to-the-Bible crusades agree on the basics? What causes them to end up fracturing themselves? Why does a man of such passionate restorationist religious convictions as Sidney Rigdon, who denies himself and his family material blessings in pursuit of spiritual priorities, wind up frustrated, apostacizing from three different restoration movements?

As for my comportment in this research, I have not deluded myself by thinking I can be totally "objective," as some claim to be. No mortal can accomplish that feat. But I want to be fair, at least, and try to acknowledge other perspectives that are just as convincing to their holders as mine are to me. In so doing, I may be the beneficiary of a broader understanding and a more tolerant spirit.*

---

* One procedural footnote should be included here. Grammatically it is the contention of this writer that words like "Biblical" should be capitalized since they include the specific title of a work. A "bibliophile" is one who loves books, but a "Bibliophile" would indicate one who loves the Bible. The word "bibliography" has no implied reference to the Bible whatsoever. Also, the argument that one should not capitalize adjectives is not consistent with practice since words like "Islamic" and "Christian" are capitalized in that form. Therefore unless university protocol prevents me from doing so, my practice will be to capitalize any references with the Bible as their root.

Table of Contents

CHAPTER

List of Figures

Introduction

RESTORATIONISM – THE CONCEPT

In May of 1984 Dr. Robert Fife, a well-known restorationist professor who at that time was directing the Westwood Christian Foundation in Los Angeles—an academic program which funded studies in early Christian history for credit in connection with U.C.L.A.—began an article by relating the following occasion:

> Some months ago a young woman came into my office to talk. After a few minutes, however, I realized this was not a casual visit, for she was greatly agitated.
>
> "What questions must I answer in order to be baptized?" She asked.
>
> I replied, "There is just one."
>
> "Oh yes? What is that?" She asked.
>
> "Do you believe that Jesus is the Messiah, the Son of God?"
>
> "Is that all?"
>
> "That's quite a bit," I replied.
>
> As we further conversed I learned the reason she was so disturbed. She had been visiting the various campus ministries to ask her question, and had received as many answers as there were ministries. She had been given books, tracts, [and] catechisms until she was utterly confused.
>
> She said, "I don't want to have to wait until I have decided which denomination is right before I give my heart to Jesus."[1]

While this is a simple dialogue, it illustrates well the conditions that form the spawning grounds for restorationism in any age. Confusion, frustration, and disenchantment with the establishment generate a reaction which, when formulated, can become a sort of antithesis or counter-culture to the predominant organization. In essence, that is what restorationism is—a rejection of the status quo.

In a book published as a centennial publication of the Ohio Christian Missionary Society, Henry K. Shaw described:

---

1   Robert O. Fife, "Evangelism or Unity—Which?", The Lamp (Los Angeles: Westwood Christian Foundation), May, 1984, p. 1.

. . .a new American religious movement as it developed on the Ohio frontier in the early part of the nineteenth century. It is primarily, however, the story of a plain people seeking a practical faith to match American ideals of democracy, freedom, and independence; a faith to provide a common ground on which they believed all Christians could unite.[2]

This movement became known as "restorationism" because it sought to restore the Christian Church to its original form, rejecting its present state of division and contention.

Whether political or cultural or religious, the philosophy of restorationism tends to emphasize the same perspectives:

1. A disenchantment with present societal conditions (eg. morality);

2. A desire to re-establish pure unadulterated "first times;"

3. A belief that the intervening times have been or have produced a corruption.

   And in the case of Christian restorationism three additional viewpoints are common place:

4. The Bible alone is the norm or pattern for the New Testament Church and the Church of today;

5. The Church should be united[3] and so division is evil;

6. Creeds and catechisms promote division, since they reinforce the existence of sects and denominations.

Some words of explanation and illustration should be said in order to elucidate each category listed above.

1. Disenchantment With The Present

Restorationism in its broadest definition is almost always dissatisfied with contemporary conditions. At the end of the Roman Republic, a time of great interest to the founding fathers of the American Republic, writers like Sallust, Livy, and others lamented the loss of innocence and virtue from an earlier age and denounced the present conditions of their society. Livy sounded the theme early in his first book when he wrote:

"I invite the reader's attention to the much more serious consideration of the kind of lives our ancestors lived. . . . I would then have him trace the process of our moral decline, to watch, first, the sinking of the foundations of morality *as the old teaching was allowed to lapse* [italics mine], then the rapidly increasing disintegration, then the final collapse of the whole edifice, and the dark dawning of our modern day when we can neither endure our vices nor face the remedies needed to cure them.

---

2   Henry K. Shaw, <u>Buckeye Disciples: A History of The Disciples of Christ in Ohio</u> (St. Louis: Christian Board of Publication, 1952) flyleaf.

3   Jesus' last prayer on Earth was for the unity of the His followers (see <u>The Bible</u>, John 17:11-21).

. . .Of late years wealth has made us greedy, and self-indulgence has brought us, through every form of sensual excess, to be, if I may so put it, in love with death both individual and collective.[4]

Whether the attempt is to restore society from moral decay or the church from moral bankruptcy, the restorationist theme is the same—the present is a corruption of a pristine past. Girolamo Savonorola, a Dominican monk in Renaissance Florence, berated Pope Julius II and his prelates with the following bitter invective in 1493:

> See how in these days prelates and preachers are chained to the earth by love of earthly things; the cure of souls is no longer their concern; they are content with the receipt of revenue; the preachers preach for the pleasure of princes, to be praised and magnified by them.
>
> . . .Men feed upon these vanities and rejoice in these pomps, and say that the Church of Christ was never so flourishing, nor divine worship so well conducted as at present. . .likewise that the first prelates were inferior to these of our own times.
>
> . . .The former, it is true, had fewer gold mitres and fewer chalices, for, indeed, what few they possessed were broken up to relieve the needs of the poor; whereas our prelates, for the sake of obtaining chalices, will rob the poor of their sole means of support. But dost thou know what I would tell thee? In the primitive church the chalices were of wood, the prelates of gold; in these days the church hath chalices of gold and prelates of wood.[5]

In the early years of the American Republic there was much opposition to officially recognized, State-sponsored churches, which may be readily evidenced in such injunctions as the Virginia Statute For Religious Freedom (1786) and the First Amendment to the U.S. Constitution (1791). Many Americans disdained the memories of Old World government-sponsored churches, such as the Anglican or Lutheran churches, which sometimes employed political or social coercion in order to gain membership or cooperation. They were also disgruntled with well-established denominations that seemed too authoritarian in this land of new-found freedom. As Nathan Hatch has observed, "No theme united the interest of insurgent groups between 1780 and 1830 more than an exaggerated opposition to official Christianity."[6]

As a result of the American Revolution, a new kind of church based on democratic principles emerged, allowing the common people to interpret the New Testament for themselves. Men like Abner Jones and Elias Smith (two New England Baptists), James O'Kelly (a Virginia Methodist), Barton W. Stone (a Kentucky Presbyterian), and Thomas and Alexander Campbell (two Pennsylvania Scotch-Irish Presbyterians), all criticized the established denominations as inconsistent with true Christianity and sought to

---

4   Titus Livius (Livy), The Early History of Rome, Bk. 1, trans. by Aubrey De Selincourt (Baltimore: Penguin Books, 1960), p. 34.

5   Girolamo Savonorola, "A Preacher of Reform," The Portable Renaissance Reader, ed. by James B. Ross and Mary M. McLaughlin (New York: Viking Press, 1968), pp. 645-646.

6   Hatch, p. 170. Furthermore, for many Americans the Republic itself came to take on a sort of quasi-religious significance.

restore the priesthood of all believers in an egalitarian faith. In a sense many saw the denominations as spiritual oppressors, the remnants of the European political oppressors who had just been evicted. Elias Smith, who published the first American religious newspaper in 1808, complained:

> Had *George the third*, when he withdrew his troops from this country, withdrawn all the principles respecting civil and religious affairs, which are in opposition to the rights of mankind, we should have been a much more united and happy people than we now are: but alas! they are left among us like the Canaanites in ancient times, to be overcome by little and little.[7]

2. The Desire To Go Back To Original Times

Norman Austin, in an introductory chapter about ancient Greek historiography, included in his anthology of Greek historians the following psychological observation:

> It has, in all periods, been difficult for men to analyze their present conditions. The past has always seemed more ordered, more inevitable even, while the present has been a confusion. It has been natural for men to look towards the past where they thought they could find an order which was lacking in the present.[8]

In a world that seems to be getting more and more complex, there is often a psychological desire to return to our roots, to find a sense of security that seems to have eluded us. Not only is there a need to reestablish a sense of stability and simplicity, but also there is the hope that by returning to the prime factors of life, one may recapture its basic essence or renew a lost perspective. Since the present state of the church was regarded to be an aberration of its earlier ideal, the solution for many was to return to the original pattern in an attempt to restore order, authenticity, and integrity. Frustrated Christian restorationists felt the desire for a reestablishment of the first principles and basic dynamics that propagated the faith. As A.T. DeGroot purported in his work The Restoration Principle, ". . .the need of every sensitive disciple is to achieve a restoration, a recapture of the faith of the Founder."[9] Today this same impulse may be evidenced by the plea for a restoration of "traditional values" in America.

With the confusion of truth claims propagated by the plethora of existing sects and denominations, some Christian primitivists sought to simplify matters, to see if they could discover those precepts commonly held by all groups, and to advocate a possible reunification based upon only the "essentials" found in the primitive church. The first century Church was their "model," and whether ecumenical or separatist in spirit, restorationists shared in common the personal conviction that faithfulness compelled them to return to the practices, doctrines, and standards of the original New Testament church.

---

7   Elias Smith, "Address To The Public," Herald of Gospel Liberty, Vol. I, No. 1 (Sept. 1, 1808), p. 1.

8   Norman Austin, The Greek Historians (New York: Van Nostrand Reinhold, Co., 1969), p. 51.

9   A.T. DeGroot, The Restoration Principle (St. Louis: Bethany Press, 1960), pp. 15-16.

They advocated the reform of Christianity, but the method of this reform was not to devise anything new but rather to restore the old—primitive Christianity. The Restoration Movement was deeply rooted in an Enlightenment idea of the primitive as an ideal, natural, and pristine state before "civilization" . . . had polluted Christianity.[10]

3. The View of History As A Corruption

Restorationism is ahistorical by nature. It tends to be rather uninterested in the intervening time between origins and the present, regarding history as a sort of corruption of that which was once unadulterated. Martin Marty has alluded to historian David Noble's assertion that many of "the custodians of America's past" were Jeremiahs, "historians against history," warning of present dangers and "constantly calling people back to the innocent and the primeval."[11] Men like Locke, Paine, and Jefferson, often argued that man's unalienable rights were "rooted" in creation and the state of nature, but were usurped by tyrants in the intervening period.

This perspective is also synonymous in Christian Restorationism. There is an identification with the church of the first century that is so strong that the intervening history is regarded as at least insignificant or aberrational, and perhaps more often as abominable and repugnant. Restorationist historian James D. North warns, "It is too easy, though appallingly attractive, to just skip from the apostolic period to the Restoration Movement." Conveniently overlooking seventeen centuries of church history, he satirically confesses that "Some of us joke, 'the apostle John died, and Alexander Campbell was born'."[12]

As may be noted in the earlier quote from Livy, primitivists tend to view the intervening period of history as a time of declension and degradation. Hence they are not in the true sense "reformers" because reformers simply want to alter what is presently there. Christian restorationists usually believe that this degeneration has become so perverted from the original that the idea of a reconstruction of the existing form seems less plausible than simply beginning over again at the beginning, **not with a new concept, but with the original one**. At the root of restorationism is the desire to remold that which exists, to break it down to its essential parts and recast it again. Hence, restorationists are usually regarded as more radical than reformers, like the Anabaptists were in comparison to the Lutherans.

Most Christian restorationists divide history into three basic periods—the Golden Age, the Fall, and the Restoration. They consider the Golden Age as having lasted until the time of the emperor Constantine, who adopted Christianity as an official religion of the Roman empire. Sometimes they even assign a specific date for the delineation, such as the years 313 or 320 A.D. The Roman Catholic Church is then usually blamed for all kinds of innovations, compromises, superstitions, immoralities, and political intrigues throughout the Medieval period.

---

10   Richard M. Tristano, <u>The Origins of the Restoration Movement: An Intellectual History</u> (Atlanta: Glenmary Research Center, 1988), p. 146.

11   Martin E. Marty, <u>Righteous Empire: The Protestant Experience In America</u> (New York: The Dial Press, 1970), p. 87.

12   James D. North, <u>Union In Truth: An Interpretive History of The Restoration Movement</u> (Cincinnati: Standard Publishing, 1994), p. 9.

In general, these leaders expressed their primitivism in the call to scuttle the elaborate, authoritarian structures of the ecclesiastical establishment and to erase and transcend all the corruptions of history and start once again at the beginning, the time of Christianity's greatest purity. The polluted stream, they believed, should be abandoned for the pure spring.[13]

4. The Bible As The Pattern For The True Church

In a video series entitled Our Restoration Vision, Bill Humble, in a definition of the Stone-Campbell Restoration Movement, expresses the "conviction that we can be the New Testament church today."[14] The word "the" in this last statement is perhaps the operative word here. Notice the wording preferred over the expression "a New Testament church." Whether Professor Humble meant to imply it or not, restoration movements commonly believe that they are the only true church and that all others are apostates. That which imparts to them this confidence is their belief that they can, and perhaps have already, faithfully reestablished the original Church in form and doctrine by using the New Testament as their guideline or model.

J.M. Powell uses the Anabaptists as an example of this approach. He claims that, "perhaps more thoroughly than any of their contemporaries they read the Bible in order to recover the *pattern* of the early church" (and hence this outlook is often referred to as "patternism," because the New Testament is regarded as a template for what the Church universal should be at all times). He lists representatives of many restorationist groups since then who were determined to reproduce the first century church "using the New Testament as a blueprint."[15] This mode has frequently led to literalism or legalism.

Author Leroy Garrett, whose religious roots are in the same tradition as Bill Humble and J.M. Powell, has re-evaluated this position:

> Primitivism thus assumes a simplistic hermeneutics that likens the New Testament to a rule book that clearly spells out the nature of the Church of Christ upon earth. That there have been scores of restorationist sects, each claiming to be the true church and each insisting it has correctly followed "the simple pattern," makes such a view of the New Testament suspect.[16]

---

13 Richard T. Hughes and C. Leonard Allen, Illusions of Innocence: Protestant Primitivism In America, 1630-1875 (Chicago: The University of Chicago Press, 1988), p. 157.

14 Bill Humble, "The Meaning of Restoration," part 2 of Our Restoration Vision (a three-part video series narrated by Bill Humble and Don DeWelt - Joplin, Missouri: College Press, 1988).

15 J.M. Powell, The Cause We Plead: A Story of The Restoration Movement (Nashville: 20th Century Christian, 1987), p. 20.

16 Leroy Garrett, The Stone-Campbell Movement: The Story of The American Restoration Movement (Joplin: College Press, 1994), p. 8 in the revised edition.

One more item is often central in the restorationist view of the Bible in order for it to be authoritative as a plumbline. Powell campaigns, "The Christianity of the first century cannot be reproduced without giving preeminence to the all- sufficiency and alone-sufficiency of the Holy Scriptures in matters of faith and life." He then cuts to the heart of the matter when he adds, "Restoration adds a recognition of the *verbal, plenary inspiration* of God's Word."[17] For those who are the most conservative and literal restorationists, this conviction often includes a belief in Biblical "inerrancy."

5. The Disunity of The Church As Illegitimate

Since Jesus had prayed for the unity of His Church, restorationists regard its disunited state as being against His will, as well as the desire of the Heavenly Father, since both share synonymous intentions for the Church. Hence, division is sinful, and denominationalism or sectarianism is division.

> Explicit is a highly developed sense of the unity of the Church of Christ and a rejection of the idea that the Church could be divided legitimately into a variety of believing bodies which determined their own corpus of belief, practice, and polity. The Restoration Movement began as an explicit rejection of denominationalism.[18]

A typical restorationist would espouse cultural uniformity over multiculturalism, and advocate the legitimacy of "one holy catholic church" instead of religious pluralism. There is only one objective truth, God's truth as revealed in Scripture, and one church is *not* as good as another. "There is neither Jew nor Greek, there is neither slave nor free, there is neither male nor female; for you are all one in Christ Jesus."[19]

In 1838 a restorationist preacher signing himself simply "J.C." submitted an article to Walter Scott's <u>Evangelist</u> entitled "The Primitive Church". He initiated the work with an idealistic laudation of the condition of the Apostolic Church:

> The church of Christ in her primitive glory, was one and indivisible; she stood before the world as the perfection of beauty and as the organ of every divine communication to man. Her charms won the admiration of an alienated world; . . . In peerless majesty she swayed the scepter of truth and love over the world, that at one time bid fair to lay their spoils at their feet and own her unrivaled authority; under her reign darkness gave place to light, error to truth, and sin to righteousness; she became the joy of the whole earth.[20]

He then proceeded to bewail its fallen status and crippling division in the intervening centuries:

---

17   Powell, p. 2.

18   Tristano, p. 3.

19   The <u>Bible</u> (RSV), Galatians 3:28.

20   "J.C.", "The Primitive Church," <u>The Evangelist</u>, ed. by Walter Scott (Carthage, Ohio), Vol. VI, No. 2 (Feb., 1838), p. 28.

The church has been planted in the world for its conversion and salvation; were it not for these objects she never would have been subjected to the storms of persecution which have beat upon her from the beginning until now. But unfortunately for her she has been so much torn and distracted by internal dissensions and wars, that for fifteen centuries, she has had more than she could do to keep herself along; she, never since the time of the Apostle, has presented a bold and united front to the world, but has been like a kingdom divided against itself.[21]

George Whitefield, a dynamic preacher during the Great Awakening, who preceded the American restoration movements, also deplored the divisions within Christendom. Preaching from a balcony at the court house in Philadelphia, he dramatically lifted his eyes toward Heaven and called out:

"Father Abraham, whom have you in Heaven? Any Episcopalians?"

"No!"

"Any Presbyterians?"

"No!"

"Any Independents? Or Methodists?"

"No, No, No!"

"Whom have you there?"

"We don't know those names here. All who are here are Christians."

"Oh, is this the case? Then God help us to forget party names and to become Christians in deed and truth."[22]

Samuel Davies, a Presbyterian preacher from Virginia, echoed his sentiments when he proclaimed:

My brethren, I would now warn you against this wretched, mischievous spirit of party . . . A Christian! a Christian! Let that be your highest distinction; let that be the name which you labor to deserve. God forbid that my ministry should be the occasion of diverting your attention to anything else . . . It has . . . been the great object of my zeal to inculcate upon you the grand essentials of our holy religion, and make you sincere practical Christians. Alas! . . . unless I succeed in this, I labor to very little purpose though I should presbyterianize the whole colony.[23]

---

21 Ibid.

22 Quoted in Winthrop Hudson, <u>Religion In America: An Historical Account of The Development of American Religious Life</u>, ed. 3 (New York: Charles Scribner's Sons, 1981), pp. 80-81.

23 Samuel Davies, <u>Sermons On Important Subjects</u>, Vol. I (New York: N.P., 1842), pp. 217-218, quoted in Hudson, p. 81.

6. The Rejection of Creeds and Catechisms

Restorationists have often criticized the proliferation of official creeds and confessions of faith, not so much because there is anything wrong in stating one's beliefs, but because they are, after all, only *interpretations* of Scripture and therefore as fallible as their human interpreters might be. "No creed but Christ; no book but the Bible," came to be a commonly-heard slogan of the Stone-Campbell movement. And since the Bible alone is the true standard for all correct doctrine and practice, creeds were superfluous. They might even be harmful, since they were used to exclude many believers who may not agree with specific denominational interpretations.

Also creeds and catechisms were seen as means to propagate denominational interests, and hence to inhibit the reunification of the church. "Are we not in a wilderness of creeds?", asked one restorationist of his Christian brethren. In 1870 a Disciples of Christ committee delegated by the Ohio Christian Missionary Society sent fraternal greetings to the Baptists of Ohio and included the following objective for their mission:

> As a people we are seeking the restoration of the Christianity of the New Testament, in letter and in spirit, in principle and in practice. We clearly see to be involved in this the over-throw of denominationalism, the repudiation of human creeds as authoritative expressions of faith or bonds of fellowship, the annihilation of party names, and the reunion of God's scattered people in one body, under the leadership of Jesus the Christ, . . .[24]

Whether naive or hopefully realistic, many restorationists believed that restorationism would prove to be a conduit for unity, because rather than combat or compromise with a creed, this position would outflank it by making it superfluous. Alexander Campbell once quixotically advised that all those who wish to follow Jesus' commandments "ought to rally under Jesus and the apostles and bury all dissensions about such unprofitable subjects as those long-vexed questions about [the] trinity, [the] atonement, depravity, election, effectual calling, etc." He then continued on to assert that he would unite in worship with any sect [of Baptists, in this instance] "if their moral and Christian behavior be compatible with the gospel, irrespective of all their speculations upon the untaught questions of their creeds."[25]

This author recognizes the endemic potential within the concept of restorationism to be claimed by most all Christian movements, since the Bible is their authoritative book and it hearkens back to an "original" culture and doctrine. Paul Conkin seems to agree:

> The problem with the label [restorationism] is its generality. Almost without exception, those who have launched new sects or schismatic splinters have claimed to restore the ancient or primitive church. All the Reformation Churches made this claim, and so have all successors in the Protestant tradition, broadly defined.[26]

24 Shaw, pp. 31-32.

25 Robert Richardson, Memoirs of Alexander Campbell, Vol. 2 (Philadelphia: J.B. Lippincott, 1868); reprinted by Religious Book Service in Germantown, Tennessee, n.d., Vol. II, p. 372 of reprint edition.

26 Paul Conkin, American Originals: Homemade Varieties of Christianity (Chapel Hill: The University of North Carolina Press, 1997), p. 2.

In the next chapter some of the *"elements"* of restorationism found throughout church history are recognized—not to establish a claim that many denominations had that concept as their *raison d' etre*, because most did not—but rather to recognize that nineteenth-century America did not invent this impulse. Nonetheless, it will later be acknowledged that restorationism blossomed on the American frontier of that time in a unique way.

Chapter
—1—

ELEMENTS OF RESTORATIONISM IN CHURCH HISTORY

Without proceeding too far down the ethereal path of Wittgensteinian linguistic analysis, this author concedes that probably any concept defined in its broadest scope and analyzed *ad absurdum* loses its distinction, and ultimately, its meaning. Taken to such extremes probably *all* Christians could be regarded as restorationists. But confined to the descriptive limits set forth in the introductory chapter, elements of restorationism may appear in certain aspects of many religious movements without that cause or crusade being, in essence, a restoration movement itself. The following pages attempt to describe some strains of restorationism present in various major religious movements in church history.

Henry Webb, in his background study of the historical roots of restorationism, recognizes its somewhat universal appeal to Christian adherents of any era:

> The need to recapture the beauty, simplicity, and effectiveness of the dynamic church reflected in the New Testament is a conviction shared to some extent by all generations of Christians. It is sometimes expressed as "reformation" and more recently as "renewal." Often, however, this need is described with more explicit focus on the church of the first century as "restoration." The concept of restoring some vital reality that has been lost or obscured is very old.[1]

To begin with, the Roman Catholic Church itself, the critical target of many of the reformers and restorationists, might even allege, if it so desired, to exemplify that restorationist paradigm. For example, it purports to *be* the New Testament Church, a direct descendant of that church established at Pentecost and in apostolic succession to Peter, the first Pope. "It *is* primitive Christianity," wrote W. E. Garrison. "Enriched, to be sure, by the wisdom

---

1 Henry E. Webb, In Search of Christian Unity: A History of The Restoration Movement (Cincinnati: Standard Publishing Co., 1990) p. 36.

of the ages, blessed with a fuller unfolding of divine truth, still it thinks of itself as identical with the primitive church in faith and structure."[2] The term restoration would seem to be an anathema to its very existence. The Eastern Orthodox tradition is equally, if not moreso, insistent in its claim to this title, as well as the distinction of being the preserver of unadulterated ordinances and correct doctrines.

However, in church history Roman Catholicism was often regarded as the Beast, the Harlot, or the Anti-Christ of the Biblical book of Revelation, by various reformers, many of whom were martyred for the expression of their beliefs. The Cathari, the Albigensians, and the Waldensians were some of these earlier "heretic" groups who called for church reform, or even more radically, restoration. The Cathari,[3] disenchanted with the immoral conditions of the Medieval church, wanted to purge and "purify" the leaders of the church, and hold them to the strict ethical standards of the New Testament. Peter Waldo, also an ascetic who sold his possessions and used the proceeds to give the Bible to people in the their own vernacular, warned church prelates that, "Whatever is not enjoined in Scripture must be rejected."[4]

Most of the reformers of the Reformation period were not, in the full sense, restorationists. They were usually more interested in correcting the moral abuses, politics, or some doctrines of the existing church rather than starting afresh at some perceived original position. Yet the very nature of the questions or problems they had with the established church often impelled them to go back to the original source, the Bible, for answers and models. Hence, many became advocates of some aspects of restorationism.

John Wycliffe, for example, espoused the authority of the Bible over that of a human infallible pope. In the year 1378 he contended:

> The Bible alone is the supreme organ of divine revelation; the church's tradition, pronouncements of the councils, papal decrees, and all other expositions of Christian doctrine must be tested on the scriptural touchstone. All truth is contained in the Scriptures. They are divinely inspired in all their parts, and they alone are a sufficient guide in all matters, religious and secular.[5]

---

2   W.E. Garrison, Religion Follows The Frontier: A History of the Disciples of Christ (New York: Harper and Brothers, 1931), p. 31.

3   This nomenclature was a virtual transliteration from the Greek word "katharoi," meaning "pure ones."

4   Quoted in J. M. Powell, The Cause We Plead: A Story of the Restoration Movement, (Nashville: 20th Century Christian, 1987), pp. 15-16.

5   Quoted in Edwin Robertson, Wycliffe: Morning Star of The Reformation (Basingstoke, England: Marshall, Morgan, and Scott, 1984), p. 39.

John Huss, who preached many of the doctrines of Wycliffe to his disciples in Bohemia, was burned at the stake for publicly preaching against indulgences and for denying the authority of the pope. Only Christ, he asserted, is the head of the Church, and the Bible is its only authoritative guide. On this Biblical basis many of his followers rejected the doctrine of transubstantiation, Purgatory, the practice of prayers for the dead, the veneration of relics and images and saints, and all the sacraments except baptism and communion. As Will Durant summarized their position, ". . .they proposed to restore the simple ritual of the Apostolic Church, and repudiated all ecclesiastical rites and robes that they could not find in early Christianity."[6]

Martin Luther, who is usually given credit as the progenitor of the Protestant Reformation, may be interpreted by some to have been a restorationist. However A.T. DeGroot refutes this notion, maintaining that, "the restoration of New Testament practices for all important phases of religion did not appeal to Luther," and adding that Luther desired a conservative reformation.[7] Allen and Hughes concur, contending that Luther simply was not interested in the question fundamental to Christian restorationists—that is, "What was the ancient tradition or pattern?" But then they concede:

> There is a sense, to be sure, in which Luther was a restorationist. For as he himself once put it, "the crawling maggots of man-made laws and regulations" had "eaten into the entire world" and had "swallowed up. ..all Holy Scripture." Thus, Luther sought to go behind the "man-made laws and regulations" of history to preach once again the primitive gospel of faith and grace.
>
> From this perspective, Luther perhaps could be called a "gospel restorationist."[8]

Alexander Campbell, a founder of the Restoration Movement in America, credited Luther with restoring the pre-eminent authority of the Bible to Christendom. Biblical knowledge was the monopoly of the authoritarian clergy of Rome, he believed, until Luther translated it into German so others could read it for themselves. "The Bible was brought out of prison, and Luther bid it March," Campbell wrote.[9]

> Luther, like any restorationist, made Scripture the ultimate authority of his reformation. When summoned before the Diet at Worms in 1521 to recant

---

6   Will Durant, The Reformation, Vol. 6 of The Story of Civilization (New York; Simon and Shuster, 1957), pp. 169-170.

7   A.T. DeGroot, The Restoration Principle (St. Louis: Bethany Press, 1960), p. 113.

8   C. Leonard Allen and Richard T. Hughes, Discovering our Roots: The Ancestry of Churches of Christ (Abilene: ACU Press, 1988), p. 121.

9   Alexander Campbell, "Prefatory Remarks," The Millennial Harbinger (Bethany, Virginia), Vol. I, No. 1 (January 4, 1830), p. 4.

his writings, Luther boldly retorted, "Unless I am convicted of error by the testimony of Scripture ...(since I put no trust in the unsupported authority of Pope or of councils...) I stand convicted by the Scriptures to which I have appealed, and my conscience is taken captive by God's word. . . ."[10]

However he was no Biblical literalist. Luther, unlike Calvin and others to follow, did not see the Bible as God's Word, but as the *revealer* of God's Word, the Divine Logos portrayed in John 1:1-14 Whose incarnation came to be identified with the person of Jesus the Christ. Hence the Bible's function for Luther was like a pair of glasses for mankind to see and understand the Savior. If the Bible were to become an object of veneration itself, that would be simple Biblioatry. This is not meant to imply that the Holy Scriptures were in any way unimportant to Luther however.

Luther is often given credit for the restoration of three major doctrines lost in the centuries of development of the Roman Catholic Church: (1) salvation by faith not works; (2) the priesthood of all believers; (3) the individual right to interpret the Scriptures. He felt so strongly about this that he translated the New Testament into the German vernacular while he was in hiding at the Wartburg Castle eluding the decree of Charles V, the Holy Roman Emperor, who had declared him to be an outlaw. In making this translation, Luther effectively placed the reading and interpretation of Scripture within the scope of the common man. According to Garrison:

> The divisive principle of Protestantism is to be found in this combination of ideas: that all Scripture is authoritative, and that the meaning of all Scripture is perfectly plain to any honest man who will simply read it.[11]

But while Luther was at the Wartburg, Andreas von Carlstadt, his senior colleague at the University of Wittenberg and his replacement as the preacher of the Castle Church there, led his parishoners in a radical reformation that resulted in rebellion and anarchy. Luther was horrified and angry, returning without permission from the prince to reclaim his pulpit and dismissing Carlstadt. He therefore stopped short of the advocacy of the democratic tendencies developed by the restoration movements later in America, which allowed anyone to interpret Scripture authoritatively for himself. Admitting the danger that one could prove most anything by Scripture through ignorance, he grumbled, "Now I learn that it suffices to throw many passages together helter skelter whether they fit or not. If this is the way to do it I certainly shall prove with Scripture that Rastrum beer is better than Malmsey wine."[12]

Nonetheless some of Luther's legacy came into the twentieth century Lutheran Church imitating restorationist form. A Lutheran book entitled

---

10   From the transcript of the trial at Worms (1521) found in Henry Bettenson, ed., <u>Documents of the Christian Church</u>, Second Ed. (London: Oxford U. Press, 1963), p. 282.

11   Garrison, <u>Religion Follows The Frontier</u>, p. 29.

12   Martin Luther, <u>Works</u> (Philadelphia Edition), Vol. 39, pp. 75-76; quoted in Hatch, p. 180.

<u>Why A Lutheran Should Not Attend Any Other Church</u> gives as the first reason: "Because the Lutheran church is the old original church."[13] Restoration churches usually reserved that claim for themselves!

Desiderius Erasmus, the Dutch humanist scholar of Rotterdam, also exhibited traits of restorationism in his caustic satire <u>Praise of Folly</u>. Reflecting the primitivist dissatisfaction with the contemporary state of the Church, he lampooned the "labyrinth" of theological divisions within the body

> . . .from the tortuous obscurities of Realists, Nominalists, Thomists, Albertists, Ockhamists and Scotists—and I've not mentioned all the sects, only the main ones. Such is the erudition and complexity they all display that I fancy the apostles themselves would need the help of another holy spirit if they were obliged to join issue on these topics with our new breed of theologian.[14]

Complaining that the fulfillment of monks in his era seemed to be in their distinctions as Cordeliers, Coletines, Minors, Minims, Bullists, Benedictines, Bernardines, Bridgetines, Augustinians, Williamists, and Jacobines—Erasmus, in disgust, admonished his readers, "They aren't interested in being like Christ but in being unlike each other. . . .as if it weren't enough to be called Christians."[15]

Ulrich Zwingli, the Swiss reformer of Zurich, in many ways also promoted the restoration of primitive Christianity. Through his personal study of Erasmus' translation of the New Testament he came to deny Christ's presence in the Eucharist and instead insisted upon communion as a memorial feast, a remembrance of the death of Christ. Some of his followers, who became known as Anabaptists ("re-baptizers") because of their advocacy that the New Testament church did not practice infant baptism but rather the adult immersion of believers, were probably the nearest representatives of restorationism during the Reformation period. Seeking to restore the early purity as well as the early doctrines of the church, many of them abandoned Christendom in favor of a communal arrangement. Such groups as the Mennonites, Hutterites, and Shakers, "spoke as if the church had ceased to exist and needed to be literally restored."[16]

These radicals were accused by many of their contemporaries of trying to divide or even destroy the church. Those who were more benign in their evaluations charged them with, at least, the desire to construct a

---

13   Quoted in Garrison, p. 33.

14   Desiderius Erasmus, <u>Praise of Folly</u> trans. by Betty Radice (Baltimore: Penguin Books, 1971), p. 156.

15   Ibid., pp. 165-166.

16   Richard M. Tristano, <u>The Origins of The Restoration Movement: An Intellectual History</u> (Atlanta: The Glenmary Research Center, 1988), 148.

new church. But A.T. DeGroot anticipated their response when he imagined that "The 'radicals' would have preferred to say that they were not building a 'new' church, but restoring the original one."[17]

Another reformer illustrative of some restoration themes was John Calvin, who established his theocracy in Geneva and became one of the foremost Protestant theologians of church history. Calvin's Institutes of the Christian Religion reflects his deep original study of the Bible and his desire to restore the order and practices of the New Testament Church. Declaring that the Roman Catholic Church had virtually abandoned original doctrine and worship, and was therefore apostate from the New Testament Church, Calvin wrote "that for several ages the pure preaching of the word disappeared."[18] According to one of his biographers, Calvin regarded himself, in relation to the Church, to be somewhat of "an architect of reconstruction."[19] When he attempted certain reforms along these lines in Lausanne, Switzerland, his efforts to remove its medieval church practices were resented by the town council, who defended them in deference to "any new-fangled fashion borrowed from the primitive church."[20] Calvin's response was simply:

> "All that we have attempted to do is to restore the native purity from which the Christian ordinances have degenerated, and to bring every practice of faith back to its [Biblical] fountain head."[21]

The English Puritans were spiritual descendants of John Calvin and were themselves radicals of a sort. Their desire was to purify the Church of England. Whether remaining as protesting members in the church or becoming "Separatists", they saw the Anglican church as corrupt and called for its purification based upon the standards of the New Testament Church. John Macleod, in his Scottish Theology published by the Free Church of Scotland, wrote of these English Puritans: "The goal for which they were making was a return of the church to the apostolic pattern. This they sought to reach all along the line not only in Faith but in Order and Discipline and Worship."[22]

But as the Puritan hopes for the restoration of the Anglican Church began to fade and imminent judgement seemed to be foreboding, a great

---

17 DeGroot, The Restoration Principle, p. 113.

18. John Calvin, Institutes of The Christian Religion, reprinted as Calvin's Institutes (Grand Rapids: Associated Publishers and Authors, Inc., n.d.), Book 4, Chapter 1, Section 11, p. 546.

19 Ronald S. Wallace, Calvin, Geneva, and The Reformation (Grand Rapids: Baker Book House, 1988), p. 133.

20 Ibid., p. 114.

21 Quoted in Allen and Hughes, Discovering Our Roots, p. 32.

22 John Macleod, Scottish Theology (N.P., Publishing Committee of The Free Church of Scotland, 1943), pp. 6-7; quoted in DeGroot, The Restoration Principle, p. 116.

migration to the New World began with the hope of constructing the resurrected Church of the New Testament. This "errand into the wilderness," Perry Miller affirms, "had a positive sense of mission." That purpose was to enter into an explicit covenant with God, establish a due form of ecclesiastical government, and become a "city upon a hill" for the eyes of the rest of the world to witness:

> There was no doubt whatsoever about what Winthrop meant by a due form of ecclesiastical government: he meant the pure Biblical polity set forth in full detail by the New Testament, that method which later generations, in the days of increasing confusion, would settle down to calling Congregational, but which for Winthrop was no denominational peculiarity but the very essence of organized Christianity.[23]

To the Puritan the essence of Christianity was the essence of life. The degree to which one preserved the integrity of the word of God and the purity of the Church paralleled man's happiness and success in this life, and his hope for the life to come. Religion was not a *segment* of one's life, as David Hall has recognized in his recent work, but rather "was embedded in the fabric of everyday life. It colored how you thought about your children and your parents. It entered into perceptions of community, and of the world that lay beyond."[24] And the Bible was not just a well written canon of books. "It was priceless, though you found it in the marketplace; it was timeless, though a printer may have dated an edition; it was living, though its matter was mere ink and paper."[25]

Hughes and Allen have postulated that, "to a degree considerably beyond what scholars have recognized, the New England Puritan enterprise took the form of a restorationist crusade."[26] T.D. Bozeman, in an Alexander Campbell bicentennial lectureship in 1988, said that the Puritan protest "arose from a will to return to the norms and ways of a primitive, sacred past." He quoted Thomas Cartwright, for example, as representing this perspective when he advocated that "whatsoever is first, that is true; and whatsoever is later, that is false." In comparing the rhetoric of Alexander Campbell to that of the Puritans he further observed:

> ...the appeal to primitive simplicity and purity was one of the most regular cliches of Puritan discourse. ...a distaste for complexity and for the addition of 'mixtures' to the first and pure is a large common denominator throughout the Puritan movement.

---

23 Perry Miller, <u>Errand Into The Wilderness</u> (Cambridge: Harvard University Press, 1956), pp. 4, 5, & 11.

24 David D. Hall, <u>Worlds of Wonder, Days of Judgement: Popular Religious Belief in Early New England</u> (Cambridge: Harvard U. Press, 1989), p. 3.

25 Ibid., p. 24.

26 Hughes and Allen, <u>Illusions of Innocence</u>, p. 32.

Flowing likewise from allegiance to the first was a deeply held belief that the norms and patterns of the great age constituted an order of fixed and changeless perfection. Preadjusted to all the circumstances and fluctuations of ordinary human history, first things were final; they defied change.[27]

This concern for "the restitution of true religion," and the sole authority of Scripture on which it is contingent, became a central feature of Puritanism. For the Puritans the Bible was the supreme authority in matters of faith and life. John Cotton, probably the most prominent minister of the founding generation, wrote:

> No new traditions must be thrust upon us. . .[but] that which [we] have had from the beginning. . . . True Antiquity. . .is that which fetches its original from the beginning. . . .no other writings besides the Scripture can plead true Antiquity. . . . All errors are aberrations from the first. [In conclusion], live ancient lives; your obedience must be swayed by an old rule, walk in the old ways. . . .[28]

The whole Puritan endeavor was to be firmly rooted and established upon a Scriptural foundation. They insisted that everyone had the right and the need to read the Bible and know God's will for himself. This strict Bibliocentricity led them to establish Harvard college, just six years after their arrival in the Massachusetts Bay colony, for the purpose of studying the New Testament pattern for their theocracy and for their lives.

Restorationist themes may be evidenced throughout the writings of the early Puritan authors. Hughes and Allen have avowed:

> The pattern of Puritan primitivism is characterized chiefly by an elemental belief in the power and exemplary authority of an ancient "first time," a time when supernatural power and presence had transformed ordinary history into an extraordinary time full of precedential authority.
>
> . . .Centered in this intense devotion to the *first*, the primitivist pattern gave rise to an array of terms that recur throughout the vast range of Puritan writings, terms such as *primitive, ancient, pattern, model, imitation, purity, simplicity, invention, addition, novelty,* and *innovation*. Such terms form a major part of the standard Puritan vocabulary and serve as signposts to the primitivist or restorationist assumptions underlying much Puritan belief and action.[29]

It could legitimately be argued that Puritanism was the earliest form of restorationism introduced into colonial America. The Roman Catholic

---

27   T.D. Bozeman, "Alexander Campbell: Child of the Puritans," found in <u>Lectures In Honor of The Alexander Campbell Bicentennial, 1788-1988</u> (Nashville: The Disciples of Christ Historical Society, 1988), pp. 6-7.

28   Quoted in Allen and Hughes, <u>Discovering Our Roots</u>, p. 51.

29   Hughes and Allen, <u>Illusions of Innocence</u>, pp. 28-29

Church in Spanish America and the Anglican Church in Virginia did not promulgate restorationist themes. But a potential threat to any primitivist cause is a developing hubristic conviction that, through the efforts of its adherents, the reanimation of the exact New Testament Church has been established exclusively with them.

> . . .the New England Puritans succumbed to just such a conceit. They soon became convinced that they had indeed restored all of God's original institutions to their purest form. John Cotton wrote smugly that the New England Churches were as close as could be to what "the Lord Jesus [would erect] were he here himselfe in person."[30]

As the years progressed however, Puritanism, like most zealous religious crusades, lost its fervor, stagnated, and entered a period of declension. The Great Awakening would revive its thrust once more briefly, but by the time of the American revolution it had begun mutating into a more complex and liberal tradition until today when most of its congregational churches have metamorphosized into the United Church of Christ.

One Puritan who followed a different path and became the progenitor of a different tradition was the Separatist Roger Williams. Disassociating himself from Jonathan Winthrop and the Massachusetts Bay colony because they would not disfellowship with the Church of England, he eventually settled in Rhode Island where he tried to establish a church based upon "the holy Scripture, the first pattern" urging his flock that God was active in ". . .His calling of His people more and more out of the Babel of confused worships, ministries, etc."[31]

Ironically, as Williams developed his thoughts further, he eventually mellowed and transformed to an advocacy of religious liberty, establishing what became the first Baptist church in America. He even permitted Quakers freedom of worship in his colony, although he ended his career quarreling with them. Yet his spiritual quest for the true Church of Christ remained in turmoil. While conceding, in his later years, that "I do profess to believe that some come nearer to the first primitive churches and the institutions and appointments of Christ Jesus than others," he nonetheless mused wistfully, ". . .if my soul could find rest in joining unto any of the churches professing Christ Jesus now extant, I would readily and gladly do it. . . ."[32]

But Williams eventually became discouraged and ended his struggle with the decision that no church could attain purity in this world. Not only had he withdrawn from the Church of England and Puritanism, but

---

30   Allen and Hughes, <u>Discovering Our Roots</u>, p. 56.

31   Perry Miller, <u>Roger Williams: His Contributions To The American Tradition</u> (New York: Atheneum, 1962), pp. 200-201.

32   Ibid., p. 253.

eventually from all other churches as well, and "from everyone but his wife."[33] In fact, he came to the conclusion that Christ's true Church had ceased to exist since the time of the emperor Constantine and hence, no authority remained for establishing new churches.

> The New Testament pattern, he believed, demonstrated that churches were formed only by apostles or those directly commissioned by them. . . .

> For Williams, therefore, restoration of the true church was a human impossibility. Only God in the divinely appointed time could do it. When that time came, God would commission new apostles to proclaim the ancient gospel with power and gather apostolic congregations. With the arrival of these new apostles there would be a new Pentecost bringing great displays of spiritual power and mass conversions. All of Christ's original ordinances—baptism by immersion in rivers, the Lord's Supper, and laying on of hands, for example—would be reinstituted and faithfully observed.[34]

Still other restorationist themes were echoed in church history. Daniel Defoe, the novelist who wrote Robinson Crusoe, courageously suggested through his character Friday, a savage saved from the cannibals, that one could become a Christian without benefit of the church or a clergyman simply by reading the Bible. John Wesley, founder of the Methodist Church, wrote a letter to Dr. Coke and Francis Asbury in America in 1784, cautioning them:

> As our American brethren are now totally disentangled both from the state, and from the English hierarchy, we dare not entangle them again, either with the one or the other. They are now at full liberty, simply to follow the Scriptures and the primitive church. And we judge it best that they should stand fast in that liberty, wherewith God has so strangely made them free.[35]

In 1814 Asbury, near the end of his ministry, reinforced this primitivist theme in his valedictory address. He insisted that the Methodist Church, more than any other, had restored the primitive order of the New Testament, and rebuffed those who doubted the possibility of returning to former apostolic days when he stressed, "But I say that we can; I say we must; yea, I say we have."[36]

James O'Kelly, a Methodist minister who opposed Francis Asbury in his desire to concentrate ministerial authority into his own hands, campaigned for a more democratic type of church government. In 1793 he

---

33 Edmond Morgan, The Puritan Dilemma: The Story of John Winthrop (Boston: Little, Brown, and Co., 1958), p. 131.

34 Allen and Hughes, Discovering Our Roots, pp. 57-59.

35 John Wesley, letter to "Our Brethren in America," London: September 10, 1784; found in John Wesley, ed. Albert C. Outler, Library of Protestant Thought series (New York: Oxford U. Press, 1964), p. 84.

36 Francis Asbury, The Journal and Letters of Francis Asbury, ed. Elmer C. Clark, J. Manning Potts, and Jacob S. Payton (Nashville: n.p., 1966), p. 478; quoted in Hatch, p. 82.

seceded from the mainline Methodist church and organized the Republican Methodist Church. Proposing an effort to unify existing denominations, a common restoration theme, he suggested:

> Let the Presbyterians lay aside the book called The Confession of Faith. Let the Baptists open a more charitable door, and receive to their communion those of Christian life and experience. . . . Let my offended brethren, the Methodists, lay aside their book of Discipline. . . . Again as each church is called by a different name, suppose we dissolve those unscriptural names and for peace's sake call ourselves Christians.[37]

The miscellaneous Baptist groups in America constitute the final significant representatives of primitivism precursive to the era of this study. In many ways they embodied the closest approximation to a restoration movement until the Stone-Campbell and Mormon movements came on the scene. While such groups as the Particular Baptists, Separate Baptists, and Landmark Baptists varied as to degree of legalism and profession of doctrines, they nonetheless sounded many of the same restorationist themes.

Morgan Edwards, a Particular Baptist and prominent preacher in Philadelphia, published a work entitled The Customs of Primitive Churches in 1768. In what was probably the first book written in America concerning the organization and practices of the Baptist church, he detailed the importance of duplicating "the customs of primitive churches" within their own fellowship, and stipulated that every church office or title should have a New Testament example. He even maintained that the Lord's Supper should be celebrated every Sunday because the Disciples gathered together on the first day of the week to break bread.[38] This form of primitivism has been called "patternism" and is probably responsible for more division than unity among churches.

Isaac Backus, an influential eighteenth-century Separate Baptist leader in New England, wrote a two-volume history of the early Baptist church in America. In it he prescribed "a return to the primitive purity and liberty of the Christian church," and he optimistically predicted, "a great and effectual door is now opened for terminating these disputes, and for a return to the primitive purity and liberty of the Christian Church."[39]

The Landmark Baptists were among the most legalistic of all primitivists. Their name derived from a tract by J.M. Pendleton which referred to Proverbs 22:28 warning the Jews, "Remove not the ancient

---

37 Marvin S. Hill, "The Role of Christian Primitivism In The Origin and Development of The Mormon Kingdom, 1830-1844" (Ph.D. dissertation, The University of Chicago, 1968), pp. 27-28.

38 Hughes and Allen, Illusions of Innocence, pp. 83-84.

39 Allen and Hughes, Discovering Our Roots, p. 67.

landmark which your fathers have set." They believed that their organization and practice was the only one faithful to that ancient landmark—the New Testament. "[40] Since they regarded the Bible to be a sort of moral and doctrinal blueprint from which there could be no legitimate deviation, they viewed all other churches as apostates.

The preachers of restoration motifs were not always well tolerated. William Penn, for example, published a little book in 1696 entitled Primitive Christianity Revived, the purpose of which was apologetic in its attempt to demonstrate that the Quaker message was synonymous with that of the primitive church. But Quakers who tried to proselyte in the state of Virginia were imprisoned without bail. Virginia also persecuted the Baptists in the early years. Rhys Isaac has labeled them "a counter culture" which was unwelcomed by the majority.[41] Their elaboration on restoration themes, such as adult immersion, was to some an annoyance, and to others heresy. In 1768 three magistrates complained, "These men are great disturbers of the peace; they cannot meet a man on the road, but they must ram a text of scripture down his throat."[42]

It would certainly not be the last occasion in which a restoration preacher would be rebuffed and vilified, but more of an omen of what was to come.

---

40 Mark Noll, A History of Christianity In The United States and Canada (Grand Rapids: Eerdman's Pub. Co., 1992), p. 237

41 Rhys Isaac, The Transformation of Virginia, 1740-1790 (New York: W.W. Norton, 1982), p. 163.

42 W.W. Bennett, Memorials of Methodism in Virginia (Richmond: Published by the author, 1871), p. 38; Earl West, The Search For The Ancient Order, vol. 1 of 4, A History of The Restoration Movement, 1800-1865 (Germantown, Tennessee: Religious Book Service, 1990), p. 2.

Chapter
—2—

A FERTILE SOIL FOR RESTORATIONISM:
THE NEW AMERICAN REPUBLIC

"Greater than the tread of mighty armies is an idea whose time has come."
So said Victor Hugo in his <u>History of A Crime</u> written in 1852.[1]

With all the primitivist elements found in the propagators and
protagonists of so many Christian denominations and sects, one might
wonder why a restoration movement happened at all in early nineteenth
century America. Most of the major denominations of the Reformation
had, in fact, been transplanted to America as well.

In the first place, though many denominational Christian leaders and
groups advocated some essential elements of restorationism, very few of
them would qualify for the appellation of restorationist. Most of them, with
the possible exception of the Anabaptists and their descendants, really
sought the reformation of the existing church rather than a more radical
restoration to the original New Testament Church.

Secondly, by the time colonial America had come to fruition as an
independent nation, some denominations had become the official state-
supported churches of various European nations, or of colonies like
Massachusetts or Virginia. Many had clergy who were rather authoritarian
and professionalized in their demeanors. Most of these denominations and
sects had also developed their own acceptable interpretations of Scripture,
traditions, and creeds.

In a recent work on the sermons and writings of Joseph Smith, Robert
Millet concludes, "The decision by some Americans to remove the 'shackles'

---

1   Found in John Bartlett, <u>Familiar Quotations . . .</u>, ed.14, ed. by Emily Morrison Beck,
     (Boston: Little, Brown and Co., 1882), p. 598. One translation of Victor Hugo, <u>History of
     A Crime</u>, trans. by Huntington Smith (New York: Thomas Crowell and Co., 1888), p. 237
     reads: "An invasion of armies can be resisted, but there is no resistance to an invasion
     of ideas."

of institutional churches and to reject religious statements opened the door to Restorationist Movements."[2] Milton Backman reinforces this observation when he elaborates:

> Like many European reformers of the sixteenth and seventeenth centuries, many Americans of the early republic earnestly sought a restoration of New Testament Christianity. These Americans determined that the leaders of the Reformation had failed to restore the fullness of the gospel and that all Christian religions had inherited from the Medieval church incorrect doctrines and practices. Such conclusions inspired the restorationists to seek the truth and to organize eventually new religions which in their opinion more closely resembled the Primitive Church.[3]

I. THE POST-REVOLUTIONARY ERA

Nathan Hatch, in The Democratization of American Christianity, argues "that the transitional period between 1780 and 1830 left as indelible an imprint upon the structures of American Christianity as it did upon those of American political life."[4] The American Revolution had proven to be the converging point of the sacred and the secular. Henry May, Bernard Bailyn, and Gordon Wood have all aptly demonstrated that the ideas of the Enlightenment brought about a revolution in the American psyche before it ever took place as a physical event. But it is no accident of history that restorationism blossomed on the heels of the American Revolution.

> From the perspective of many who lived during and following the Revolution, that event was the infinitely grand, cosmic battle that, now at last in these latter days, had begun the process of making the primordium contemporary. "Behold, all things have become new" was the common sentiment. And so they had. [5]

The principle of revolution itself, with its correlative idea that "governments are instituted among men, deriving their just powers from the consent of the governed," became ingrained into the American way of thinking. More than that, as Gordon Wood expressed it, "Americans had in fact institutionalized and legitimized revolution."[6] Such a mind set could not be confined to the political sphere alone.

---

2   Robert Millet, ed., Joseph Smith: Selected Sermons and Writings (New York: Paulist Press, 1989), p.9.

3   Milton V. Backman, Jr., American Religions and the Rise of Mormonism (Salt Lake City: Deseret Book Co., 1970), pp.237-238, as quoted in Millet, pp.9-10.

4   Hatch, p.6.

5   Hughes and Allen, Illusions of Innocence, p.20.

6   Gordon S. Wood, The Creation of the American Republic, 1776-1787 (New York: W. W. Norton, 1969), p.614.

Independence thus became not only political but moral. Revolution, republicanism, and regeneration all blended in American thinking. . . .The repeated calls of the clergy for a return to the temperance and virtue of their ancestors made sense not only in terms of the conventional covenant theology but also, as many ministers enjoyed noting, in terms of the best political science of the day.[7]

By the time of the birth of the American Republic around a dozen major religious groups had been exported from Europe to America. Of these, five—the Congregationalists, Presbyterians, Baptists, Anglicans (Episcopalians), and Methodists— accounted for about 75 percent of all religious adherents.[8] According to church historian Henry Webb, a common estimate of historians of the era holds that only about ten percent of the population held membership in any church.[9] Though church attendance was significantly higher than that number,[10] still the denominations had to struggle and compete for members, and the last quarter of the century presented some further problems.

Some denominations, like the Anglicans and Methodists, cut off from their hierarchies and financial support in England, had to rebuild their structures and their coffers. The Anglicans also suffered because much of their clergy and laity proved to be Tories during the Revolution. Even the Quakers found scorn added to ridicule for their pacifist stance during the struggle for independence.[11]

Also, whereas in earlier colonial days some churches had political backing to either compel or pressure people to become members or pay dues for their support, now they would have to compete for their allegiance. From the climate of the Revolution Americans became infected with strong sentiments about natural rights, and among these rights was the freedom to decide one's own religious convictions and attachments. They were persuaded that no denomination should be favored by law, nor should the law interfere in the internal functions of the churches.

The Enlightenment and American Revolution had bequeathed a legacy of freedom to the American way of thinking—freedom from superstition, from intolerance, and from an oppressive government.

---

7   Ibid., pp.117-118.

8   See chart in Mark Noll, <u>A History of Christianity In The United States And Canada</u> (Grand Rapids: Eerdman's Publishing Co., 1992), p. 153.

9   See Henry Webb, <u>In Search of Christian Unity</u> (Cincinnati: Standard Publishing Co., 1990),p. 27. See also Winthrop Hudson, <u>Religion In America</u>, Third Edition (New York: Charles Schribner's Sons, 1981), p. 129.

10   See Hudson, p. 130, for explanation of reasons.

11   Hill, p.6.

Symbiotic with that legacy grew the desire for freedom from similar problems within the denominations, especially those which had enjoyed political positions of privilege. This did not mean that most Christians then sought a form of ecclesiastical anarchy. Jon Butler has offered the following distinction: "The post-revolutionary denominations embraced authority, but not authoritarianism."[12]

Sidney Mead has observed that this desire for religious freedom did not mean that people wanted to give up commonly shared basic Christian beliefs. Instead it meant that they rejected the idea that any religious group should have the coercive power of the state behind it. In other words, force would be supplanted by persuasion as the motivation for church participation and doctrinal beliefs.[13]

Yet many also came to view the denominations themselves as having become encrusted with the corruptions of time. People accused the established churches of having confusing theologies, distorted interpretations and doctrines, meaningless traditions, exclusivist creeds, and an entrenched clerical class. Many sought for a revival of true faith, and their search led them to reexamine the roots of Christianity. "What makes the American religion so American," advocates Harold Bloom, "is that the Christianizing of the American people, in the generation after the Revolution, persuasively redefined what Christianizing meant, by returning history to origins and to essentials."[14]

Drew McCoy, in The Elusive Republic, refers to an occasion when Thomas Jefferson reminisced about what he called "the revolution of 1800." He was using the term revolution, not in the sense that a radical new political order had been created, but in reference to "a return to first principles, . . . a restoration of original values and ideals that had been overturned or repudiated." He was yearning for a regeneration of the true republican spirit of 1776.[15]

In a similar vein, Jefferson believed he saw what had been the degradation of Christianity over the centuries. As a Deist Jefferson did not share the same convictions as Christian restorationists about the deity and miracles of Jesus. In a letter to William Short he lampooned the "pseudo-followers" of Jesus for their "falsehoods," "charlatanisms,"

---

12   Jon Butler, Awash in a Sea of Faith: Christianizing The American People (Cambridge: Harvard U. Press, 1990), p. 272.

13   Sidney E. Mead, The Lively Experiment: The Shaping of Christianity in America (New York: Harper and Row, 1963), p. 63.

14   Harold Bloom, The American Religion: The Emergence of the Post-Christian Nation (New York: Simon and Schuster, 1992), pp.28-29.

15   Drew McCoy, The Elusive Republic: Political Economy In Jeffersonian America (New York: W. W. Norton, 1980), p.185.

"misconstructions," "interpolations," and "theorizations" that would expose Jesus as an imposter to any sound-thinking person.[16]

Yet even Jefferson recognized the damage done to Christianity by the various interpretations and divisions within the Church, and acknowledged the potential power of Jesus' message to unify mankind. In 1821 he wrote to Timothy Pickering:

> ...when, in short, we shall have unlearned everything which has been taught since [Jesus'] day, and got back to the pure and simple doctrines He inculcated, we shall then be truly and worthily His disciples; and my opinion is that if nothing had ever been added to what flowed purely from His lips, the whole world would at this day have been Christian. . . . The religion-builders have so distorted and deformed the doctrines of Jesus, so muffled them in mysticisms, fancies and falsehoods, have caricatured them into forms so monstrous and inconceivable, as to shock reasonable thinkers, to revolt them against the whole, and drive them rashly to pronounce its Founder an imposter. Had there never been a commentator, there never would have been an infidel. . . .As the Creator has made no two faces alike, so no two minds, and probably no two creeds. . . .So there may be peculiarities in your creed and in mine. They are honestly formed without doubt. I do not wish to trouble the world with mine, nor to be troubled for them. These accounts are to be settled only with Him who made us; and to Him we leave it, with charity for all others, of whom, also, He is the only rightful and competent Judge. I have little doubt that the whole of our country will soon be rallied to the unity of the Creator, and, I hope, to the pure doctrines of Jesus also.[17]

What Jefferson was expressing was not an impulse unique to him alone. Many Americans were frustrated and befuddled with the fragmented state of Christianity in America. A ground swell of desire for some sort of syncretism or unifying focus prepared the theological soil for those who would come with ecumenicity in their messages.

A man named James Madison (a doctor of divinity who was *not* the later-to-be U.S. president), made the following plea in a sermon to the Protestant Episcopal Church of Virginia in 1786:

> I will then venture earnestly to recommend to all Christians to reject every system as the fallible production of human contrivance, which shall dictate articles of faith, and adopt the Gospel alone as their guide. . . . The Proposition is indeed simple and plain; it is, "That those Christian societies will ever be found to have formed their union upon principles, the wisest and the best,

---

16   Thomas Jefferson, letter to William Short, Monticello, August 4, 1820. Found in Thomas Jefferson: Writings, Vol. 15 of The Library of America Series, ed. by Merrill D. Peterson (New York: The Library of America, 1984), p. 1435.

17   Thomas Jefferson, letter to Timothy Pickering, Monticello, February 27, 1821. Found in The Writings of Thomas Jefferson, Vol. XV, ed. Andrew A. Lipscomb (Washington D.C.: The Thomas Jefferson Memorial Association, 1904), pp. 323-324.

which impose the fewest restraints upon the minds of their members, making the Scriptures alone, and not human articles or confessions of belief, the sole rule of faith and conduct. . . . Those things alone should be held as *essentials*, which our Lord and Master, hath fully and clearly expressed, and which therefore cannot require the supposed improvements and additions of men. . . it is also the particular duty of a Christian church to frame their mode of public worship upon a plan so liberal, so free from all matters of theological disputation, so truly scriptural, that all who call themselves Christians may come to the same communion . . . .[18]

John Wesley displayed the same sentiments in 1841 in an expose' on his priorities as a Methodist:

I, and all who follow my judgment, do vehemently refuse to be distinguished from other men, by any but the common principles of Christianity, — the plain, old Christianity that I teach, renouncing and detesting all other marks of distinction....

But from real Christians, of whatsoever denomination they be, we earnestly desire not to be distinguished at all, . . .Dost thou love and serve God? It is enough. I give thee the right hand of fellowship.[19]

One of the many ways in which the new spirit of freedom and ecumenicity expressed itself was in a fascination with the concept of primitivism. The desire to restore Christianity back to its basic earlier forms resulted, not only in the sabotage of coercive authoritarian structures, but also in an obliteration of the traditional lines between clergy and laity as a separate order of men.[20]

Although the power of the clergy and the old creeds still held sway among some traditionalists, the stronger impulse was to renounce the guidance of any external guides and to elevate an already strong reverence for unmediated scripture. "No creed but the Bible" and "The Bible alone is good enough for me" became the watchwords of the day.[21]

Bible and tract societies worked hard to put Scripture in the hands of ordinary lay people, especially the unchurched. Barlow postulates that, by

---

18   Quoted in Webb, pp.35-36.

19   John Wesley, "The Character of a Methodist," found in The Works of John Wesley (Third edition), Vol. 8 (Grand Rapids: Baker Book House, 1991), pp. 346-347.

20   Hatch, p.9. See also Sidney Ahlstrom, A Religious History of the American People, Vol. I (Garden City, New York: Doubleday and Co., 1975), p. 463, who argues that because churches no longer were subsidized by taxes or the crown, they depended upon the voluntary support of a committed laity. Because they had to *compete* for members and support, "ministers were obliged to please their constituencies, and hence lost authority and status."

21   Philip L Barlow, Mormons and The Bible: The Place of The Latter-Day Saints In American Religion (New York: Oxford University Press, 1991), p.7.

the time of Andrew Jackson's egalitarian age, "privately interpreted scripture rivaled or surpassed the clergy and the traditional creeds as the preeminent religious authority of the land."[22] And Nathan Hatch argues, "In a culture that increasingly balked at vested interests, symbols of hierarchy, and timeless authorities, a remarkable number of people awoke one morning to find it self-evident that the priesthood of all believers meant just that— religion of, by, and for the people."[23]

Another result of the American Revolution, though perhaps less directly, was the emergence of a millennial hope among many Christians. The American exceptionalism that said to the world, "we shall be as a city upon a hill" and "we are the great experiment in democracy" eventually nurtured an optimistic world view in the early nineteenth century which matured into a common conviction that it was the place and time of the Biblically- prophesied millennium, a thousand-year reign of peace and prosperity before Christ returned for His flock. This view is known to history as postmillennialism because Christ would return *after* the thousand years, not at the outset (premillennialism).

Contributing to this optimistic spirit were such things as the beginning of the Industrial Revolution, the seemingly endless abundance of land and other natural resources, and the freedom one experienced on the frontier. America was a land that was not yet defiled by the complexities and corruptions of advanced civilizations. To many Americans it was as if man was being allowed by God to enter Eden a second time, to start afresh unencumbered by the corrosion of European civilization and the established Church.

Drew McCoy relates that many Americans of this period had believed in "the four stages theory" of civilization, which said that all societies proceeded from a simple, pure condition to a civilized complexity. Like America, the nations of Western Europe had once existed in that idyllic former state. But the demands of modern commercial society had despoiled their virgin purity. The fourth and final stage, that of commerce, represented civilization on the decline, and mercantilistic Europe was seen to be in that stage. When the Federalist platform called for increased commerce with the Old Country, many quipped that all that the United States could draw from intercourse with Europe was "infection."[24]

A parallel attitude may also be found toward European religion. Time had corrupted the Roman Catholic Church and fractured Protestantism. While the Church remained in this condition the Apocalypse would be postponed. When the pristine Church would be resurrected, then Christ would return for His bride. Two recent authors have stressed that:

---

22   Ibid. p.3.

23   Hatch, p.69.

24   Drew McCoy, see especially pp.19, 57, and 101.

Most scholars writing on this subject, however, have failed to recognize that generally implicit in the rhetoric of American newness and millennialism was the fundamental theme of recovery—recovery of something primal, ancient, and old. . . .

Implicit in this conception is the notion of a fall from primal purity and rightness, and it was history—the long duration of human time—that embodied the disastrous aftermath of that fall. Understood in this way, millennialism was itself a kind of recovery of sacred time.[25]

But while the concepts of freedom and independence were now in vogue, Americans soon came to realize that some sort of unification was also desirable, and even necessary. Their experience during the Revolution, and their common needs as a nation afterward, helped them see the need for cooperation with each other. Hence the Articles of Confederation had been enacted, and not long after, the Federal Government under a Constitution. Thus political unity was attained.

Likewise, a similar desire began to be felt for religious unity. Fawn Brodie wrote, "Although the authority and tradition of the Christian religion were decomposing in the New World's freedom, there was a counter-desire to escape from disorder and chaos."[26] Errett Gates, in his research on the early nineteenth-century relationships of Baptists and Disciples of Christ, summarized the era in the following way:

It was not difficult to convince the Christian communities of that time of the evils of sectarianism and division. Their task so far was an easy one. It was a beautiful vision, a glorious ideal that looked down upon them. The realization of it was a task worthy of the most earnest effort. A united church, of one mind and spirit, marching together to the conversion of the world and the overthrow of infidelity—this had been the prayer of the Master and the dream of the church in all ages, and was to be the immediate achievement of the present generation of Christians, if the churches would only abandon their divisive creeds and confessions, their human systems of doctrine and discipline, and their sectarian names, and return to the Christianity of Christ and his apostles. . . . this plan was convincing and captivating to multitudes who saw the millennium in the not distant future through its acceptance. There was power of appeal in it, because there was something in it worthwhile. Then too it was easily understood. Many preachers of mediocre talent found their greatness in its advocacy.[27]

---

25 Hughes and Allen, <u>Illusions of Innocence</u>, p.2.

26 Fawn M. Brodie, <u>No Man Knows My History: The Life Story of Joseph Smith, The Mormon Prophet</u> (New York: Alfred A. Knopf, 1960), p.90.

27 Errett Gates, <u>The Early Relation and Separation of Baptists and Disciples</u> (Chicago: The Christian Century Company, 1904), p.87.

II. THE NEW FRONTIER

Among the first settlers of the eastern Appalachian piedmont, the Scotch-Irish were significant in numbers [see figure 1]. Back in England they had battled famine, greedy landlords, and religious discrimination as Presbyterians. Many of them relocated in Northern Ireland to escape the reach of the Anglican Church, but earning a living there was a terrible burden as well, even though they came to outnumber the Roman Catholics in several northern counties.

During the eighteenth century many of them emigrated to the new colonies, most of them settling in the tolerant colony of William Penn. Restless and independent, they pushed westward to the plush farmlands in the rolling hills of western Pennsylvania. At first the proprietors of the colony welcomed their presence there, for they were regarded as a barrier between the settled colonial villages and the Indians.[28]

But soon problems arose, as they tended to settle on the best land they could find, which also happened to be claimed by others back east. Spreading southward into the western portions of Maryland, Virginia, and the Carolinas, they squatted on whatever good land was available. An unkind quip was sometimes heard that Scotsmen were good at keeping the Sabbath, and whatever else they could lay their hands on![29]

But permanent settlers they weren't, at first, gaining a reputation as a rootless people, and moving numerous times from one area to another. As the Germans behind them closed in, they proved ready to sell their stakes and relocate. "They sat lightly on the land, ready to sell out, pack up, and move on to flee the onset of new people and closer settlement. They were a deliberately marginal people . . . ," noted Dennis W. Meinig.[30]

It has been estimated that by 1775 about 175,000 Scotch-Irish had migrated to the colonies, making them second only to the English in numbers and comprising around 7% of the total population.[31] Yet wherever they went they retained a tendency toward independence and were challengers of established authority, whether secular or sacred. As Presbyterians, many had an intense faith. Yet, due to their experiences under the oppression of the Anglican Church, they were no theocrats, but rather stubborn opponents of established churches in America.[32]

---

28   Robert A. Divine, et al., <u>America: Past and Present</u>, ed. 5 (New York: Addison Wesley Longman, Inc., 1999), p.101.

29   Thomas A. Bailey, David M. Kennedy, and Lizabeth Cohen, <u>The American Pageant: A History of The Republic</u>, ed. 11 (Lexington, Mass.: D.C. Heath, 1998), p.84.

30   Dennis W, Meinig, <u>Continental America, 1800-1867</u>, Vol 2 of <u>The Shaping of America: A Geographical Perspective On 500 years of History</u> (New Haven: Yale University Press, 1993), p.246.

31   Bailey, Kennedy, and Cohen, p.83.

32   Ibid., p.87.

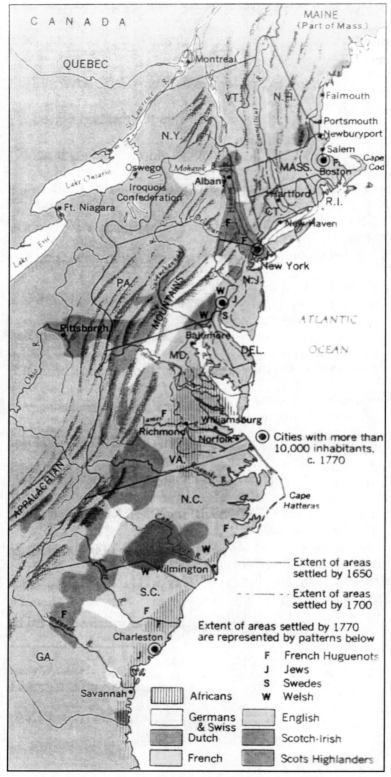

Figure 1. Map of Immigrant Settlement (Permission granted -CCC)

In 1763 the London government had issued a proclamation prohibiting settlement beyond the Appalachian Mountains in order to prevent problems between the Indians and the land speculators and settlers who were pouring into their territories.[33] But the treaty that ended the American Revolution nullified that barrier and fixed the western boundary of the United States at the Mississippi River. The first general census taken in 1790 revealed that only 200,000 people, or 5% of the total U.S. population, lived west of the Allegheny Mountains. Yet Americans were pushing westward nonetheless. In 1790 nearly one third of the nation's population lived in counties that had been virtually unpopulated before the American Revolution. Ten years later over 40% of all Americans lived on land unsettled before 1760. From the end of the revolution to the turn of the century the population of western Pennsylvania almost tripled, from 33,000 to 95,000, and the years 1775 to 1790 saw the population of Kentucky mushroom to around 75,000, while Tennessee increased to 35,000 people.[34]

The Northwest Ordinance of 1787, the Battle of Fallen Timbers in 1794, and the Louisiana Purchase in 1803, all proved catalystic to westward migrations. Yet in 1810 the new west still had only 13.3% of the total population.[35] The War of 1812 and the depression that followed it were major interruptions in the development of western lands and immigration slowed somewhat. The next strong surge awaited the building of the Erie Canal in 1825.[36]

Regarding Ohio itself, even though migration westward was rather extensive after the Revolution because of depressed economic conditions along the East Coast, the settlement of Ohio was delayed until a territorial government was provided for that area by the Ordinance of 1787. Then in 1788 the first permanent settlement was made on the Ohio River, to be called Marietta, by settlers moving in from Kentucky. But the Ohio country was still looked upon as a source of revenue for the Federal Government, and a source of profit by various land speculators. Once the lands were acquired and developed they were sold. In a study done covering the years 1800-1810, only 82 of 188 property owners retained their land during that decade.[37]

---

33 For a description of the British and Indian concerns regarding colonial encroachments, see Richard White, The Middle Ground: Indians, Empires, and Republics In The Great Lakes Region, 1650-1815 (New York: Cambridge University Press, 1991), pp. 305-314.

34 Statistics provided in a study done by Nathan Hatch for The Democratization of American Christianity, p. 30.

35 Henry F. May, The Enlightenment In America (New York: Oxford University Press, 1976), p.307.

36 Meinig, p.227.

37 R. Douglas Hurt, The Ohio Frontier: Crucible of The Old Northwest, 1720-1830 (Bloomington, Indiana: Indiana University Press, 1996), p.176.

According to figures quoted in Mary Agnes Smith's thesis on the Mahoning Association, in the year 1800 the Northwest Territory could boast a population of only 51,000 people in five states, with Cincinnati being the largest town containing only 750 people.[38] Yet apparently the state of Ohio itself numbered 42,000 in 1800, and 26 years later totaled 800,000—a growth that according to F. P. Weisenburger "is perhaps without a parallel in the history of this or any other country."[39] During these same three decades Ohio rocketed from eighteenth to fourth place among the states in the Union in population.[40] By 1850, it had attained a population of almost two million people, over 30% of which was under ten years of age and almost 84% of which was under forty years of age.[41]

In a 1998 article entitled "Did Religion Follow the Frontier?", W. Clark Gilpin takes issue with authors like William Warren Sweet, who attempted to describe "the Americanizing of Christianity" on the basis of Frederick Jackson Turner's 1893 "Frontier Thesis." He vilifies Sweet's proteges for concluding that the American religion was a sort of frontier creation, as if the church was only a passive recipient of the molding forces of social evolution. In contrast, he seems to prefer the viewpoint of W. E. Garrison who saw frontier religion as only one phase of a continuous evolution of the Church *responding* to the political, social, and economic circumstances around it.[42]

It is true that there are facets of the Christian Church that seem to transcend time and culture. But there can be little doubt that the reception and success of religion is an interplay of forces back and forth—that is, that the surrounding culture influences the Church and that the Church, in turn, influences its community. In reference to three of the most prominent religious movements of the early nineteenth century frontier, Hughes and Allen have maintained:

> Mormons, Baptists, and "Christians" were no mere cults, destined to strut upon the American stage and then to die. In fact, one of the principle reasons for their immense, collective appeal to so many thousands of Americans at the time was their uncanny accuracy in reflecting the myth of first times that was so central to the American ethos. One might even argue that Mormons and "Christians" were, in fundamental ways, creations of that ethos.[43]

---

38   Mary Agnes Smith, "A History of the Mahoning Baptist Association" (Master's thesis, West Virginia University, 1943), p.11.

39   Francis P. Weisenburger, The Passing of the Frontier, 1825-1850, Vol. III of The History of the State of Ohio, ed. By Carl Wittke (Columbus , Ohio: The Ohio State Archaeological and Historical Society, 1941), p.4.

40   Parkin, p.25.

41   Weisenburger, pp. 3 and 55.

42   W. Clark Gilpin, "Did Religion Follow the Frontier?", Discipliana (Nashville: The Disciples of Christ Historical Society), Summer, 1998, pp.40-43.

43   Hughes and Allen, Illusions of Innocence, p. XIV.

Whitney Cross has described the multifarious religious upheavals of the early nineteenth century in western New York State as yielding a "burned-over district."[44] Ivan Barrett has expressed the belief that the many revivals there had significant influence in the readying of men's minds for the restoration of the Gospel because they sharpened interest in the Millennium.[45] I would further add that another factor in this preparation was the proliferation of doctrines among the many contenders in that area, which caused a great deal of confusion regarding the tenets of the Christian faith. "The frontiersman cherished simplicity," wrote Garrison and DeGroot, "practiced direct action, and was suspicious of experts, round about procedures, and complicated systems imposed by authority or hallowed by tradition. He was addicted to shortcuts."[46]

Most frontiersmen were permeated with this primitivistic attitude. They simply wanted an opportunity to build a new life and live close to the soil. To these pioneers the virgin land of the west was a panorama of the new, the fresh, and the innocent. "People on the frontier were rugged individualists who were dependent upon their own resources. They expected very little from their central government, and they wanted it that way."[47]

The stark simplicity of the frontier life and frontier survival bequeathed to the pioneers a desire to boil religion back down to the basics. Centuries of creeds, catechisms, and doctrinal developments had confused their faith, and many pioneers "hungered and thirsted" to start over again at the beginning of the church, when the doctrines and practices were just being incubated. In other words, they wanted to "restore" original New Testament Christianity in regard to its pristine forms and teachings, and they resolved to "go back to the Bible" as their only authoritative source of faith and practice.

James B. North, in his new restorationist history, stresses that:

These people were also wide open to the basics of the Restoration Movement as it hark[en]ed back to the simple gospel message and church structure of the New Testament. Ideologically, the frontier had already opted for that kind of viewpoint in society, politics, and culture. Since the Restoration Movement presented the same idea as a religious option, many people accepted it wholeheartedly. Thus the American frontier was a ready-made field for the message of this Restoration Movement. The preachers got nods

---

44   See Whitney Cross, The Burned-Over District: The Social and Intellectual History of Enthusiastic Religion in Western New York, 1800-1850 (Ithaca, New York: Cornell University Press, 1950).

45   Barrett, p.11.

46   W. E. Garrison and A. T. DeGroot, The Disciples of Christ: A History (St. Louis: Bethany Press, 1948), p.79.

47   James B. North, Union In Truth: An Interpretive History of The Restoration Movement (Cincinnati: Standard Publishing Co., 1994), p.5.

of agreement when they pointed negatively to the hierarchical structures of numerous denominations—they were the religious counterparts of the elite societies of Europe that the frontiersmen despised. The preachers got the same agreement when they called for an elimination of the legalism and restrictions that marked denominational control over the lives of church members. The frontiersmen felt the same way about social regulations in general, and the words of these preachers perfectly matched their sociology. For these reasons, the Restoration Movement was able to get a running start on evangelizing the frontier.[48]

Early on, many frontiersmen were not very interested in religion, however. They had escaped the rigors of puritanical restraints in New England and became restless individuals who engaged in rowdyism, drinking, swearing, and gambling. Many places on the frontier seldom saw a minister, and great tracts of territory inhabited by as many as 20,000 to 50,000 people had no resident preacher from any denomination.[49]

Churches like the Episcopal Church with its hierarchy of officials and formal liturgy had no appeal for this down-to-earth bunch. Those who were converted were moved by a more personal, individual, emotional appeal that presented the Gospel in its simplest forms. Great stress was placed upon religious experience through the indwelling of the Holy Spirit. W. E. Garrison has commented that, "The emotional tone of revival preaching fitted the mental state of people who, unaccustomed to the discipline of hard thinking, found relief in ardent feeling."[50]

The two great rising churches that represented this simple approach were the Baptists and the Methodists. Henry May has pointed out that, while New England was solidly Federalist in conviction, these two denominations were even more solidly Jeffersonian. By the year 1800 Isaac Backus, the great Baptist leader, was advocating the convergence of Jefferson's election and the Great Revival as harbingers of the coming millennium.[51]

III. THE WESTERN RESERVE

The northeast portion of what is now the state of Ohio was known in colonial days as the Western Reserve. In 1662 King Charles II of England had granted the colony of Connecticut a charter-right to all of the lands in

---

48 Ibid., pp. 5 - 6.

49 Walter W. Jennings, <u>Origin and Early History of the Disciples of Christ</u> (Cincinnati: Standard Publishing, 1919), p. 33. In this chapter Jennings either summarizes or quotes the observations and impressions of numerous Bible society missionaries.

50 Winfred Earnest Garrison, <u>Religion Follows The Frontier: A History of The Disciples of Christ</u> (New York: Harper and Brothers, 1931), p. 58.

51 Henry May, pp. 317 and 304.

the New World contained between the 41st and 42nd latitudinal parallels. Because of the limited geographical expertise of the Europeans at this time, the western boundary was set at the Pacific ocean.[52] However the states of Virginia, New York, and Massachusetts, also claimed title to that territory by virtue of royal charters from the King of England, and there were disputes over the area throughout the eighteenth century.

In the latter part of the eighteenth century the Western Reserve acquired the recognized boundaries of Lake Erie on the north, Pennsylvania on the east, the 41st parallel on the south, and the counties of Sandusky and Seneca in the west. While this section comprises only one seventh of the present state of Ohio, it was at that time virtually an unbroken forest containing about 175,000 more acres than its mother state of Connecticut. The total area of the Western Reserve amounted to about 3,800,000 acres.[53]

Late in the Revolutionary War period the Continental Congress requested of the states that they give up their land claims to the west of the Appalachian Mountains. This action had been a condition established by Maryland in return for its pending ratification of the Articles of Confederation.[54] In 1781 all of the states, with the exception of Connecticut, ceded their claims to the new central government. Yet even though Connecticut finally surrendered jurisdiction of her land claims to the west of the Western Reserve in 1786, it still persisted in its demand to retain that estate as a "reserve" for hardships suffered during the Revolution. Congress confirmed its right to that territory on September 14, 1786.[55]

In 1792 a half million acres was subtracted from the Western Reserve and donated by the state of Connecticut to certain inhabitants of New London, whose homesteads had been burned down when the traitor Benedict Arnold entered their harbor and burned their city. Hence this territory—now the counties of Huron and Erie—became known as "the fire lands" of Connecticut.[56] As for the rest of the territory, Indians had made settlement of this area unsafe before the Greenville Treaty in 1795. But by May of that year the legislature of Connecticut was selling lands to various other citizens of that state and of other states as well. On the 4th of July, in 1796, the first surveying party, headed by Moses Cleaveland, prepared the area for development by the Connecticut Land Company, a group of

---

52   A. S. Hayden, Early History of the Disciples On The Western Reserve (Cincinnati: Chase and Hall, 1875), p. 14.

53   P. P. Cherry, The Western Reserve and Early Ohio (Akron: R. L. Fouse, Pub., 1921), pp. 56-64.

54   See Jack N. Rokove, The Beginnings of National Politics: An Interpretive History of The Continental Congress (New York: Alfred A. Knopf, 1979), pp. 285-288.

55   Harry F. Lupold, "Origin of Mentor Township," The Historical Society Quarterly (of Lake County Ohio), August, 1975, pp. 1-2.

56   Cherry, p. 56.

speculators who had bought up much of the land in the Reserve. They built an infrastructure of roads, towns, mills, inns, and sometimes model farms, in order to increase the value of the property and lure settlers for purchase.[57]

By the turn of the nineteenth century there were only about one thousand people living in the Western Reserve Territory. In 1800, Congress came to regard the Western Reserve as being under the jurisdiction of the United States and of the Northwest Territory. However, Connecticut would not formally cede her claim to the Federal Government until May 30, 1801. Ohio entered the Union in 1803, and by 1832 eight counties comprised the Western Reserve—Ashtabula, Geauga, Cuyahoga, Lorain, Huron, Trumball, Portage, and Medina.[58]

As for Cleveland itself, which would become the predominant city in the Western Reserve area, General Moses Cleaveland arrived at the mouth of the Cuyahoga River with his scouting party on July 22, 1796. While there he surveyed and laid the foundations of the city. The map maker christened the city after its founder but, apparently never having seen Cleaveland's name spelled, erroneously dubbed the site "Cleveland," his error remaining undetected until it was too late.[59]

The growth of Cleveland would be insignificant until after the War of 1812. In 1810 the total population of the mosquito-infested city was only 57 people.[60] John Melish, a visitor to Cleveland in 1811, described the city as "a paltry *village*, containing a few houses only."[61] Other towns, such as Painesville, Youngstown, and Hudson, rivaled it in the early years. Even as late as 1830, Cleveland was a small village of scarcely a thousand inhabitants, in comparison to Cincinnati which then had a population of around 25,000. But the Forest City—a nickname which Cleveland would inherit later—was on the verge of a population boom, and by 1850 it boasted over 17,000 people.[62]

The Western Reserve was somewhat extraordinary in comparison with the rest of the early nineteenth-century frontier of the time. Whereas Kentucky, Tennessee, and much of the rest of Ohio had been settled by the descendants of backwoodsmen pouring in from Virginia and the Carolinas, the Western Reserve was heavily populated by Connecticut Yankees of Puritan stock. As such, their educational level

---

57 See Hayden, p. 15; Lupold, p. 2; and Meinig, p. 225.

58 See Hurt, p. 166; Cherry, p. 61; and Parkin, p. 27.

59 See Hayden, p. 16, and Hurt, p. 199.

60 Hurt, pp. 201-202.

61 John Melish, "The Western Reserve," An Ohio Reader: 1750 To The Civil War, ed. Thomas H. Smith, Director of The Ohio Historical Society (Grand Rapids: Eerdmans Pub. Co., 1975), p. 117.

62 Weisenburger, pp. 10-13.

tended to be higher and their approach to religion perhaps a bit more rationalistic than that of their southern counterpart revivalists. R. Douglas Hurt contends that, before the onset of the nineteenth century, "they formed the most homogenous settlement of New Englanders in the Old Northwest." It seems that the deep forests of the Western Reserve did not tend to attract large numbers of foreign immigrants until after the frontier period had ended.[63]

These Connecticut Yankees established a Congregationalist Church in many townships where they settled. Several communities, such as Hudson and Oberlin, reflect this prototype even today with their central "common" areas and their white-spired churches. A certain smug pride about their blue-blooded ancestry could be evidenced in such people as P. P. Cherry, who bragged that, "The descendants of these people have no equal in intelligence, integrity and good order generally."[64] Calling the Western Reserve "the last stand of Puritanism," he went on to sermonize:

> All that was pure, that was noble, that was of humanity and of God, we have inherited from them, the first state to be settled by representative Americans, children of the old colonies; of Revolutionary sires—a chosen people—children of destiny. God-risen we have a mission to perform and when we forget it and all that has made us great we shall sign our death warrant and seal the doom of our children.[65]

The formal demeanor and rigid doctrines of the Calvinists, however, tended to alienate these freedom-loving and independent-spirited pioneers. In the 1830's any Oberlin College student who traveled on Sunday was expelled, and in 1837 a member of the Oberlin church was brought to trial for drinking tea.[66] Three modern scholars have summed up the conflict between the five points of Calvinism and the free-spirited pioneers in the following way:

> The idea of total depravity did not stand up well to the belief that individuals had the inherent capacity to shape their own destinies. The concept of unconditional election also seemed to deny that people were fully capable of determining the course of their own lives. The Calvinistic idea of a limited atonement in which the benefits of God's action in Christ were restricted to the "elect" was an affront to the equality of which the Declaration of Independence spoke. Irresistible grace seemed offensive to the American idea that uncontrollable power was evil. True, American Evangelicals might continue to believe in the perseverance of the saints, but they did so as much for their confidence in themselves as in God.[67]

63 Hurt, p. 250.

64 Cherry, p. 59.

65 Ibid., p. 65.

66 Weisenburger, pp. 177 and 162.

67 John D. Woodbridge, Mark A. Noll, and Nathan O. Hatch, <u>The Gospel In America: Themes In The Story of America's Evangelicals</u> (Grand Rapids: Zondervan, 1979), p. 32.

Some rebelled and behaved "like freed prisoners." [68] But other God-
fearing "seekers" eventually came to seek some other way. The Baptists and
Methodists arrived on the Western Reserve in the early part of the
nineteenth century and soon, as Alanson Wilcox complained, arrived "all
kinds of religious and infidel fads."[69]

Revivals broke out in many parts of the territory. In Ashtabula
County these occurrences were common. Some people would hop like
frogs and others would crawl on all fours, showing their teeth and barking
like dogs.[70] Men like Lyman Beecher complained to Charles Finney, the
prominent revivalist preacher on the Western Reserve, about these excesses.
But criticism would not stop these revivals as long as converts were being
won to the church. Eventually, however, many people of the Reserve were
offended by these "excesses", and the seeds of restorationism found a fertile
soil from which to germinate.

The Appalachian frontier culture of the new American republic
proved to be quite conducive to the spread of Christian primitivism.
Sidney Mead has adeptly summarized the factors promoting such
acceptance and growth:

> . . .the constellation of ideas prevailing during the Revolutionary epic
> in which the denominations began to take shape were: the idea of pure
> and normative beginnings to which return was possible; the idea that
> the intervening history was largely that of aberrations and corruptions
> which was better ignored; and the idea of building anew in the American
> wilderness on the true and ancient foundations. It is notable that the
> most successful of the definitely Christian indigenous denominations
> in America, the Disciples of Christ, grew out of the idea of a "new
> reformation" to be based, not on new insights, but on a "restoration"
> of the practices of the New Testament church—on which platform, it
> was thought, all the diverse groups of modern Christendom could unite
> as they shed the accumulated corruptions of the church through the
> centuries. Typically American, this beginning over again was not
> conceived as a new beginning, but as a picking up of the lost threads
> of primitive Christianity.[71]

---

68   See Parken, p. 17 and McKiernan, p. 18.

69   Alanson Wilcox, <u>A History of The Disciples of Christ in Ohio</u>, (Cincinnati: Standard
       Publishing, 1918), p. 40.

70   Parkin, p. 13.

71   Sidney Mead, p. 111.

Chapter
—3—

THE INCEPTION OF PRISTINE ECUMENICAL RESTORATIONISM ON THE FRONTIER

Neither the Stone-Campbell Movement nor the Mormons could accurately claim to be the first restoration pioneers in America. Many advocates of primitivism, such as the Separate or Landmark Baptists, had plowed the ground before them. But the *degree* to which the "Campbellites" and Mormons emphasized restorationism, and their incredible success in doing so—especially in the nineteenth century—cannot be denied.[1]

The Stone-Campbell Movement began as a restoration effort *within* the confines of the Presbyterian Church. There were men of the same sentiments in other denominations as well who developed relationships with the Stone-Campbell Movement. Elias Smith and Abner Jones were Baptists, and James O'Kelly was a Methodist, for example.

But Barton W. Stone and Thomas Campbell, who both began their work of restorationism on the frontier in the first decade in the nineteenth century, were Presbyterians. Both held the unification of all Christians to be their primary goal, and both believed that restorationism was the only means to achieve that unity. Because their ultimate concern was for unity, neither one placed an emphasis upon examining theologies or defining doctrines. In fact, official interpretations or mandated opinions were, they warned, the causes of division. They both agreed that unity could only be achieved through restorationism, but they differed as to the direct object, or basis, of restorationism. Campbell was very Bibliocentric, believing that unity would be achieved by an agreement on the few fundamental "facts" of the Bible. Stone was, however, very Pneumatocentric, contending that Christians can only be one in the Holy Spirit. Nonetheless, the obsession of both men was for unity, and this remained in the forefront of all their writings and activities.

---

1 Statistical growth numbers will be presented later in this work (see especially the end of Chapter 7).

PART I. BARTON STONE AND HOLY SPIRIT RESTORATIONISM

Barton Stone was born near the town of Port Tobacco in the state of Maryland on Christmas eve in the year 1772. His father died when he was still a youth, and a few years later in 1779, during the American Revolution, his mother moved the family to the back woods of Virginia. Many of their fellow backwoodsmen were called upon to fight against the British and the Tories, including his own brothers. Stone even relates an occasion when General Nathaniel Green fought Lord Cornwallis at Guilford Courthouse in North Carolina only thirty miles away from his home. They could hear the roar of the cannons, and, in fear, took to the woods to hide some valuable horses which they needed for the work of their farm. Recalling an impression cemented in childhood, Stone wrote:

> From my earliest recollection I drank deeply into the spirit of liberty, and was so warmed by the soul-inspiring draughts, that I could not hear the name of British, or tories, without feeling a rush of blood through the whole system.[2]

When the soldiers returned from the war they were hailed as heros and admired. But this proved to be a bane rather than a blessing because they brought back with them many vices, such as swearing, sensuality, drunkenness, gambling, quarreling, and fighting. Their influence at first demoralized, and then spread into, the society around them. The problem was intensified because many of the Anglican priests, whose salaries had been paid by Britain, left and returned to England. "Every man did what seemed right in his own eyes;" moaned Stone, "wickedness abounded, the Lord's day was converted into a day of pleasure, and the house of worship deserted."[3]

Figure 2. Barton W. Stone (1772 - 1844) (From http://www.therestorationmovement.com/stone,bw.htm)

In 1789 Stone went away to Guilford, North Carolina, to study law at Caldwell Academy. While he was there, many of his roommates heard the revival preaching of James McGready and "got religion." This influenced

---

2   Barton W. Stone, <u>The Biography of Elder Barton W. Stone, Written By Himself: With Additions and Reflections By Elder John Rogers</u> (Cincinnati: J.A. and U.P. James, 1847), p. 3. Hereafter referred to as <u>Autobiography</u>.

3   Ibid., pp. 2-4.

Stone to become a "seeker", and after a period of confusion, despondency, and despair, he was converted to Christ in the spring of 1791 by a preacher named William Hodge, whose theme of God's love led Stone to join the Presbyterian church. He became licensed and preached for awhile in North Carolina, Virginia, and Tennessee.

But religious apathy and public debauchery began to discourage the preachers of the frontier. "I seem to labor in vain," said one depressed cleric, and another admitted "No doubt I contribute my part to this declension of religion as well as others."[4] In 1798 the general assembly of the Presbyterian church issued a general letter blaming the corruption of public morals on the declension of religion. Complaining that "profaneness, pride, luxury, injustice, intemperance, lewdness, and every species of debauchery and loose indulgence greatly abound," they were joined by the Methodist and Baptist churches in denouncing the sin prevalent in society.[5] Christians entered into covenants with one another to spend much time in prayer imploring the Lord to send a revival.

It was at about this time that Barton Stone, too, was preaching in despair. The Calvinistic doctrine of the Presbyterians held that sinners could do nothing to effect their own salvation. The only people who would be saved were God's Elect, and He had predetermined who they were from before the foundation of the world. The only thing that anxious "seekers" could do was to implore God to send them a revelation confirming that they were of the chosen. Stone's mind struggled with the injustice of this system, and at first he would dismiss these heretical thoughts by imputing them to be the blasphemous suggestions of Satan. But his evangelistic desire for the universal salvation of mankind would not let him rest. He complained:

> Calvinism is among the heaviest clogs on Christianity in the world. It is a dark mountain between heaven and earth and is amongst the most discouraging hindrances to sinners from seeking the kingdom of God,. . . .[6]

Yet already a spiritual awakening had begun on the frontier. James McGready, along with others like William Hodge, John Ranken, William McGee, and John McGee, had ignited much of Kentucky in the year 1800 with revivals of unrestrained emotionalism. Though questioned at first by many, especially Presbyterians, as to their legitimacy, the large attendance and phenomenal results soon convinced people that it was the work of God. News of the strange and wonderful occurrences spread rapidly. The faithful and the curious anxiously awaited the announcement for the location of the

---

4   See John Boles, <u>The Great Revival: Beginnings of The Bible Belt</u> (Lexington: The University of Kentucky Press, 1972), p. 63.

5   B.B. Tyler, <u>Concerning The Disciples Of Christ</u> (Cleveland: The Bethany C.E. Company, 1897), p. 17.

6   Stone, <u>Autobiography</u>, pp. 33-34.

next revival, and then journeyed from as far away as one hundred miles "expecting an extraordinary display of religious fervor."[7]

In 1801 Stone married Elizabeth Campbell and purchased one hundred acres of land near Cane Ridge, Kentucky, for five hundred dollars. While there he established a ministry with two churches—one at Concord and one at Cane Ridge.

Stone had known McGready since his days at the Guilford Academy. He had heard about the success of the revivals in Logan county and was anxious to hold one in Bourbon county. The plans for a revival to be held at Cane Ridge were publicized for over a month, and when the event was finally held, a thunderous crowd of thousands covered the hillside.[8] The composition of the crowd varied widely, "from the Governor of the State to prostitutes, blacks as well as whites, the blackleg and the robber as well as the devout worshiper."[9]

The clamor alone was infectious. Sermons were shouted, hymns resounded around the hillsides, and mournful wailing and ecstatic Hosannas filled the air. "The noise was like the roar of Niagara [Falls]. The vast sea of human beings seemed to be agitated as if by a storm."[10] James B. Finley described the scenes involving the great multitudes:

> [They were] swept down in a moment, as if a battery of a thousand guns had been opened upon them, and then immediately followed shrieks and shouts that rent the very heavens. . . .My heart would beat tumultuously, my knees trembled, my lip quivered, and I felt as though I must fall to the ground.[11]

The emotional level of the revival was magnified by the many campfires, candles, and lamps illuminating the dark background of night. Passions increased as they fed upon each other until people began gyrating in strange "exercises."

Stone described these in his autobiography. In the "falling" exercise, which was common among all classes "from the philosopher to the clown," a person would "fall like a log on the floor, earth, or mud, and appear as

---

7   Boles, p. 51-55..

8   This author has seen numerous estimates ranging from 10,000 to 30,000 in attendance. See Boles, pp. 64-65; Murch, p. 29; Garrett, p. 74; Woodbridge, Noll, and Hatch, p. 43; and Garrison and DeGroot, p. 101, for example.

9   See Leroy Garrett, p. 74.

10 An extract from a letter written by the son of Reverend James Finley, September 20, 1801, printed in Boles, p. 65.

11 James B. Finley, <u>Autobiography of Rev. James B. Finley...</u>, ed. W.P. Strickland (Cincinnati: Printed at "the Methodist book concern for author," 1859), pp. 172-173; quoted in Woodbridge, Noll, and Hatch, p. 143.

dead." After awhile he or she would rise with a heavenly smile and speak of the love of God to all around.

The "jerking exercise" created spasms in the body:

> When the head alone was effected, it would be jerked backward and forward, or from side to side, so quickly that the features of the face could not be distinguished. When the whole system was effected, I have seen the person stand in one place, and jerk backward and forward in quick succession, their head nearly touching the floor behind and before.[12]

Stone also described the "barking exercise," which was often nothing more than the jerking exercise forcing a grunt out of a person that sounded like the bark of a dog. In his Autobiography, Stone portrayed an old Presbyterian preacher who went to the woods for his private devotions and was suddenly seized with the jerks. Grabbing hold of a small sapling to prevent a fall, he helplessly grunted repeatedly as air was forced from his mouth. An observer who came upon him satirically quipped that he found him "barking up a tree."[13]

Barking was not always the result of forced air however. In lower Kentucky one eye-witness reported:

> It was common to hear people barking like a flock of spaniels on their way to meeting. . . . There they would start up suddenly in a fit of barking, rush out, roam around and in a short time come barking and foaming back. Down on all fours they sometimes went, growling, snapping their teeth, and barking just like dogs.[14]

Stone described the "dancing exercise" which, he said, was peculiar to professors of religion, though there was nothing in it that would cause people to laugh. He further explained the "laughing exercise," the "running exercise," and the "singing exercise." In the latter, the sound issued not from the mouth or even the nose, but entirely from the breast, an emanation which yielded a mystical experience to all hearers.[15]

Thousands made professions of faith, and Stone was openly excited about the results. Though he may have questioned some of the emotional excesses, he did not doubt that the spirit of God was working in the crowd and transforming the multitudes.

---

12 Stone, Autobiography, p. 39-40.

13 Ibid., p. 41.

14 David Benedict, A General History of the Baptist Denomination In America, Vol. II (Boston: N.P., 1813), p. 256; quoted in William Garrett West, Barton Warren Stone: Early American Advocate of Christian Unity (Nashville: The Disciples of Christ Historical Society, 1954), p. 36.

15 Stone, Autobiography, pp. 40-42.

> That there were many eccentricities, and much fanaticism in this excitement, was acknowledged by its warmest advocates; indeed it would have been a wonder, if such things had not appeared, in the circumstances of that time. Yet the good effects were seen and acknowledged in every neighborhood, and among the different sects it silenced contention, and promoted unity for awhile; . . . .[16]

Stone also seemed to be impressed that Presbyterians, Baptists, and Methodists were working *together* to gain this success. Boles claims that as many as eighteen Presbyterian preachers were present, and that the number of Baptist and Methodist ministers exceeded that.[17] Garrett suggests that the number of preachers may have been as high as forty, and that they worked together "with more harmony than could be expected," forgetting their creeds and confessions and simply preaching the gospel.[18]

> This leveling of denominational distinctives belonged to the very essence of the revivals. Preaching in a revival context generally ignored what divided Christians and focused instead on beliefs held by all Christians—namely, that all people are sinners to whom God offers forgiveness and that the essence of Christianity was holy living inspired by the Holy Spirit.[19]

Some scholars have analyzed that this kind of revivalism results from a sort of self hypnosis. My own take on it is that heightened expectation of miracles and wonders often yields a self-fulfilling prophesy of unrestrained emotionalism. Authors like Harold Bloom attribute the atmosphere of emotional contagion to a deep-seeded psychosexual excitement that so engulfs a multitude that they become " awash in a sea of faith" as a form of displacement or sublimation.[20] Sidney Mead, however, believes that the successes of such meetings really had more to do with the spiritual frustrations of a simple frontier people with complex, judgmental, or exclusivistic, theological doctrines and practice.

> . . .revivalism tends to produce an oversimplification of all problems both because the effective revivalist must appeal to the common people in terms they can understand and because he must reduce all the complex of issues to a simple choice between two clear and contrasting alternatives. Said one convert,. . . "he made salvation seem so plain, so easy, I wanted to take it to my heart without delay."[21]

But many people, and especially the Presbyterians, were disturbed by the rampant eccentricities produced by these open-air camp meetings, and

---

16   Ibid., p. 42.

17   Boles, p. 65.

18   Garrett, p. 74.

19   Hughes, <u>Reviving The Ancient Faith</u>, p. 96.

20   Harold Bloom, <u>The American Religion: The Emergence Of The Post-Christian Nation</u> (New York: Simon and Shuster, 1992), p. 64.

21   Mead, p. 123.

began to oppose the work. One Presbyterian preacher addressed the people at length "in iceberg style," denouncing the hysteria that was overwhelming them in the guise of true faith. Barton Stone, who was very sick and spitting up blood at the time, nonetheless attended the meeting and pronounced that "its influence was deathly."[22] In a series of lectures on Christian union delivered in 1841 in Illinois, Stone, reminiscing nostalgically about the era of the great revivals, lamented:

> In the beginning of the present century the standard of heaven was almost forsaken—all having enlisted under the party standards of the day. There was a great and general revival of religion—the attention of Christians of every name was taken—they flowed together in one spirit—worshiped together, and loved one another as brethren. But the jealous demon of partyism became alarmed, for fear their party would lose. This alarm was spread, and the most blessed work I ever beheld on earth was marred.[23]

Stone also came to realize and regret that, apparently, some preachers had entertained more sinister intentions of such cooperation:

> At first they were pleased to see the Methodists and Baptists so cordially uniting with us in worship, no doubt, hoping they would become Presbyterians. But as soon as they saw these sects drawing away disciples after them, they raised the tocsin of alarm—the confession is in danger!—the church is in danger! Oh Israel to your tents!

> . . .The sects were roused. The Methodists and Baptists, who had so long lived in peace and harmony with the Presbyterians, and with one another, now girded on their armor, and marched into the deathly field of controversy and war. These were times of distress. The spirit of partyism soon expelled the spirit of love and union—peace fled before discord and strife, and religion was stifled and banished in the unhallowed struggle for pre-eminence. Who shall be the greatest, seemed to be the spirit of the contest—the salvation of a ruined world was no longer the burden, and the spirit of prayer in mourning took its flight from the breasts of many preachers and people.[24]

There were five Presbyterian preachers—Richard McNemar, John Thompson, John Dunlavy, Robert Marshall, and Barton Stone—who had participated in these revivals and were suspected, probably correctly, of differing with the Philadelphia Confession of Faith, and therefore teaching subversive doctrines. A Presbytery in Ohio summoned McNemar and charged him with preaching anti-Calvinistic ideas, and from there his case came before the synod at Lexington. The consequence of the hearings, although protested by all five men, led to their separation from association

---

22 Stone, <u>Autobiography</u>, pp. 42-43.

23 Barton W. Stone, "The Union of Christians," found in <u>The Works of Elder B.W. Stone</u>, ed. by Elder James M. Mathes, Vol. 1 (Cincinnati: Moore, Wilstach, Keys & Co., 1859), p. 251.

24 Stone, <u>Autobiography</u>, pp. 45-46.

with the synod. Therefore, they decided to form their own presbytery in 1803, which they called the Springfield Presbytery. But repeated attacks against them and misrepresentation of their positions from Presbyterian pamphlets and pulpits prompted them to sever their relationship with the denomination.

Soon after the separation Stone gathered his supporting congregations together and announced that he could no longer conscientiously promulgate Presbyterian doctrine. Then, in their presence, he tore up the contract which obliged them to pay his salary in order to release them from any persecution they might receive for supporting a *persona non grata*. In less than a year he and his fellow protestors came to the conclusion that the Springfield Presbytery itself "savored a party spirit," and they decided to dissolve it in favor of a more ecumenical endeavor. In the place of *Presbyterian* they took the name *Christian* because it was the name first given to Jesus' disciples at Antioch, and because it would be the most universal in recognition.[25] Stone opined:

> Party names have always produced bad effects and have exerted a mighty influence against Christian union. As soon as a man is called a Methodist, the Presbyterian looks at him with a jealous eye, and attaches to him all the errors of that sect, which as a dark cloud rolled before the view of his mind, [stands] in the way of union.[26]

The document which nullified their association was entitled "The Last Will and Testament of The Springfield Presbytery." This work was, in effect, their declaration of independence from any one denomination in particular. It gave them the freedom they needed to proceed on a broader ecumenical basis unencumbered by tradition and creed. Signed on June 28, 1804, the proclamation willed the death of the Presbytery and determined that it would "sink into union with the Body of Christ at large." It proceeded to advocate that candidates for the ministry receive their licence to preach from God rather than any man-made organization. It advocated a congregational form of government responsible only to God, with the power to choose their own minister and support him by a free will offering. Denying the legitimacy of any creed, the document declared that the Bible was the only sure guide to Heaven and that people should spend their time praying more and disputing less.[27]

---

25 Ibid., pp. 49-50. Boles (p. 63) either misunderstands or misstates Stone's position on this name, calling him the "founder of the Disciples of Christ movement." Stone always preferred the name Christian, and the churches he founded took that name. It was Alexander Campbell who preferred the name "Disciples of Christ" for his movement.

26 Stone, "Christian Union," Found in <u>The Works Of Elder B.W. Stone</u>, p. 314.

27 Robert Thompson, et. al., "The Last Will and Testament of The Springfield Presbytery," found in many sources, but also in Stone's <u>Autobiography</u>, pp. 51-53.

Not long after his exit from the Presbyterian church, Stone and others were accused of attempting to start a new denomination. The very thought of such an endeavor was repugnant to him. In an address to the churches Stone asserted:

> Often it is said of us, that we are laboring to establish a party. I deny the charge, with respect to myself, with abhorrence of the thing. Our very profession is leveled at the destruction of partyism, as the bane of Christianity. . . .

> Partyism is a foul blot on Christianity, and among the blackest stains on the character of its professors. An apostle calls such "carnal." Partyism is directly opposed to the plan of heaven, which is to gather into one, or unite all, in Christ Jesus.[28]

While admitting that there were Christians present in all denominations, Stone and his followers exhorted them to leave their various parties and unite upon the foundation of the one apostolic church. The divisions within Christendom represented by the denominations were "to be consigned to the rubbish heap upon which Christ died."[29] Stone predicted, "The time is not far distant, when Christians of every name shall be more solicitous for the salvation of souls, than for the promotion of a party."[30]

From 1812 to 1832, Stone worked to bring about unity among churches, but progress was slow and discouraging. For awhile, after the death of his first wife, he moved to middle Tennessee and established the roots of what would become a restorationist stronghold in the nineteenth and twentieth centuries. But efforts to bring about unity between New England, New York, and Southern Christian Churches were stifled, especially in 1826 when an attempt to form a united western convention failed.[31]

In November of 1826[32] Stone initiated a periodical entitled The Christian Messenger. Published monthly, a theme running throughout his fourteen-volume work advocated self-effacement in deference to ministry to the poor, the hungry, widows and orphans. Another constant motif was the abandonment of sectarianism in favor of Christian unity. In an editorial in the first issue, he opens with a statement of purpose:

---

28 Stone, "An Address To The Churches," found in The Works of Elder B.W. Stone, pp. 157-158.

29 Quoted in Allen and Hughes, Discovering Our Roots, p. 3.

30 Stone, "An Address To The Churches," p. 60.

31 Paul Conkin, American Originals: Homemade Varieties of Christianity (Chapel Hill: University of North Carolina Press, 1997), pp. 12-13.

32 Richard Hughes in his Reviving The Ancient Faith (p. 108), and Conkin in his American Originals (p. 13) both list the starting year as 1827, but two issues were published before that—one on November 25, 1826, and the other on December 25, 1826. William West, in his Barton Warren Stone, (p. 104) erroneously lists the year as 1824, too early.

It is universally acknowledged, by the various sects of Christians, that the religion of heaven, for centuries past, has fallen far below the excellency and glory of primitive Christianity. The man who honestly investigates the cause of this declension, and points the proper way of reformation, must certainly be engaged in a work, pleasing to God, and profitable to man. This is our design;. . .

That there are errors in the doctrines, as well as in the lives and practices of the various religious denominations now living, I presume no Protestant will deny. Their various, jarring creeds—their bitter strife and uncharitable opposition to one another—their multiplied divisions and disunion among themselves—their pride and worldly spirit—their death and cold formality;—these are undeniable evidences of the melancholy fact. To have these errors corrected and removed from the church, and to have truth restored in her heavenly, captivating robes, unadorned with the tinsel of human wisdom, are certainly the pious wishes of every honest Christian. Therefore, unappalled at the dangerous attempt, not discouraged at the attendant difficulties, we will boldly, though humbly, advance to the work.[33]

The thrust of Stone's admonition was primarily ethical and spiritual, not doctrinal, and focused on the achievement of inner piety and outward holiness. While the Stone movement was restorationist, it centered more on holy and righteous living than on the forms and structures of the early church. With the slogan "Let the unity of Christians be our polar star," Stone often elaborated on his viewpoint regarding four different kinds of union. There was "book union," based upon creeds and confessions; "head union," relying on human opinion and interpretation; "water union," based upon the immersion of a believer; and "fire union," created by the presence of the Holy Spirit. The latter was the only permanent union possible because it was created and sustained by the direct intervention of God.

Christians could never hope to unite on any creed, as the denominations propounded, because they are simply human translations, and therefore opinions, inferred from God's Holy Word. "We must be fully persuaded, that all uninspired men are fallible, and therefore liable to error," wrote Stone. "I think that Luther, in a course manner, said *that every man was born with a Pope in his belly*; by which I suppose he meant, that every man deemed himself infallible."[34]

Nor can professed Christians unite in one body without they possess the same Spirit—the Spirit of Christ. We may abandon all human creeds and formularies as bonds of union—we may relinquish the idea of making opinions of truth a test of fellowship—we may take the Bible alone, and

---

33 Barton W. Stone, editorial, The Christian Messenger (Georgetown, Kentucky), Nov. 25, 1826, p. 1. Reproduced by the Disciples of Christ Historical Society on microfilm, Nashville, 1958.

34 Ibid., p. 2.

Bible facts, without note or comment, as the only standard of faith and practice, and of Christian union; yet without the Spirit union can never be effected, nor continued. The attempt to unite righteousness and unrighteousness, piety and impiety, the Spirit of Christ and the spirit of the world, is as vain as the attempt to unite fire and water, or light and darkness.[35]

According to one contemporary observer, in 1811 there were about 13,000 Christians associated with Stone's unity movement.[36] Stone was not by nature contentious, except for the cause of Christian unity. "There are many preachers in this world," he complained, "who often zealously preach the doctrine of union, and they eulogize it in high terms; yet these men, though they know and preach the truth, remain inactive in promoting it. Like the pharisee doctors, *they say and do not.*"[37]

Stone, however, was a "doer." In 1832 the Stone and Campbell movements met together in Lexington, Kentucky, to consider the possibility of unification. Alexander Campbell was not even present. He seems to have had some misgivings, or at least questions, about some of Stone's doctrines. He also was concerned about the formal "structure" that such a union would entail, and so he believed the occasion to be premature. But Stone had made his position clear years ago about the subject:

> Oh, my brethren let us repent and do the first works, let us seek for more holiness, rather than trouble ourselves and others with schemes and plans of union. The love of God, shed abroad in our hearts by the Holy Ghost given unto us, will more effectually unite than all the wisdom of the world combined.[38]

With his ecumenical priority, Stone was willing to overlook any differences with Campbell and concoct a spiritual union (political union was not possible since both movements had forgone denominational structure). Effectively bypassing Campbell, though not opposed by any protestation, "Racoon" John Smith represented the Disciples of Christ while Barton Stone was the spokesman for the "Christians". They met for four days around Christmas in Georgetown, and on New Year's Day at Lexington, where they addressed the crowd and then, rather spontaneously, rose up and shook hands, agreeing to recognize each other as Christian brothers. In this informal way, unity between the two groups was consummated.

In his jubilation over the event, Stone immediately published in the Christian Messenger:

---

35 Stone, "Christian Union," pp. 313-314.

36 Hughes and Allen, Illusions of Innocence, p. 90.

37 Stone opening editorial, The Christian Messenger, Nov. 25, 1826, p. 17.

38 Quoted in Robert Richardson, Memoirs of Alexander Campbell, Vol. II. (Reprinted in Germantown, Tennessee: Religious Book Service, original copyright date 1897), p. 374.

We are happy to announce to our brethren, and to the world, the union of Christians in fact in our country. A Few months ago the Reforming Baptists, (known *individually* by the name of Campbellites,) [sic.] and the Christians, in Georgetown and in the neighborhood, agreed to meet and worship together. We soon found that we were indeed in the same spirit, on the same foundation, the New Testament, and wore the same name, *Christian*. We saw no reason why we should not be the same family. The Lord confirmed this union by his presence; for a good number was soon added to the church. . . .

Never did we witness more love, union, and harmony, than was manifested at these meetings. Since the last meeting we have heard of the good effects. The spirit of union is spreading like **fire in a dry stubble** [my bold].

It may be asked, is there no difference of opinion among you? We answer, We do not know, nor are we concerned to know. We have never asked them what were their opinions, nor have they asked us. If they have opinions different from ours, they are welcome to have them, provided they do not endeavor to impose them on us as articles of faith. They say the same of us. We hear each other preach; and are mutually pleased and edified.[39]

It seemed that the simple restorationist ecumenical hopes of Stone were coming to fruition. Robert Richardson, Alexander Campbell's biographer, evaluated the results of the event in the following manner:

Multitudes were added to the churches throughout the state, and an impetus was given to the cause by the union of the two people, which served to illustrate the overwhelming power which the gospel would exert upon the world if, in like manner, all the sad divisions of Protestants could be healed.[40]

History would prove that Stone was willing to compromise or sublimate many of his beliefs for the greater good of Christian union, even to the extent that he faded into the background of the movement, as the Campbells came to the fore.

---

39 Barton W. Stone, "Union of Christians," found in The Christian Messenger, ed. by B.W. Stone and John T. Johnson (Georgetown, Kentucky), January, 1832, pp. 6-7.

40 Richardson, vol. II, p. 387.

THE INCEPTION OF PRISTINE ECUMENICAL RESTORATIONISM ON THE FRONTIER:

PART II. THOMAS CAMPBELL AND MINIMALIST DOCTRINAL RESTORATIONISM

As a restorationist Alexander Campbell has been given plenty of recognition and a place of prominence. But, with the exception of Lester McAllister, authors have not accorded Thomas Campbell, Alexander's father, his rightful place of ascendency as the *ecumenical* restorationist of the Disciples of Christ. If Alexander Campbell was the Lenin of the movement, Thomas Campbell was the Karl Marx. He was the visionary who set forth the initial and basic ideology, and then his son defined, developed, and actualized the principles involved into a movement. "It may be said then that the father created the movement and that the son gave it life, that Alexander was the popularizer and Thomas the creative genius behind the movement."[1]

Many have approached Thomas Campbell as a precursor

Figure 3. Thomas Campbell (1763 - 1854)
(From www.therestorationmovement.com/tcmbl.htm)

---

1   Lester G. McAllister, <u>Thomas Campbell: Man Of The Book</u> (St. Louis: The Bethany Press, 1954), p. 12.

who was eclipsed by his more dynamic son for the leadership of the movement. Such a position is understandable, and certainly even defensible, because Alexander was an openly voracious advocate of restoration principles, an active debater, an avid journalist, and even a socially and politically prominent personality. But Thomas was not only the harbinger who pointed the direction of the movement; he provided the initial impetus for his church to develop the ecumenical plea it would advocate—though to varying degrees often alter or de-emphasize— throughout its history. McAllister has argued:

> It is evident from the facts that [Thomas] Campbell influenced the "brotherhood" known as Disciples of Christ much more fundamentally than has been commonly recognized. In organization patterns, in methods and publications, and in institutional development, the communion may have followed Alexander Campbell, Scott, and others but in its inner spirit and its penetrating emphasis on the Scriptures the influence was primarily that of the elder Campbell.[2]

Thomas did not originate in America, and there were many old-world influences that effected his thinking. He was one of the Scotch-Irish immigrants who migrated to America in the early nineteenth century. But he had been profoundly instilled with the principles of the English Enlightenment before he ever made the journey.

Allen and Hughes have postulated that the roots of influence on Thomas Campbell may be evidenced as far back as 1624, when Lord Herbert of Cherbury, deeply distressed over the causes of the Thirty Years War (1618-1648), wrote a book entitled _De Veritate_ [Concerning The Truth]. At least the first three stages of that conflict were between feuding religious groups, mainly Protestant against Catholic. Herbert came to regard the clamor over Biblical interpretation to be the source of agitation for the conflict.[3]

Concerned about the disastrous results of Christian disunity, he sought a rational panacea for this dilemma. He came to advocate that God was not the author of one book, but two instead. The first was the Bible, but the second was the book of Nature which, as the handiwork of the Creator, revealed His intended moral order to the world. These doctrines were clearly evident, and agreed upon by all religions in their basic teachings. He therefore urged that men abandon their disagreements about the Bible and, instead, adopt a religion of reason based upon God's revelation in Nature. In doing so he would later become recognized as the father of Deism.

---

2   Ibid., p. 269.

3   Edward, Lord Herbert of Cherbury, _De Veritate_ (London, n.p., 1635); as interpreted by Allen and Hughes, Discovering Our Roots, pp. 77-78.

The True Catholic Church is not supported on the inextricable confusion [of] oral and written tradition to which men have given their allegiance. Still less is it that which fights beneath any one particular standard, . . . The only Catholic and uniform Church is the doctrine of Common Notions which comprehends all places and all men. This Church alone reveals Divine Universal Providence, or the wisdom of Nature.[4]

Thomas Campbell certainly was no Deist. But, like Herbert, he was perplexed by religious division and sought to find a unifying factor for mankind. Both sought a platform on which all people of reason should be able to agree. For Herbert that answer was to be found in the obvious moral precepts of nature. For Campbell, however, only the clear and indisputable teachings of the Bible would suffice.

In the latter part of the same century, John Locke also came to share Herbert's concerns. He was similarly distressed over the causes of religious wars and persecutions, and was greatly troubled by the obstinate intolerance of one Christian group for another. In 1689 he was moved to write his Letter Concerning Toleration against any kind of enforced religious orthodoxy. In his essay Locke wrote, "For every church is orthodox to itself; to others erroneous or heretical."[5]

In seeking an answer for this quandary, Locke opted for what would become a typical restorationist position—the advocacy of a return to original conditions. He recommended to the different denominations a reduction of their doctrinal requirements for church membership down to the basic principles upon which they could all agree. Thomas Campbell would echo the same concept a century later. Locke proposed his idea in the following manner:

> But since men are so solicitous about the true church, I would only ask them here, by the way, if it be not more agreeable to the Church of Christ to make the conditions of her communion consist in such things, and such things only, as the Holy Spirit has in the Holy Scriptures declared, *in express words* [italics mine], to be necessary to salvation; I ask, I say, whether this be not more agreeable to the Church of Christ than for men to impose their own inventions and interpretations upon others as if they were of Divine authority, and to establish by ecclesiastical laws, as absolutely necessary to the profession of Christianity, such things as the Holy Scriptures do either not mention, or at least not expressly command?[6]

---

4   Edward, Lord Herbert of Cherbury, *De Veritate*, trans. Meyrick H. Carre' (Bristol, England: Published for the University of Bristol by J.W. Arrowsmith LTD., 1937), p. 303.

5   John Locke, "A Letter Concerning Toleration," found in Great Books Of The Western World, Vol. 35, ed. by Robert Maynard Hutchins (Chicago: Encyclopedia Britannica, Inc., 1952), p. 6, col. 2.

6   Ibid., p. 5, col. 1.

To Locke, there were certain ideas in Scripture that were easily self evident to any reasonable person. Reducing Christian requirements down to these few items, he believed, might restore the unity which was lacking in Christendom. This theological interpretation of requirements has been labeled by the term **"minimalist"** because only the very basic doctrines of Christianity would require consent. "By eliminating human deductions, the purity of Scripture would be restored and the causes of sectarian division removed."[7]

The Campbells admired Locke, who made reading the Bible a personal priority. Even though he was a member of the Anglican church, he downplayed the importance of promoting any denomination:

> I design to take my religion from the Scripture; and then, whether it suits or suits not any other denomination, I am not much concerned; for I think, at the last day it will not be inquired whether I was of the Church of England or Geneva, but whether I sought or embraced truth in the love of it.[8]

In 1695, John Locke added another work entitled The Reasonableness of Christianity, in which he maintained that Christianity is a reasonable religion. Restoration authors have appreciated Locke's perspective in this work:

> Locke concluded that Christianity is a reasonable faith, especially in its essentials: the Messiahship of Jesus and obedience to his clear commands. All other biblical teachings Locke viewed as non-essential issues which individual Christians might devoutly embrace but over which they should never coerce, fight, or kill.[9]

It is interesting to note that the Puritans in America were dealing with some of the same thoughts at this same time. Cotton Mather praised reason for its faculty to apprehend the truth of God and stated, "Did men Act Reasonably they would Live Religiously." But at the same time he refuted Deism's demand to abandon Scripture in favor of the reasonable interpretation of nature. He retorted, "The more of Gospel there is in our Preaching, the more of Reason there is in it. Scripture is Reason, in its highest elevation." And just a few years later Jonathan Russell reaffirmed this symbiont relationship between faith and reason when he announced, "Let our principles be Rational, those that are not Rational, are not Scriptural."[10]

---

7   Tristano, pp. 18 and 79.

8   See references and quote in Alexander Campbell's Millennial Harbinger (Bethany, Virginia) Vol. IV, No. 12 "New Series" (December, 1840), p. 548; and Vol. VII, No. 11 (November, 1836), p. 528.

9   Allen and Hughes, Discovering Our Roots, pp. 78-79.

10 Perry Miller, The New England Mind: From Colony To Province (Cambridge: Harvard University Press, 1953), pp. 420-421.

Being Scotch-Irish, Thomas Campbell was even more directly influenced by the Common Sense rationalism of Thomas Reid. In 1763, the same year in which Thomas Campbell was born, Reid joined the faculty at the University of Glasgow as Professor of Moral Philosophy. Essentially a proponent of the empirical rationalism of John Locke, Reid's thoughts came to represent a conservative reaction against the skepticism of David Hume. In his work entitled <u>An Inquiry Into The Human Mind, On The Principles Of Common Sense</u> published in 1764, Reid maintained that there were certain self-evident spiritual realities which could not be called into question. Some of these were: the real existence of the external world; the necessary causal connection of natural events; the moral character of actions; the existence of the human soul; the Providential establishment of natural laws; and the human mind's ability to comprehend their particular end or purpose.[11] This innate knowledge was shared by all humans, and a rational examination of Scripture might reveal the implications of such truths.

Thomas Campbell attended the University of Glasgow from 1783 to 1786. Reid's ideas appear to have been predominant at the university, even after his death in 1796, and it seems reasonable that Campbell was influenced by them. This common sense philosophy also infiltrated most American universities around the turn of the nineteenth century, and exercised a major influence on American thought when Thomas Campbell arrived in 1807.[12] Alexander Hamilton, Thomas Jefferson, and James Madison, were among many who were philosophical disciples of Reid.[13]

As has already been explained, there was a large and steady migration of Scotch-Irish to the colonies in the eighteenth century and early nineteenth century. Thomas Campbell was one of these. But he arrived here with no *tabula rasa* of religious conceptions. He brought with him many already established ideas about the church.

> The thought of the disciples was influenced in many obvious ways by [their Scotch-Irish] ethnic roots. The legalistic emphasis of the movement was in the tradition of Scottish Presbyterianism and German sectarianism. The intense individualism and iconoclasm of the early disciples leaders, their fervent confidence in the destiny of the nation, and their practical "common sense" approach to religion were all nurtured by their ethnic as well as their social heritage.[14]

11   Thomas Reid, <u>An Inquiry Into The Human Mind on the Principles of Common Sense</u>, ed. Derek R. Brookes (University Park, Pennsylvania: Penn State University Press, 1997). See also McAllister, p. 27.

12   Tristano, p. 26

13   West, p. 50.

14   David Edwin Harrell, <u>Quest For A Christian America: The Disciples Of Christ And American Society To 1866</u>, vol. I (Nashville, The Disciples of Christ Historical Society, 1966), pp. 49-50.

Another influence on the Campbells, especially regarding their hermeneutical approach to the Scriptures, was the inductive philosophy of Sir Francis Bacon. Thomas and his son Alexander attempted to apply Bacon's "scientific method" to the Bible, which they regarded to be mainly a set of facts. Rationally and systematically examined, these facts would then yield the great overriding principles of God for our lives. Alexander agreed with those who credited Bacon with helping to rid the Church of unreasonable authoritarianism:

> But the greatest of all the services which Bacon rendered to natural philosophy, was, that he perpetually enforced the necessity of laying aside all preconceived opinions and learning to be a follower of nature. . . .

> For men still leaned upon authority, and accepted as a test of truth the *appearance* [italics mine] of completeness and scientific consistency.[15]

One other strain of influential men must be acknowledged in formulating the views of the Campbells—the Glasites. John Glas (1695-1773) was a Scottish Presbyterian clergyman who questioned the Scriptural basis for a nationalized Presbyterian church. Along with others, like Robert and James Haldane, he also disdained the formalism, sterility, and institutionalism of the established church.

> As always in a state-supported church whose "livings" are at the disposal of a landed aristocracy, there were too many ministers who were mere place-holders and who acted on the theory that the church was performing its function if it continued to exist, maintained its dignity, administered the ordinances of religion, and furnished them a comfortable income.[16]

Concluding that the church should be autonomous in relation to the State, and that it should follow no particular creed, but rather only the Bible, Glas was summoned before his Presbytery in 1726. Finding his answers unsatisfactory, the Presbytery suspended him in 1728 and he was officially deposed in 1730. The former date is recognized as the official origin of the Glasite churches in Scotland.

Following his lead, the Campbells came to emphasize the Scriptures as the sole rule of faith and practice. At least four of the practices of the old Glasite churches seem to have been adopted by the Campbells: (1) weekly communion; (2) a plurality of elders; (3) a distinction of the Lord's Day from the Sabbath; (4) the use of Scriptural names such as "Church of Christ" to designate local congregations. But a negative consequence may have

---

15   Alexander Campbell, ed., "Sir Francis Bacon - Extract From The General Preface To His Works," The Millennial Harbinger [Fifth Series], Vol. III, No. 5 (May, 1860), pp. 256-257.

16   Winfred E. Garrison, Religion Follows the Frontier: A History of The Disciples of Christ (New York: Harper and Brothers, 1931), p. 80.

hitchhiked with this primitivistic emphasis, and that is legalism. The Glasites believed there was only one authorized form of worship established in the book of Acts, and they rigidly attempted to follow this pattern. Therefore, the Glasites had a propensity to divide among themselves when they could not agree on specific interpretations of doctrine or practice. As will be discussed later, so did the restoration movements.[17]

On one occasion John Glas visited the University at Edinburg where he met Robert Sandeman, a student at the university who would later become his son-in-law. In time Sandeman became the principle exponent of the Glasite viewpoint, and established Glasite congregations around Scotland. It has been estimated that there were eventually around thirty of these Glasite churches in Britain.[18]

Some Stone-Campbell denominational historians have attempted to down play the amount of influence bequeathed to their movement because of the negative implications that eventuated in history. W.E. Garrison criticized Glas and Sandeman—as well as the Haldane brothers and Greville Ewing, who held similar restorationist views—by noting that, "It will be observed that the union motive was virtually nonexistent among these restorers of the primitive order. Their object was not to be united with other Christians, but to be right."[19] On the centennial of Alexander Campbell's birthday, a professor at Southern Baptist Theological Seminary wrote a book critical of the Disciples of Christ Movement in which he spoke of the "arrogance of the Scottish Sandemanians," and leveled the accusation that "the Disciples of Christ are the direct descendants of the Sandemanians. . . ."[20] The next year a Disciple author named G.W. Longan responded with a work which contended that the Campbells agreed with only four of the Sandemanian's distinctive fifteen points of doctrine.[21]

Garrison and DeGroot have also been quick to distance the Stone-Campbell movement from Sandemanianism:

> The outstanding difference was the total absence of the unity motive in Sandeman and its primacy with Campbell. The Sandemanian churches were completely preoccupied with the duty of restoring the practices of the primitive church. They had no interest in unity, and not enough evangelistic zeal to keep themselves alive.[22]

---

17 John Owston, "The Scotch-Baptist Influence On The Disciples Of Christ," found in Leaven (Malibu, California: Pepperdine University) Winter Quarter, 1997, pp. 38-39.

18 Ibid., p. 38.

19 W.E. Garrison, Religion Follows The Frontier, pp. 37-38.

20 William Whitsitt, Origin Of The Disciples Of Christ (Campbellites) (New York: A.C. Armstrong and Son, 1888), pp. 110-111.

21 See Garrison and DeGroot, The Disciples Of Christ: A History, p. 49.

22 Ibid., p. 50.

History has confirmed at least the last part of this statement, because the only remaining Sandemanian church in America expired in 1890.[23]

Henry Webb has attempted to summarize the issue with the following distinction:

> Thus, while other restoration efforts sought primarily to be "right" in God's sight, regardless of how many others were "wrong," the movement under study did not come into being with such disregard for the rest of the "erring" followers of Christ. Rather, it sought to be Biblically faithful because it held that such Biblical fidelity is the only viable basis on which to appeal to other followers of Christ to achieve the unity for which the Lord of all Christians earnestly prayed.[24]

While living in Northern Ireland, Thomas Campbell was a member of the Old Light, Anti-Burgher, Seceder, Presbyterian church. But Scripture passages like John 17: 11-21 had produced in him a profound distaste for the many divisions within Christ's Body. He not only regarded them as deeply sinful, but also harmful to the evangelistic effort of the church. Robert Richardson, who knew him personally, wrote the following:

> Schooled amidst such schisms in his own denomination, and harassed by the triviality of the differences by which they were maintained, it is natural to suppose that one of so catholic a spirit as Thomas Campbell conceived the greatest antipathy to party spirit in all its workings and manifestations. . . .[25]

Hence, when an ecumenical effort within the Presbyterian church occurred in 1804, Thomas Campbell eagerly participated in its promotion. The Synod of Ireland met at Belfast to consider the reunification of the Burgher and Anti-Burgher factions within the church, and Campbell took advantage of the situation to address the conference. After opening with a lament about the "unhappy division" that had occurred earlier for political reasons, he enumerated the negative consequences of such disunity:

> It appeared to us, indeed, a matter truly deplorable, that, in the circumstances in which the Lord has placed us, there should not exist the most perfect harmony among all the sincere friends and lovers of the truth as it is in Jesus; and that all such were not united in one common, energetic cooperation in the grand cause of truth and righteousness, under the banner of one common, comprehensive, and faithful testimony. More especially that a respectable body of professing Christians, . . . should be divided among ourselves;. . . .

---

23   See reference in <u>The New Encyclopedia Britannica (Micropaedia)</u>, Ed. 15 (1998), Vol. 5, p. 295.

24   Webb, p. 38.

25   Richardson, Vol. I, p. 56.

This, our unhappy division, appeared to us an evil of no small magnitude,.
. . . For has it not exposed the zealous contenders for a reformation, on
both sides, to the contempt and jeer of the scorners, and filled the mouths
of scoffers with reproach and obloquy? Has it not been fraught with the
awful consequence of distracting, disturbing, and dividing the flock of the
Lord's heritage, and of sowing discord among the brethren? Has it not
been productive of a party spirit, . . . ? Has it not had a very embarrassing
tendency with respect to many of the serious and well-meaning, when
they, seeing our division, upon inquiry, find that the subject-matter of our
difference is not to be found either in the Old or New Testament.[26]

The strain of Campbell's many labors in preaching and teaching, and
the stress of political and religious dissensions probably contributed
significantly to a break down of his health, and his doctor recommended a
change in environment. Some of Campbell's friends had resettled in
America and were urging him to join them. Reluctantly, but with the
encouragement of his son Alexander, he made the journey in the spring of
1807. Upon arrival, he sought the fellowship of his comrades, who
recommended him highly to the Associate Synod of North America. In
May he was appointed to serve in the Presbytery of Chartiers in
southwestern Pennsylvania, and given fifty dollars to launch a circuit-
riding ministry.[27]

But Thomas Campbell soon discovered that the schisms of the Old
World had been transplanted into the New World as well. Not only
members of other denominations, but even members of other branches of
the Presbyterian church were considered to be pariahs. Many years later
Robert Richardson would reminisce:

There are few, in fact, of the present generation, who have grown up under
the influence of the liberalizing institutions of the United States, and the
more enlightened views of Christianity since presented, who can form a
proper idea of the virulence of the party spirit which then prevailed. Each
party strove for supremacy, and maintained its peculiarities with a zeal as
ardent and persecuting as the laws of the land and usages of society would
permit. The distinguishing tenets of each party were constantly thundered
from every pulpit, and any departure from the "traditions of the elders,"
was visited at once with the severest ecclesiastical censure. Covenanting,
church politics, church psalmody, hyper-Calvinistic questions, were the
great topics of the day; and such was the rigid, uncompromising spirit
prevailing, that the most trivial things would produce a schism, so that

---

26 Thomas Campbell, "Address of Thomas Campbell To The Synod of Ireland", found in
    Memoirs Of Elder Thomas Campbell, p. 210. It is interesting to note that, while
    Thomas Campbell's plea failed to bring about an immediate unification, both sides did
    finally unite in 1820, after the Campbells had relocated to America. See Errett Gates,
    The Early Relation and Separation of Baptists and Disciples (Chicago: The Christian
    Century Co., 1904), p. 10.

27 For greater detail see Richardson, Ch. 5, and McAllister, pp. 56-69.

old members were known to break off from their congregations, simply because the clerk presumed to give out, before singing, *two* lines of a psalm instead of *one*, as had been usual custom.[28]

Not long after his entrance into the Presbytery, Campbell was requested to pay a pastoral visit to some of his Anti-Burgher Presbyterian brethren who lived near Pittsburgh, and to officiate at a sacramental religious service for them. Realizing that there were members from other branches of the Presbyterian church in his congregation, and sympathizing with the fact that they had been denied the Lord's Supper for quite some time, Campbell expressed his regret at the existing divisions in the church and invited all who wished to participate in an open communion celebration. William Wilson, a fellow seceder minister who had accompanied him on the trip, was offended by this action and reported it to the presbytery. After a long process which included seven charges being leveled at Campbell, and his response to each one of them, the presbytery "censured" him and, by its subsequent actions, sought his suspension from the Associate Synod of North America. Campbell then composed a "Protest and Appeal" for the occasion of its meeting on May 19, 1808, pleading for the union of all Christians on the basis of Scripture alone and denying that his intentions were schismatic. Addressing them like a suppliant, he requested:

> . . .permit me to add, my sincere desire to unite with you. . . . if I did not sincerely desire a union with you, I would not have once and again made application for that purpose. . . . I am, therefore, through His grace, ready to forebear with you; at the same time, hoping that you possess the same gracious spirit, and therefore will not reject me. . . .[29]

Campbell was at first simply "rebuked and admonished" by the Synod, but as the year progressed other seceder ministers stirred the coals of rumor and innuendo and Campbell became a *persona non grata* among the seceders. However, he was not at a loss for opportunities to preach, for he was still in great demand by the laity, and he continued to minister around the area of Washington, Pennsylvania. On September 14, 1808, Campbell submitted a paper *in absentia* to the Synod. Part of it read:

> . . .I find myself in duty bound to refuse submission to their decision as unjust and partial; and also finally to decline their authority, while they continue thus to overlook the grievous and flagrant maladministration of the Presbytery of Chartiers. And I hereby do decline all ministerial connection with, or subjection to, the Associate Synod of North America, on account of the corruptions and grievances. . . .[30]

---

28 Richardson, Vol. I, pp. 245-246.

29 Thomas Campbell, "Protest and Appeal," found in <u>Memoirs Of Elder Thomas Campbell</u>, p. 15.

30 McAllister, p. 94.

By the following May Campbell had returned the original fifty dollars given him by the synod to launch his ministry, and the synod had accepted his resignation from the seceder church. Seeing the opportunity to now form an association with other Presbyterians, as well as some from other communions and some who were unaffiliated but agreed with his principles, Campbell and other Christian leaders inaugurated the Christian Association of Washington. In drawing up their platform for the association it was agreed upon that its purpose would be to emphasize a return to original New Testament Christianity and abandon anything that was not authorized in the Bible. This determination was expressed in a slogan often repeated today among the Stone-Campbell descendants: "Where the Scriptures speak, we speak; and where the Scriptures are silent, we are silent."[31] We are informed that there was a long period of silence at the meeting while the representatives tried to evaluate the merits of such a plea. After a while a bookseller and postmaster from Cannonsburg, who was a member of the Seceder church, quipped, "Mr. Campbell, if we adopt *that* as a basis, then there is an end of infant baptism." Campbell immediately retorted, "Of course if infant baptism be not found in Scripture, we can have nothing to do with it."[32]

After erecting a log building on the Sinclair farm for meeting purposes, members of the association allowed Campbell to draft a document which would express more fully the objectives of the association. The resultant publication became known as the Declaration and Address, and is regarded by Campbellites today as the foundational and most important document, other than the Bible of course, in the history of their restoration movement.

It was about this time, in the fall of 1809, that Thomas Campbell's family joined him in America. His oldest son Alexander, who is the subject of the next chapter, had the opportunity to read the proof-sheets of the Declaration and Address, and approved of its sentiments whole-heartily. But when a Presbyterian minister named Riddle also had the chance to examine them, he responded, "Sir these words, however plausible in appearance, are not sound. For if you follow these out, you must become a Baptist."[33] No one at the time, except perhaps Mr. Riddle himself, realized how prophetic his words would prove to be.

The Declaration and Address was read, approved, and ordered to be printed by the Association on September 7, 1809. It is a pamphlet of fifty-six pages divided into four sections: (1) A Declaration consisting of three

---

31 Richardson, Vol. I, p. 236. Leroy Garrett (p. 104) believes this motto to be original with Thomas Campbell.

32 Ibid., pp. 236-238.

33 Ibid., p. 250.

pages and outlining the reasons, purposes, and organization of the association; (2) The Address, consisting of eighteen pages promoting the goal of, and suggesting the means for, the achievement of Christian union; (3) An Appendix of thirty pages of response to anticipated criticisms; (4) A Postscript of three pages in which Campbell tries to prompt the process with two suggestions.

In the Declaration Campbell expresses his desire to restore the unity, peace, and purity, of the original church. Moreover, he laments that he is "well aware from sad experience, of the heinous nature and pernicious tendency of religious controversy among Christians; tired and sick of the bitter jarrings and janglings of a party spirit,. . . ." He also expresses the hope that all Christians would come to reject human opinions and creeds as authoritative.[34] Henry Webb expresses the opinion that Campbell hoped that other associations like the Christian Association of Washington would be formed in every community and cause the various sects and denominations to surrender their entrenched positions in favor of Christian unity.[35]

In the Address portion of the writing, Campbell often makes reference to "our brethren of all denominations," demonstrating that his Association was not meant to be exclusivistic by being the one with the correct doctrine, but rather *inclusivistic* by advocating principles upon which all Christians should be able to unite. Listing thirteen propositions as principles upon which to proceed, the essence of his plea may be realized in the following excerpts:

> Proposition one: That the Church of Christ upon earth is essentially, intentionally, and constitutionally one; consisting of all those in every place that profess their faith in Christ and obedience to Him in all things according to Scriptures,. . . ;
>
> Proposition two: That although the Church of Christ upon earth must necessarily exist in particular and distinct societies, locally separate one from another; yet there ought to be no schisms, no uncharitable divisions among them. They ought to receive each other as Christ Jesus hath also received them to the glory of God;
>
> Proposition three: That in order to this, nothing ought to be inculcated upon Christians as articles of faith; nor required of them as terms of communion; but what is expressly taught and enjoined upon them, in the word of God;

---

34 Thomas Campbell, Declaration and Address, Centennial Edition (Caraopolis, PA.: Record Publishing Co., 1909), pp. 3-4. (originally published in Washington, PA.: Brown and Sample, 1809).

35 Webb, In Search of Christian Unity, p. 78.

Proposition four: . . .the New Testament is as perfect a constitution for the worship, discipline and government of the New Testament church, and as perfect a rule for the particular duties of its members; as the Old Testament was for the worship, discipline, and government of the Old Testament church, . . . ;

Proposition ten: That division among Christians is a horrid evil, fraught with many evils. It is antichristian, as it destroys the visible unity of the body of Christ; as if he were divided against himself, ... It is antiscriptural, . . . it is antinatural, . . . in a word, it is productive of confusion, and of every evil work.[36]

Condemning those "sad divisions" among Christians which cause "its professed subjects to bite and devour one another," Campbell eloquently portrays the situation:

What awful and distressing effects have those sad divisions produced! what [sic] aversions, what reproaches, what backbitings, what evil surmisings, what angry contentions, what enmities, what excommunications, and even persecutions!!! And indeed, this must in some measure, continue to be the case so long as those schisms exist, for, said the apostle, where envying and strife is, there is confusion and every evil work. What dreary effects of these accursed divisions are to be seen, even in this highly favored country, where the sword of the civil magistrate has not as yet learned to serve at the alter.[37]

Apparently feeling the impending significance of world events of that day, Campbell seemed apocalyptic in his motivation. Napoleon was widely regarded as the beast of Revelation, and Campbell probably included a millennial perspective in his desire for Christian unity.[38] In an effort to show his willingness to be reasonable and pliable, Campbell promised, "that there is nothing we have hitherto received as a matter of faith or practice, which is not expressly taught and enjoined in the word of God, either in express terms, or approved precedent, that we would not heartily relinquish, that so [sic] we might return to the original constitutional unity of the Christian church."[39]

---

36   Thomas Campbell, <u>Declaration and Address</u>, pp. 16-18.

37   Ibid., p. 6.

38   Thomas Campbell's biographer, Lester McAllister (pp. 112-113), claims that he had a "premillennarian cast to his appeal for Christian union. . .," and that "He appears quite clearly to have identified current events with the predictions of the Apocalypse." Thomas Campbell, for example (p. 8), discusses the significance of the recent French Revolution and asks, "Is it not the day of the Lord's vengeance upon the anti-Christian world; the year of recompences for the controversy of Zion? Surely then the time to favor her is come; even the set time."

39   Ibid., pp. 10-11.

The isolation of the Christian Association of Washington did not seem, however, conducive to its highest priority—the unity of all believers upon the basis of the Bible alone. Errett Gates cleverly enunciated the incompatibility of their position when he wrote, "It began to dawn upon the Campbells that they were in danger of becoming another sect among the sects, and to stand in the ridiculous light of a sect pleading for the destruction of sectarianism."[40] So Thomas Campbell approached the Synod of Pittsburgh, being willing to concede many differences, in order to be received back into the Presbyterian church. But on October 4, 1810, the synod declined Campbell's request, believing that it would be destructive to the peace of the church.[41] Alexander does not seem to have encouraged the overture, but he and others nonetheless seem to have anticipated its outcome. Richardson wrote:

> For a party to have admitted into its bosom those who were avowedly bent on the destruction of partyism, would of course have been perfectly suicidal. It would have been only to repeat in another form, and with a full knowledge of the object in view, the story of the wooden horse of Troy, and to have the gates of its well-walled ecclesiastical city thrown open to its enemies.[42]

There was irony in the fact that the Synod's Confession of Faith declared that the Bible was the only legitimate rule of faith and practice, and yet the Synod excluded the Campbells for insisting upon virtually the same thing. Thomas became even more convinced that people had to be liberated from creedalism and sacerdotalism. He asked:

> What is the great difference between withholding the Scriptures from the laity, as the Romanists do, and rendering them unintelligible by arbitrary interpretation, forced criticisms and fanciful explanations, as many Protestants do, or making the people believe that they are nearly unintelligible by urging the necessity of what is called a learned clergy to explain them?[43]

Thomas was an advocate for the inclusion of all who agreed upon a few basic essentials, rather than the exclusion of those who differed on the details. He believed that the second chapter of Acts highlighted all that was necessary for one to become a Christian:

> Here, then, we have the faith once delivered to the saints, namely: what the apostle preached concerning Christ and Him crucified, with the belief and obedience of it by the three thousand, and the happiness, the joy, and

---

40   Gates, p. 15.

41   McAllister (p. 142) has reprinted an entry from the minutes of the meeting, a portion of which accuses Campbell of "promoting division, instead of union."

42   Richardson, vol. I, pp. 330-331.

43   Ibid., Vol. II, p. 41.

consolation that followed. Here, then, we have the ancient Gospel exhibited in its purity and power; . . . .[44]

Dean Walker alludes to the fact that Disciples of Christ churches today still use only the "Good Confession" of Peter for baptism and membership, and that the essence of this short testimony is more of an "oath of allegiance" than a consent to a creed.[45] "The question, therefore, in regard to faith," Richardson asserted, "was not, in the beginning, '*What* do you believe?' the eager and sole inquiry of modern religious parties; but '*In whom* do you believe?'." He continues on to regretfully admit, ". . .men have unhappily substituted a trust in the accuracy of their doctrinal knowledge—a confidence in the orthodoxy of particular tenets; as if correctness of religious opinion could secure the Divine favor, ..."[46]

It must be acknowledged, of course, that not all of Thomas Campbell's associates and biographers evaluate his intentions as altruistic, pacific, or even courageous. Many of his colleagues in the Seceder Church honestly believed him to be in error and undermining the efforts of the church. And some of them had been his friends. Even McAllister, perhaps Campbell's most enthusiastic supporter, admits that:

> It was evident that the synod, while it could not justify the method of the presbytery, felt called on to pass censure on Thomas Campbell's actions, and so virtually sustained the spirit and purpose of the charges originally brought against him. It is just as obvious that Campbell must have been somewhat petulant and that his sense of right was outraged. Furthermore, he may have been poorly advised at times during the trial. From the minutes it may be concluded, however, that the synod was doing its best to reach a decision satisfactory to all parties.[47]

William Whitsitt was not so gentle in his assessment of Campbell. He referred to him as "a timid, inefficient person," who was eventually "in subjection to the imperious will of his son," due to his "rather exceptional weakness of character."[48] Later on in his work he rather harshly stated that, "If he ever had an original idea, he took pains to avoid giving expression to it in such of his writings as have been submitted to the inspection of the public."[49]

However with Campbell's distaste for sectarian division, it is reasonable to suppose that he was sincere and purposeful in his irenic and

---

44   Thomas Campbell, letter to Jane Campbell (his wife), dated April, 1830, found in <u>Memoirs of Elder</u> <u>Thomas Campbell</u>, p. 149.

45   Walker, p. 9.

46   Richardson, Vol. I, p. 411.

47   McAllister, p. 90.

48   Whitsitt, pp. 63-65.

49   Ibid., p. 112.

ecumenical desires. In the <u>Declaration and Address</u>, proposition one, he states that the Church of Christ on earth consists "of all those in every place that profess their faith in Christ and obedience to Him *in all things according to the scriptures. . . .*"[50] Since Thomas Campbell did not elaborate on what obedience in "all things" meant, he may be legitimately accused of either naivete, or perhaps of timidity. But it must also be considered that this well-educated man may have *intentionally* left that phrase uninterpreted, realizing that further definition of his ideas could precipitate a greater barrier to dialogue between the denominations.

McAllister adds that, "Campbell was disturbed, not only by the division of the Church, but also because he sincerely felt that such a spirit was a hindrance to many individuals in accepting the gospel."[51] Certainly a "kingdom divided against itself cannot stand," but it also would not be very credible or convincing! If Christians could eradicate these divisions among themselves, the only legitimate occasion for controversy would then be with those who deny the deity of Jesus, the resurrection, or the divine authority of the Bible, and in those days not many held to those positions.

---

50 Thomas Campbell, <u>Declaration and Address</u>, p. 16.

51 McAllister, p. 52.

ALEXANDER CAMPBELL AND THE DEMARCATION AND ORGANIZATION OF RESTORATIONISM

On October 1st in 1808, Thomas Campbell's family boarded a ship at Londonderry with the intention of joining him in the New World. Only six days into the journey an inept and half drunk crew ran into the strong winds of a storm and they were shipwrecked off the coast of Scotland. Fearing the hazards of a winter voyage, Mrs. Campbell postponed the voyage until the next year. In the meantime, Alexander enrolled in the University at Glasgow and studied under Greville Ewing, somewhat of a free-spirited restorationist.

Upon completion of his study, and after much soul searching, the 21-year-old found himself in opposition to the sectarian myopia of his Seceder church and separated himself from its fellowship. This event amounted to an interesting coincidence since, at the time, he knew nothing of his father's expulsion from the same church in America.

Arriving in Pennsylvania in 1809, Alexander was pleased with the text of the <u>Declaration and Address</u> and reluctantly supported his father's efforts to re-establish a relationship with the Presbyterian church. But when the Synod of Pittsburgh rejected Thomas Campbell's overture in 1810, Thomas was willing to overlook the rejection and pursue no further public action. Alexander, however, whose nature was more contentious

Figure 4. Alexander Campbell (1788 - 1866) (From www.therestorationmovement.com/cmbla.htm)

than his father's, became convinced that some kind of public response should be made, and he attempted to do so through the auspices of the Christian Association of Washington. This incident may illustrate a next step in the evolution of the Restoration Movement on the frontier—its adolescence—and Alexander's personality and abilities were appropriate for that stage of development. McAllister evaluated the two Campbells in his biography in the following manner:

> The essential difference between Thomas and his son is brought to the forefront in their attitude toward this matter. The son was to give evidence of an aggressive and disputatious nature in contrast to the indecisiveness and avoidance of conflict so apparent in the father. In fairness, however, it must be said that much of the difference in attitude was but that of a young and ambitious man in contrast to a man thrust in middle age into an unfamiliar environment.[1]

The vigor and expression of Alexander's response to the synod did much to propel him to a position of leadership among the reformers. But it also further isolated them from the orbit of the Presbyterian church. Richardson offered this comparison of the personalities and approaches of Thomas and Alexander Campbell:

> The father, full of affectionate sympathy and over-sensitive in regard to the feelings of others, could not bear to inflict the slightest pain, and would rather withhold than confer a benefit which could be imparted only by wounding the recipient. The son, with more mastery of his emotional nature, could calmly contemplate the entire case and, for the accomplishment of higher good, could resolutely inflict a temporary suffering. The former was cautious, forbearing, apologetic; the latter decided, prompt and critical. The one displayed the gentle spirit of Melanchthon, the other the adventurous boldness of Farel and the uncompromising spirit of Knox. Both were alike anxious to promote the great interest of humanity; but while the father relied perhaps too much upon emollients to remedy the spreading cancer of sectarianism, the son, with less reverence for consecrated errors, but equal love for men and greater sagacity and skill, preferred the knife of the surgeon. Both were equally desirous of winning men away from the idols of religious bigotry, but while the one sought to persuade with gentle words, the other would seize with powerful grasp the image at the shrine, and break it in pieces before the eyes of its worshipers.[2]

Since they were no longer in good standing with Presbyterian churches, the Campbells decided to reorganize the Christian Association as a church, which was organized on May 4, 1811. W.E. Garrison charges that by this act they constituted themselves as a separate denomination, even

---

1   McAllister, p. 147.

2   Richardson, Vol. I, pp. 482-483.

though they were only one small country church with a membership of thirty people.[3] The members had a communion service together the next day—Sunday, May 5th—with Alexander Campbell preaching. However, the inaugural service in the Brush Run Church building was held on June 16, 1811. Thomas Campbell was chosen to be its elder (minister), and Alexander was licensed to preach.[4]

Within a year, on January 1, 1812, the Brush Run Church ordained Alexander to the ministry, a further act which demonstrated their contempt for the officially recognized ecclesiastical authorities. It would be through the auspices of the Brush Run Church—and later the Mahoning Association and the Christian Baptist periodical—that Alexander Campbell defined and structured the simple and unstructured plea of Thomas Campbell into an organization. These actions, in retrospect, probably initiated the degeneration of a realistic hope for denominational unity, and engendered the foundation of what would eventually become a loosely-organized denomination itself. But Robert Richardson, Alexander Campbell's primary biographer, certainly regarded these developments as a positive and necessary step in the evolution of the movement:

> It is certain . . . that had it not been for the bold assaults, the incisive logic and the determined spirit of the son, the reformatory movement initiated by the father would speedily have disappeared from view, as the wave created in the river by the passing steamer quickly subsides into the general current.[5]

The first step toward defining the doctrinal positions of the Restoration Movement was initiated by the birth of Alexander Campbell's first daughter on March 13, 1812. Alexander had married Margaret Brown, the eighteen-year-old daughter of a carpenter named John Brown, on March 12, 1811. Since his wife and parents were still members of the Presbyterian Church, shortly after the birth the question of infant baptism presented itself. Up to this time Campbell does not seem to have given the subject of baptism a great deal of thought. So he gathered as many books as he could in favor of infant baptism and investigated the subject. However, studying the Greek New Testament along with these books, he came to the conclusion that infant baptism was an invention of men. In the Bible all the occasions of baptism seemed to involve only adult believers. Therefore, he decided to forgo the sprinkling of his young daughter Jane.

However, further reflection caused him to question the validity of his own experience in baptism, having himself been sprinkled as an infant in the Seceeder Presbyterian Church. Some members of the Brush Run Church had already decided that the adult immersion of believers was a

---

3   W.E. Garrison, Religion Follows the Frontier, p. 100.

4   Richardson, Vol. I, pp. 367-371.

5   Ibid., Vol. I, p. 483.

matter of significant importance, and Alexander Campbell began to consider the issue for himself.

> Admitting that infant baptism was without warrant, the question began to assume quite a different aspect, and was no longer, "May we safely reject infant baptism as a human invention?" but, "May we omit *believer's baptism*, which all admit to be divinely commanded?"[6]

Connecting the act of baptism as a part of the process of salvation (Mark 16:16; Acts 2:38; et al.), Alexander went to visit his father and ask his opinion on the matter. Thomas does not seem to have had strong feelings one way or the other, and made no significant objections to his son's plans for immersion. Alexander, having become acquainted with a Baptist preacher named Matthias Luce, requested that he perform the sacrament. At first Pastor Luce balked at performing the ceremony because Alexander insisted upon the omission of the "testimonial of religious experience," alleging that such a requirement was not to be found in the Bible. But eventually Luce consented and agreed to baptize him simply upon the confession that Jesus was the Son of God. On Wednesday, June 12, 1812, Alexander and Margaret Campbell, along with his sister Dorothea and two members of the congregation, were immersed in the clear waters of Buffalo Creek.[7]

To Alexander's surprise and delight, Thomas and Jane Campbell, Alexander's parents, were also immersed in the ceremony. Thomas had come to agree that there was neither express terminology nor precedent in the Scriptures to authorize the practice of infant baptism. By the same token, even though he regarded his baptism as an act of obedience important for him to culminate, he did not want to offend his paedobaptist friends. He had earlier insisted that the ordinance was not to be mandated:

> But as for those who are already members of the Church and participants of the Lord's Supper, I can see no propriety, even if the scriptural evidence for infant baptism be found deficient, in their unchurching or paganizing themselves, or in putting off Christ, merely for the sake of making a new profession; thus going out of the Church merely for the sake of coming in again.[8]

Thomas continued to stress that the issue of baptism should be sublimated to the greater issue of Christian unity. In a long address he

---

6   Ibid., Vol. I, pp. 393-394.

7   A research paper on file at the Disciples of Christ Historical Society claims that Sidney Rigdon baptized Alexander Campbell, which is simply not true. See Thomas Lee Scott, Sr., Apostasy on The Western Reserve: Selected Disciples of Christ Experiences In The 1830's (Research paper for Phillips University, Enid, Oklahoma, April 13, 1978), p.6 (though pages are not numbered).

8   Richardson, Vol. I, p. 251.

attempted to explain why he regarded it as incumbent upon him to submit to the fulfillment of an important divine institution. But, Richardson reports:

> This was a necessity which he had evidently longed to avoid since he was aware it would at once erect an impassable barrier between him and the paedobaptist community in which he had labored, and frustrate all his hopes of winning it over to his views of Christian union.[9]

William Whitsitt, one of the Campbells' most vitriolic critics, claims that the Campbells would never have abandoned the practice of sprinkling if they had not been pressured to do so by the majority of the Brush Run congregation.[10] This seems unlikely, however, because, up to this point at least, the Campbells had not been reluctant to place principle above affiliation. Also their conclusions and resultant actions were certainly consistent with the basic principles expressed in the Declaration and Address.

Robert Richardson identifies this occasion as a significant transition point in the Campbellite Restoration Movement, saying that, "From the moment that Thomas Campbell concluded to follow the example of his son in relation to baptism, he conceded to him in effect the guidance of the whole religious movement."[11] McAllister appraised, "It may be said then that the father created the movement and that the son gave it life," and that while Thomas was "the creative genius behind the movement," Alexander was "the popularizer."[12] As far as Restoration Movement objectives were concerned, the pendulum began to swing from a unity emphasis based upon those New Testament doctrines agreed upon by all denominations, to an attempt to define what basic New Testament principles were and implore others to accept them. "There needed, at this crisis, one to take the lead," Richardson explained, "who was of a more adventurous spirit, and who, realizing better the real posture of affairs, could recognize the truth that peace could be reached only through victory."[13]

Thomas Campbell had adopted the slogan of a German, Rupertus Meldenius, for his Restoration Movement: "In essentials unity; in non-essentials [matters of opinion] liberty; in all things charity [love]."[14] He had earlier consigned the issue of infant baptism as a matter of private judgement to the category of non-essentials. Now, for the first time in the Campbell movement, it seemed that a specific element was defined in the list of "essentials" for unity that had not been there before. At least it can be said that that is how some

---

9   Ibid., p. 400.

10   Whitsitt, p. 79.

11   Richardson, Vol. I, p. 401.

12   McAllister, p. 12.

13   Richardson, Vol. I., p. 401.

14   Powell, p. 22..

perceived it. And whereas the facts of the good confession of Peter (Mt.16:16) had been agreed upon by all Christian churches and therefore could perhaps form a realistic basis for unity, belief in the importance of adult immersion of believers was a minority opinion and certainly not a platform for unity without outright conversion. In the opinion of one author:

> Christian union . . . was no longer simply a matter of persuading churches to unite on the beliefs which Christians already held. Now it was felt necessary to persuade them also to accept the "positive ordinance" of baptism which at that time only the Baptists believed to be commanded in the New Testament. It now seemed most important to seek first the reformation of the church, the restoration of it to the purity it had known in the New Testament days, and *then* to work for the union of Christianity.[15]

This conversion of the Brush Run Church into a fellowship of immersed believers proved to be quite a marvel to the community around them, and quite an offense to the paedobaptist clergy. At this time on the frontier of Western Pennsylvania, the power of the ecclesiastical establishment was almost supreme, and the Campbells were anathematized as disorganizers and even spiritual outlaws. On one occasion, when Alexander Campbell was traveling and noticed that a thunderstorm was about to overtake him, he was refused shelter at the house of a lady when she found out who he was. On other occasions, when baptisms were being held in the river, crowds on the riverbank would mock them, threaten personal violence, and even throw sticks and stones into the water where they were.[16]

The impression that the Campbells were moving into the Baptist orbit did not sit well with some who pressed for ecumenical Restorationism. Barton Stone, for example, who had been advocating the "fire union" of the Holy Spirit for all Christians, suggested that this emphasis upon "water union" would have " a chilling effect" upon their movement.[17] Later, in his <u>Christian Messenger</u>, Stone warned about the consequences of making immersion a condition for Christian unification:

> Should they make their own peculiar view of immersion a term of fellowship, it will be impossible for them to repel, successfully, the imputation of being sectarians, and of having an authoritative creed (though not written) of one article at least, which is formed of their own opinion of truth; and this short creed would exclude more christians from union than any creed with which I am acquainted.[18]

---

15   McAllister, p. 160.

16   Richardson, Vol. 1, pp. 430-431.

17   Ibid., Vol. 2, pp. 197-198.

18   Stone, <u>The Christian Messenger</u>, August 30, 1830, p. 201.

Stone had, for many years, fellowshipped with the unimmersed as well as the immersed, regarding them all as Christian brothers and sisters. Alexander Campbell, on the other hand, seemed to be establishing the first condition, beyond belief in Jesus as the Christ, for fellowship in their restoration movement. Even Robert Richardson, Alexander Campbell's personal friend, colleague, doctor, and biographer—whose purpose it was to praise him in his biography—admitted this comparison between Stone and Alexander:

> With the former, the idea of uniting all men under Christ was predominant; with the latter the desire of an exact conformity to the primitive faith and practice. The one occupied itself chiefly in casting abroad the sweep-net of the gospel which gathers fishes of every kind; the other was more intent upon collecting "the good into vessels" and casting "the bad away." Hence the former engaged mainly in *preaching*—the latter in *teaching*.[19]

But Alexander Campbell still very much regarded his movement as a unity movement. Being a rationalist of the Lockean Enlightenment tradition, he believed that faith was simply belief in the testimony of the facts in the Bible. A rational examination of Scripture, devoid of preconceived prejudices, should lead any sincere and discerning Christian to a clear understanding of basic Biblical doctrines. Thus he believed that one of these clear requirements for all Christians was baptism, the rite of initiation for salvation. Hence, he continued the restoration plea for the unity of all denominations, although it was a conditional appeal. Twenty years later his plea still retained the same tone:

> Such is the measure of light and liberty which I now enjoy under Jesus Christ, that I could unite in all Christian communion and co-operation with all the *baptized believers* in all the sects of America., so far as their *opinions* are considered; provided only, that they hold *the head*, Jesus; believing all the *facts* attested concerning Him, and are obedient *to His commands*. And farther than this, we humbly conceive, *christian* union, communion, and co-operation can never legitimately extend.[20]

Despite the fact that no unimmersed believer was recognized as being "duly prepared" to participate fully in the worship service, or was invited to partake of the Lord's Supper, Alexander Campbell was probably not as discriminatory as he appears to have been. Even William Whitsitt, who portrays him as a narrow-minded chauvinist, admits that Campbell's "arrogant policy of exclusion" was not followed "continuously and consistently," contending that if it had been, this country would never have "been burdened with the evils of Mormonism," the

---

19   Richardson, Vol. II, pp. 198-199.

20   Alexander Campbell, "Introductory Remarks," <u>The Millennial Harbinger</u> (Bethany, Virginia), Vol. 3, No. 1 (January 2, 1832) p. 5 (p.1 orig.).

growth of which was fertilized by the restorationist principles of the Disciples' movement.[21]

Because the Campbells harbored benevolent feelings toward those who may be sincere but mistaken, and because they had a fresh recollection of their own struggles with creeds and clergies, they would not deny that their "erring brethren" were Christians. While that position may not impress most of us as being overly liberal, Alexander Campbell was eventually questioned, and even criticized, for such magnanimity by some of his followers. On July 8, 1837, a well-meaning lady from Lunenburg, Virginia, wrote Campbell and asked him if anyone who was unimmersed could truly be regarded to be a Christian. His reply to "this conscientious sister," which ignited some controversy among "the Brotherhood," was as follows:

> Who is a Christian? I answer, everyone that believes in his heart that Jesus of Nazareth is the Messiah, the Son of God; repents of his sins and obeys Him in all things according to his measure of knowledge and of his will. . . .

> I cannot, therefore, make any one duty the standard of Christian state or character, not even immersion into the name of the Father, of the Son, and of the Holy Spirit, ...

> Should I find a Pedobaptist more intelligent in the Christian Scriptures, more spiritually-minded and more devoted to the Lord than a Baptist, or one immersed on a profession of the ancient faith, I could not hesitate a moment in giving the preference of my heart to him that loveth most. . . .

> There is no occasion, then, for making immersion, on a profession of the faith, absolutely essential to a Christian. . . .[22]

The Campbellite advocacy of adult immersion caused the Baptists to become interested in their movement. Some of the Baptist churches invited Thomas and Alexander Campbell to preach for them and, pleased with what they heard, frequent invitations were extended to the Brush Run Church to join the Redstone Baptist Association. But Alexander Campbell, a college-educated man with a classical education, was not impressed with the Baptist leaders.

> I had no idea of uniting with the Baptists more than with the Moravians or the mere Independents. I had unfortunately formed a very unfavorable opinion of the Baptist preachers as then introduced to my acquaintance, as narrow, contracted, illiberal, and uneducated men. This, indeed, I am sorry

---

21   Whitsitt, p. 85.

22   Alexander Campbell, "Any Christians Among Protestant Parties", <u>The Millennial Harbinger</u>, Vol. 1, No. 9 (Sept. , 1837), pp. 411-414 (p. 35 orig.).

to say, is still my opinion of the ministry of that Association at that day; and whether they are yet much improved, I am without satisfactory evidence.[23]

Campbell's opinion was not maintained exclusively by him. The Virginia Anglicans held a similar lack of respect for these itinerant, dissenting preachers. The Reverend Patrick Henry[24] once complained about their preaching, "I wish they could be prevented, or, at least be oblig'd to show their credentials."[25] Henry May has also observed that, "Sometimes their long hatred of upper-class establishments, Congregational or Episcopalian, led Baptists in this period to be positively hostile to education."[26]

Campbell's impression of the Baptist laity, nonetheless, was very different. Admitting that, "The people, however, called Baptists, were much more highly appreciated by me than their ministry,"[27] he relented and decided to attend the next meeting of the Redstone Association, which he dates as being held in the Fall of 1812. Many years later Campbell recalled his motivation to do so, and the impression it left on him:

> I confess, however, that I was better pleased with the Baptist people than with any other community. They read the Bible, and seemed to care but little for any thing else in religion than "*conversion*" and "*Bible doctrine*." They often sent for us and pressed us to preach for them. We visited some of their churches; and, on acquaintance, liked the people more and the preachers less. Still I feared that I might be unreasonable, and by education prejudiced against them; and thought that I must visit their Association at Uniontown, Pennsylvania, in the autumn of 1812. I went there as an auditor and spectator, and returned more disgusted than I went. They invited me "to preach;" but I declined it altogether, except one evening in a private family, to some dozen preachers and twice as many laymen. I returned home, not intending to ever visit another Association.[28]

On his way home from the meeting, however, Campbell learned that the Baptist people themselves, who had attended the meeting, did not like the spirit and style of the speakers. They assured him that the meeting was an aberration, continued their invitations for him to preach,

---

23 Alexander Campbell, "Anecdotes, Incidents and Facts, connected with the origin and progress of the current reformation, some of which have never before been published," No. 2, The Millennial Harbinger, Series III, Vol. 5, No. 6 (June, 1848), p. 345. See also Richardson's Memoirs, p. 438.

24 This is **not** the American patriot of Revolutionary renown.

25 Isaac, p. 150.

26 May, pp. 322-323.

27 Alexander Campbell, "Anecdote, Incidents, and Facts . . .," No. II, Millennial Harbinger, Vol. V, No. 6 (June, 1848) p. 345.

28 Ibid., p. 346.

and kept coaxing him to join the Brush Run Church with the Association. The congregation finally discussed the matter in the Fall of 1813, according to Alexander Campbell.[29] A decision was made to apply for membership with certain conditions delineated in an eight to ten page document, with probably the paramount provision being the repudiation of all human creeds.

There were a few individuals who, for various reasons, opposed the Brush Run entry into the Redstone Association. But the majority welcomed them, perhaps unaware of some of their views at that time, or else not perceiving their differences as very significant. In 1832, after the expulsion of the Campbellite churches from the Redstone Association, Alexander regretted that his congregation had not preserved a copy of the document, because the Association clerk declined to provide it for them when requested.

> In forming a union with the Baptists we protested against their constitution, and refused to unite with them if any other creed than the New Testament was presented to us. A document of several pages to this effect was presented to the Redstone Association in the year 1813, and is now, or ought to be, in the hand of William Brownfield, Secretary of the Association, who then opposed, and always opposed our union, unless we would worship the Philadelphia idol, the little book drawn up by a few English Baptists in 1689 against Arminianism, and adopted in Philadelphia in 1742 by an Association of Baptists.[30]

B. A. Hinsdale—a minister who became president of Hiram College, Superintendent of Cleveland Schools, Professor of Education at the University of Michigan, and a prolific writer—identified the incompatibility in the Campbellite marriage to the Baptists which eventually led to the divorce in 1829:

> Thus, immersion was the bridge over which the Campbells passed from the Presbyterian to the Baptist order. In fact, however, they never were

---

29 Ibid. Alexander Campbell and Robert Richardson (Vol. 1, pp. 450 and 459) both give this date as the fall of 1813 (though Richardson in a footnote on page 458 erroneously lists the year of entry into the Union for the state of Ohio as 1802). Most Stone-Campbell historians have simply accepted that date as correct.

However, McAllister (p. 169) and W. K. Pendleton (1867 Millennial Harbinger, p. 42) both list the date as 1815. Jim North (Union In Truth, pp.114 and 115) gives a well-researched and convincing argument for the latter date, based mainly upon a reprint of the Minutes of the Redstone Baptist Association. No mention is made of the Brush Run application for membership in the 1813 entry, but the 1815 entry acknowledges receipt and approval of it. North also gives a firm date of 1814 for the Uniontown meeting.Still, however, Campbell recollects an interval of "some two or three years" (p. 347) between Association membership and the composition and delivery of his famous "Sermon on The Law," which has an uncontested date of 1816.

30 Alexander Campbell, "Introductory Remarks," Millennial Harbinger, Vol. III, No. 1 (January 2, 1832) pp. 1-2 (p.1 orig.).

Baptists; and the union formed in 1813, although it lasted ten years or more, was never a very happy one.

The Campbells continued to preach their newly gained views. They departed more and more from the old Calvinistic Doctrines and methods of preaching. They attempted to pour the new wine into the old bottles, in which attempt they met with very different results.[31]

During the duration of time from 1813 thru 1819, Alexander Campbell was occupied primarily with preaching at the Brush Run Church, teaching restoration principles, farming, and trying to provide for his growing family. In 1811, when the Christian Association had been considering relocating to Zanesville, Ohio, John Brown, Alexander's father-in-law, deeded him the family farm at "Buffaloe," Virginia, hoping he would remain in the area. He did, and the Brush Run congregation, not wanting to move without him, also stayed. He became a rather industrious farmer, but his preaching engagements still retained priority.

In 1816 Alexander Campbell re-ignited some repressed Baptist hostilities when he delivered his now famous "Sermon On The Law" to the Redstone Association assembled at Cross Creek. To a gathering of people, most of whom believed in those days that every part of the Bible was equally authoritative, Campbell advocated the obsolescence of the Old Testament law by the New Testament Covenant. Claiming that Christians are no longer bound to the law of Moses but instead are subjects of the grace of Christ, he was actually brought to trial for heresy before the Association the following year. Though he was acquitted, his adversaries continued to fan the glowing embers until, in 1823, another trial with even more substantial charges was proposed to the Association. However, as will be seen in chapter eight, Campbell anticipated the move by his detractors and adeptly outflanked the planned confrontation by leaving their jurisdiction in forming a new congregation.[32]

The year 1820 proved to be one of great significance in Alexander Campbell's life, as well as for our study here. It was not then uncommon for Presbyterian ministers to enter towns and challenge Baptist ministers to debate. Baptists were not usually inclined to accept, since the former were usually superior in education. But in the Fall of 1819 a Seceeder Presbyterian minister named John Walker, in Goliath-like demeanor, challenged a Baptist preacher named John Birch, or any other Baptist champion of his choosing, to debate him on the issue of baptism. Birch immediately implored Campbell to respond, but Alexander declined because:

---

31 B. A. Hinsdale, A History of The Disciples In Hiram, Portage County, O. — A Discourse Delivered to the Church on Sunday, March 26, 1876 (Cleveland: Robison, Savage and Co., 1876), p.8.

32 For the text of the "Sermon On The Law" see The Millennial Harbinger, Vol. III, No. 9 (September, 1846), pp. 493-521.

. . . the feelings of the Reformers were at first decidedly opposed to *public* oral debate even on scriptural themes, as being not favorable to the promotion of Christian union, since persons thus publicly committed to the support of particular views were too often tempted to strive for victory, rather than for truth, ...[33]

Nevertheless, eventually Campbell was induced to accept the invitation, and the debate took place on June 19 and 20, 1820, in Mount Pleasant,[34] Ohio—only twenty-three miles from his home in Buffaloe (later Bethany), Virginia (later West Virginia). The topic of the debate was: Who is the Proper Subject and What is the Proper Mode of Baptism? The debate lasted for seven days, during which time the Baptists were impressed with, and cheered on, their new champion. But Campbell was uncomfortable in the role of being their hero, confessing to them three years later after a second such debate with a Presbyterian preacher named McCalla:

> Brethren, I fear that if you knew me better you would esteem and love me less. For let me tell you that I have almost as much against you Baptists as I have against the Presbyterians. They err in one thing and you in another; and probably you are each nearly equidistant from original apostolic Christianity.[35]

In August of the same year as the Campbell-Walker Debate, the Mahoning Baptist Association was organized by ten churches in the town of Nelson, located in the Western Reserve area of Portage County, Ohio.[36] A minister named Adamson Bentley, one of its founders and perhaps its most influential authority, having read a published copy of the debate, decided to visit Mr. Campbell in the summer of 1821. He had been hearing that Campbell was being criticized and opposed by the Redstone Association for some of his views, though he personally expressed the conviction that, "Mr. Campbell had done more for the Baptists than any man in the west."[37] Hence, he determined to journey to Campbell's home at Bethany, along with his brother-in-law Sidney Rigdon, for the ultimate purpose of enticing him to join the more liberal[38] Mahoning Association.

---

33   Richardson, Vol. II, pp. 13-15.

34   There are two Mt. Pleasants in Ohio. This one is the easternmost, along the Ohio River.

35   Ibid., Vol. II, pp. 88.

36   Mary Agnes Smith, "A History of the Mahoning Baptist Association" (Master's thesis, University of West Virginia, 1943), p.25.

37   Richardson, Vol. II, pp. 44-45.

38   Smith, Appendix A. The first paragraph of the constitution of the Mahoning Association reads in part [errors not mine] ". . . not pretending to Halve Athority over any man's nor over the churches whose representatives form this Association. But we act as advisory council only. Disclaiming all superiority, Jurisdiction, Coercive Right, and Infalibility, and acknaledging the Independence of every Church which has received Authority from Christ to Perform all Duties enjoyned respecting the Goverment of his Church in this world."

Campbell was intrigued enough by the suggestion that he decided he would at least scrutinize the annual meetings. He reported that, "I became a regular attendant, and found in them much pleasure and profit," and later claimed that the Mahoning Association had done much to eliminate "prejudice" among the Baptist ministry of their jurisdiction, and had "prepared the way for a very great change of views and practice all over those 3,000,000 acres of nine counties, which constitute the Western Reserve."[39] In 1823 he and his new Wellsburg congregation joined that Association.

Having felt defeated and embarrassed by Walker's performance in the 1820 debate, the Presbyterians selected the more capable William McCalla to debate Campbell again— this time in early October of 1823 in the town of Washington, Kentucky. Campbell "appeared as the defendant of the Baptist community against their assailant Mr. McCalla, who had been, for some time, smoke in their eyes and thorns in their side."[40] But in the process of the debate on the mode of baptism—immersion versus sprinkling—Campbell developed the non-Calvinist view that the *purpose* of immersion was for forgiveness of sins.

> For the "Christians in the West," this message was a godsend, for it provided what they wanted most: immediate certainty of salvation and an end to waiting and mourning. No longer would a sinner anxiously await for months or even years, seeking an experience that might ratify his or her election. Instead the sinner simply would hear the gospel and submit to immersion for the forgiveness of sins. Immediately all doubts would be erased; the sinner would know that he or she was now saved.[41]

In 1832 Campbell wrote, "That the christian religion has been for ages interred in the rubbish of human invention and tradition, is confessed and felt by many, very many in all societies."[42] He accurately read the pulse of society for his time. Nathan Hatch has observed:

> The most telling evidence of the revolt against history and against Calvinist control is the distinctive way that many populists chose to read the Bible. Any number of denominations, sects, movements, and individuals between 1780 and 1830 claimed to be restoring a pristine biblical Christianity free from all human devices.[43]

---

39 Alexander Campbell, "Anecdotes, Incidents, and Facts . . .", No. III The Millennial Harbinger, Vol. V, No IX (September, 1848) p. 524.

40 Ibid., No. V (November , 1848) p. 613.

41 Allen and Hughes, Illusions of Innocence, p. 115.

42 Alexander Campbell, "Introductory Remarks," The Millennial Harbinger, Vol. III, No.1 (January 2, 1832), p.6.

43 Hatch, p. 179.

But Alexander Campbell was not only a good analyst of the mood of the era, he also personally believed and practiced the same convictions. Whereas reformers like Luther and Calvin wanted the people to read the Scriptures, they did not go so far as to advocate that they could completely understand them without interpretations from the clergy. Campbell went one step further. "The German Reformer gave to the people the opportunity of *reading* the Scripture. It was the part of Mr. Campbell to convince them that they could *comprehend* it— . . . ."[44]

Richardson wrote that Campbell acted upon the same principles he advocated, and was "accustomed to contemplate the Bible as if it had just fallen into his hands from heaven, and utterly disregarding all systems and theories, and even his own previous conclusions, he was wont to study it constantly with a free and unbiased mind."[45] Campbell himself corroborated this observation when he wrote, "I have endeavored to read the Scriptures as though no one had read them before me; and I am as much on my guard against reading them to-day, through the medium of my own views yesterday, or a week ago, as I am against being influenced by any foreign name, authority, or system, whatever."[46]

Samuel S. Hill, Religion Professor at the University of Florida, advanced the opinion at the Bicentennial Campbell Lectureships for the Disciples of Christ Historical Society, that Campbell's unfolding of a major new emphasis in Protestant Christianity could not have occurred at an earlier or later time in American history. Emphasizing that this time and this place were fertile for the restorationist seed to be planted, he wrote:

> Campbell touched the concerns and aspirations of a great many western Americans. Those people probably had not formulated these perceptions when they heard about the Restorationists' principles and system. Nor would most of them have managed to do any formulating of a public theology. That is what leaders do. But when the frontier men and women heard the message, they recognized it and they liked it. It struck a chord. They were ready for it, indeed in some real if inchoate sense they believed it already.[47]

As B. A. Hinsdale so eloquently phrased it:

---

44   Richardson, Vol. II, p.42.

45   Ibid.

46   Alexander Campbell, "Reply" (to R. B. S.) , The Christian Baptist, ed. by Alexander Campbell (Buffaloe, Virginia), Vol. III, No. 9 (April 23, 1826), reprinted as "Seven Volumes in One" (Joplin, Missouri: College Press, 1983), p. 229.

47   Samuel S. Hill, "Campbell-Stone On The Frontier: The Only Ones Weren't the Only Ones," Lectures In Honor of the Alexander Campbell Bicentennial, 1788-1988 (Nashville: Disciples of Christ Historical Society, 1988), p. 68.

It was, therefore, the good fortune of the Campbells, and of their co-laborers, to begin their work where the material at hand was plastic; also their good fortune to see this material, as society grew in culture and in age, harden, thus retaining the impression that they had made. They wrote neither upon iron nor in the water.[48]

One of the many who became enthused with Campbell's message was a Baptist preacher named Sidney Rigdon. Restless and searching, he became convinced that he had found "the true faith" at last. He would become one of the Restoration Movement's most avid and eloquent proponents. . .for awhile.

---

48 Hinsdale, p. 7.

Chapter
—6—

SIDNEY RIGDON AND THE ATTRACTION OF RESTORATIONISM

Sidney Rigdon was born on February 19, 1793, in St. Clair Township of Allegheny county, Pennsylvania.[1] His parents, William and Nancy Rigdon, had four children—three boys and a girl—and Sidney, the second son, grew up working on the family farm. He received only a rudimentary education by attending a common school, which met at a log school house nearby in winter time when the chores on the farm were minimal. Typical of many children during that era, Sidney was not permitted to attend school further, even though he greatly desired to do so, because he was fit enough to do the important manual labor on the farm and an education was deemed of limited practical value for the frontier of that era. One of his brothers (Laommi), however, was "too sickly and feeble" to work on the farm, so Sidney's parents allowed Laommi to finish school and, eventually,

Figure 5. Sidney Rigdon (1793 - 1876) (From www.jfs.saintswithouthalos.com/images/rigdon.htm.)

---

1   Henry Webb's new "Campbellite" history entitled <u>In Search Of Christian Unity</u> (Cincinnati: Standard Publishing Co., 1990), p. 142, erroneously lists his birth date as 1795. John W. Rigdon, Sidney's son—in a lecture to the Washington State Historical Society on Sept. 20, 1883—mistakenly lists the county as Washington County (see typescript in Special Collections at Lee Library of B.Y.U., p. 2). A plethora of credible sources confirm the birth information written here.

From *Sidney Rigdon: The Benedict Arnold of the Restoration Movement* originally published in SCJ 6.1 (Spring, 2003). Reprinted by permission of Stone Campbell International.

go to medical school in Lexington, Kentucky, where he became a doctor. When Sidney insisted upon going with him, and his parents again denied him the opportunity, "he said to them in anger he would have as good an education as his brother got and they could not prevent it." Also forbidden the use of candles to read at night, Sidney nonetheless became self-taught by gathering up hickory bark for the fire place and reading the Bible, history books, and grammar texts, after his parents were in bed.[2]

While Sidney envied Laommi his opportunity, he dutifully remained on the farm until he was twenty-six, because his father, who had died in 1810 when he was seventeen, had willed him a section of land and he was still needed there to work it. But Sidney's heart was not in farming because, from early childhood, he felt himself to be called by God to preach the Gospel. His family were members of the Peter's Creek Baptist Church near his home, and Sidney was familiar with the requirement of a personal divine experience for church membership. After a personal struggle as a "seeker" for such a confirmation, Rigdon later admitted, "When I joined the church I knew I could not be admitted without an experience: so I made up one to suit the purpose, but it was all made up, and was of no use."[3] On the basis of his testimonial, Pastor David Phillips baptized him.

> But there was so much miracle about his conversion, and so much parade about his profession, that the pious and discerning Pastor, entertained serious doubts at the time in regard to the genuineness of the work. He was received, however, by the church, and baptized by the Pastor, with some fears and doubts upon his mind. Very soon, Diotrephes like, he began to put himself forward and seek the preeminence, and was well nigh supplanting the tried and faithful minister who had reared, and nursed, and fed the church, for a long series of years. So thoroughly convinced was Father Phillips by this time, that he was not possessed of the spirit of Christ, not withstanding his miraculous conversion, and flippant speech, that he declared his belief, "that as long as he (Sidney) should live, he would be a curse to the church of Christ!"[4]

In late 1818 Rigdon left the family farm[5] and traveled westward to Beaver county in order to get a theological apprenticeship with Reverend Andrew Clark, the minister of the Providence Regular Baptist Church there, since there were no Baptist seminaries in Western Pennsylvania at the time.

---

2   John W. Rigdon, "Lecture On The Early Mormon Church," Sept. 20, 1883, Special Collections, Lee Library, Brigham Young University, Provo, Utah, pp. 2-3.

3   See Harmon Summer's statement in J.H. Kennedy, <u>Early Days Of Mormonism</u> (London: Reeves and Turner, 1888), p. 64; also cited in Van Wagoner, p. 8.

4   Hans Rollman, "The Early Baptist Career Of Sidney Rigdon In Warren, Ohio," <u>Brigham Young University Studies</u>, Vol. 21, No. 1 (Winter, 1981), p. 43.

5   McKiernan (p. 15) says that Sidney's mother Nancy sold it, but Van Wagoner (p. 9) claims that Sidney left it to his brother Carvel's oversight.

Spending the winter under Clark's tutelage, Rigdon obtained a "license"[6] to preach, and gradually became preoccupied with the task of finding the "fullness of the gospel" for his life. As F. Mark McKiernan would later express it, "Rigdon believed that he could find in the New Testament the ordinances of Christ's church, which could be established in the nineteenth century through the direction of God's Holy Spirit in the lives of righteous men."[7]

Most historians of the subject have written that Rigdon left the Providence Church to join Adamson Bentley and his ministry at Warren, Ohio, in the Western Reserve area, in May of 1819. But evidence now seems to support the date of his arrival as being in March of 1820. Based upon the Warren church records, his letter of dismission from the Providence church was dated August 4, 1819. Hans Rollman has suggested that Rigdon may have had a short preaching engagement in Pittsburgh before joining the Warren congregation.[8]

Adamson Bentley had also been born in Allegheny county, Pennsylvania, in the year 1785, but this author is unaware of any personal familiarity between the two men before this time. In an interesting coincidence though, Bentley *had* met the Campbells. In 1809, while engaged in the mercantile business and traveling to Philadelphia to purchase goods, he encountered them as the family was joining Thomas after their journey from Ireland.[9] In the next year, on May 19, 1810, Bentley was ordained, and in 1811 he became the Pastor of the Concord Baptist Church, which was organized in Warren in 1803 and by 1811 had 27 members. His ministry there lasted twenty years, the longest tenure of any other minister since the church started.[10]

While co-laboring with Bentley, Rigdon met Mrs. Bentley's sister Phebe Brooks, and on June 12, 1820, they began a marriage of 56 years in which she remained faithfully supportive of his many moves.[11] Living in

---

6   A distinction was made between "licensed" and "ordained" pastors, with the former being allowed to preach but not administer the sacraments. See William Warren Sweet, Religion On The American Frontier: The Baptists 1783-1830 (New York: Henry Holt, 1931), p. 40. See also Van Wagoner, p. 10.

7   F. Mark McKiernan, The Voice Of One Crying In The Wilderness: Sidney Rigdon, Religious Reformer, 1793-1876 (Lawrence, Kansas: Coronado Press, 1971), p. 11.

8   For more detail, see Rollman, p. 39. For an example of the earlier date, see McKiernan, p. 17.

9   See Richardson, Vol. I, pp. 215-217. A good biography needs to be written about Bentley.

10 Thorn Pendleton, et. al., The History of Central Christian Church , Warren, Ohio, 1803-1988 (published by the church, 1988), see esp. pp. 3 and 20.

11 McKiernan, (p. 17) mistakenly wrote, "They lived together in harmony, regardless of the hardships they endured, until she died in 1886." But Sidney died in 1876.

Warren, Rigdon worked as a circuit-riding preacher for congregations that could not afford a minister. At Warren, Bentley and Rigdon together baptized fifty-six people in the first twelve months of his ministry there, making the church of ninety-one members one of the largest Baptist churches in Ohio.[12]

Before 1820 the Baptist churches of the western Pennsylvania and eastern Ohio area were members of the Beaver Baptist Association, a body created to regulate the orthodoxy of the ministers to the frontier churches. Bentley had become "the most influential preacher of the Association."[13] Rigdon's name appears for the first time in the minutes of the 1819 annual meeting, and the minutes of the August, 1820, meeting report his ordination, which must have happened between April and August of that year.[14]

Four days after the close of the annual meeting, on Wednesday, August 30, the Beaver Association restructured into three parts. The Mahoning Association—named for the river which encompassed its territory in Ohio—was one of these, born in 1820. It was in this Association that Bentley, Rigdon, and Alexander Campbell would all construct a movement together. Bentley's name especially, features prominently in the minutes of all the meetings.

The Mahoning Association, not long after its inception, began to develop a "liberal" strain within that would cause other associations, like the Redstone Association, to question it and, eventually, disfellowship with it. Adamson Bentley, for one, began to question the harsh and arbitrary nature of the Calvinist doctrine of salvation, which the Baptist church then taught:

> I used to take my little children on my knee, and look upon them as they played in harmless innocence about me, and wonder which of them was to be finally and forever lost! It can not be that God has been so good to me as to elect all my children! No, no! I am myself a miracle of mercy, and it can not be that God has been kinder to me than to all other parents. Some of these must be of the non-elect, and will be finally banished from God and all good. And now, if I only knew which of my children were to dwell in everlasting burnings, oh! how kind and tender would I be to them, knowing that all the comfort they would ever experience would be here in this world![15]

---

12   Milton Backman, "The Quest For A Restoration: The Birth Of Mormonism In Ohio," Brigham Young University Studies, Vol. 12, No. 4 (Summer, 1972), p. 352.

13   Rollman, p. 46.

14   Ibid., pp. 45-48.

15   Quoted in A.S. Hayden, A History Of The Disciples Of Christ On The Western Reserve (Cincinnati: Chase and Hall, 1875), p. 103.

Rigdon would soon join his brother-in-law in the refutation of predestinationist doctrines, and his refusal to teach them would, within a few years, propel him out of the Regular Baptist orbit.

In 1820 Bentley and Rigdon discovered a pamphlet recording the text of Alexander Campbell's debate with John Walker. Both men were so impressed with Campbell's thoughts that, in the summer of 1821, they traveled eighty-five miles to Buffaloe (Bethany), Virginia, just to talk with him. Fascinated with what Campbell had to say, the men conversed with him from evening until the next morning. As they were leaving the next day, Rigdon candidly confessed to Campbell his realization that, if he had taught one error from the pulpit within the last year, he had taught a thousand! Campbell later observed, "At that time he [Rigdon] was the great orator of the Mahoning Association— though in authority with the people, second always to Adamson Bentley."[16]

But Campbell was reluctant, after their discussions, to encourage Bentley and Rigdon to become spiritual revolutionaries, stirring up resentment and resistance. He also may not have yet fully trusted them, perhaps fearing misrepresentation of his viewpoints. Sensing their excitement about his new restorationist perspective when "they went on their way rejoicing," he tried to caution them to be careful in their teaching:

> I found it expedient to caution them not to begin to pull down any thing they had builded until they had reviewed, again and again, what they had heard; nor even then rashly and without much consideration. Fearing that they might undo their influence with the people, I felt constrained to restrain, rather than to urge them forward, in the work of reformation.[17]

However, within a year, they had laid the groundwork for many members of the Mahoning Association to be receptive to Campbell's ideas. Both Bentley and Rigdon attended the meeting that fall, which convened at Palmyra, in Portage county, Ohio. The minutes of the two-day meeting reveal Rigdon's accelerating influence in the Association. On the first day he was invited to a seat in the council, and on the second day he was voted to be the Mahoning Association's messenger to the Grand River Association, and to write the "Corresponding Letter" for its members the following year.[18]

While both Campbells advocated the twin goals of restoration and unity, Sidney Rigdon was probably much more of a restorationist than an

---

16 Alexander Campbell, "Anecdotes, Incidents and Facts," No. III, The Millennial Harbinger, Series III, Vol. V, No. IX (September, 1848), p. 523. See also Hayden, p. 19, and Richardson, Vol. II, p. 45.

17 Ibid.

18 Nathan Coffin, clerk, "Minutes Of The Mahoning Baptist Association, September 5 and 6, 1821, Special collections, The Western Reserve Historical Society, Cleveland, Ohio.

ecumenist. His personality tended more toward legalism and rigidity than tolerance and compromise. His energy seemed limitless, his ambition high, his preaching dynamic, and his demeanor sometimes pugilistic. "The restoration of Christ's true religion as revealed in the New Testament," wrote McKiernan, "became a compulsive, consuming passion, which led Rigdon to follow solely the dictates of his own religious understanding and to scorn all other viewpoints."[19]

Apparently Campbell was soon impressed with Rigdon. The "Sage of Bethany" had roots and influence in the Pittsburgh area, still being a member of the Redstone Association through the Brush Run church, and in 1822 he induced Sidney to accept a call to a growing Baptist congregation there that was "favorable to reformation."[20] Sidney's father-in-law also urged him to accept the position, "as it was not very often a young minister received such an offer. It might be the making of him and give him a great reputation."[21]

So Sidney left Warren on January 5, 1822,[22] and began his ministry at the First Baptist Church of Pittsburgh in February.[23] Even though he was still a young man of twenty-nine years, in less than a year Rigdon had united the church into the largest congregation in the city, and gained a reputation as one of Pittsburgh's most eloquent preachers.[24] Richardson confirmed this by relating that, "he was a man of more than ordinary ability as a speaker, possessing great fluency and a lively fancy which gave him great popularity as an orator."[25]

While Rigdon was ministering to this church, Alexander Campbell made an effort to introduce him to a man with whom he would eventually become friends and, five years later, set the Western Reserve on fire evangelistically. This man was Walter Scott, whom Campbell met in 1820 as he had arrived recently from Scotland. At this time Scott was a rather rebellious Presbyterian, while Rigdon was somewhat of a reforming Baptist—both moving in the direction of complete restorationism. Campbell later recalled the occasion:

I was at all pains to have Sidney Rigdon and the church in Pittsburgh introduced to Brother Scott and the brethren with him. They were,

---

19 McKiernan, p. 11.

20 Richardson, Vol. II, p. 47. Jim North, <ins>Union In Truth</ins>, p. 190, believes that this same church had been established "some years previously" by Thomas Campbell.

21 John W. Rigdon, "Lecture On The Early Mormon Church," pp. 4-5. "Wickliffe," as he was commonly known then, said that Sidney had preached there before, on occasion.

22 Rollman, p. 50.

23 Joseph Smith, <ins>History Of The Church</ins>, Vol. I (Salt Lake City: Deseret Book Co., 1978), p. 121. Henry Webb, <ins>In Search Of Christian Unity</ins>, p. 142, wrongly lists the year as 1821.

24 John W. Rigdon, p. 5.

25 Richardson, Vol. II, p. 47.

however, for a considerable time very shy of each other. Each community was very sensitive on the subject of its own peculiarities.[26]

The feelings of admiration between Alexander Campbell and Sidney Rigdon must have been mutual, for in October of 1823 Rigdon accompanied Campbell for three hundred miles on horse back to his debate with William L. McCalla in Washington, Kentucky. After what many had regarded as Campbell's stinging defeat of John Walker in 1820, the Presbyterians believed they could have a much better representation of their views through this preacher from Augusta, Kentucky, so Campbell had accepted a second challenge. Rigdon took notes for the occasion and these, combined with some of Campbell's notes, were soon published as a volume of over four hundred pages.[27]

Earlier that summer Campbell had narrowly averted being evicted by the Redstone Association by forming the new church in Wellsburg, Virginia, and joining it with the Mahoning Association. Still somewhat frustrated and angry, Campbell's Redstone enemies transferred their hostility toward some of his colleagues in the reformation. Since Rigdon's church at Pittsburgh was still a member of the Redstone Association, they went after him, even though he had built up his church to be "one of the most respectable and popular churches in the city of Pittsburgh."[28] John W. Rigdon, Sidney's son, later wrote:

> At lenght [sic] an old Scotch Divine came to Pittsburgh and wanted to know of my father if he preached and taught the Baptist Confession of Faith., Infant Damnation. He told him he did not as he did not believe it and would not teach it. The Scotch Divine replied to him that he would have to teach it as it was part of the Baptist Confession of Faith. My Father replied to him that he did not care if it was a part of the Baptist Confession of Faith. It was to him too horrible a doctrine for him to teach and he would have nothing to do with it. His refusal to teach the Babpitst [sic] Confession of Faith occasioned quite a stir among the congregation. The older members of the chu ch [sic] thought he ought to teach it as it was a part of their Confession of Faith while the younger members thought he acted wisely in refusing to teach the doctrine. My father seeing there was to be a division in the Church tendered his resignation and the Church got another minister.[29]

---

26 Alexander Campbell, "Anecdotes, Incidents and Facts," No. IV, The Millennial Harbinger, Series III, Vol. V, No. X (October, 1848), p. 553.

27 Richardson, Vol. II, p. 95. The proceedings of the debate may be read today in Alexander Campbell, A Public Debate on Christian Baptism Between The Rev. W.L. Maccalla, A Presbyterian Teacher, and Alexander Campbell (London: Simpkin and Marshall, 1842); Reprinted in Kansas City, Missouri, by The Old Paths Book Club, 1948).

28 A.B. Phillips, The Restoration Movement and The Latter-Day Saints (Independence, Missouri: Herald Publishing, 1929), p. 312.

29 John W. Rigdon, p. 5.

There is some discrepancy in the sources as to how and when Rigdon left the church. According to the Baptist version, Rigdon was *excommunicated* for "doctrinal heresies" by a council of ministers and messengers held in Pittsburgh on October 11, 1823.[30] But according to Mormon and Disciples' sources, Rigdon *resigned* in August of 1824.[31] A small opposition group of twelve to twenty people—led by a man named Winter who apparently later divided some other churches—had begun as early as 1822 in Rigdon's own church, and it may be that Rigdon's supporters of some seventy or eighty people, and Winter's group, ended up trying to disfellowship each other.[32] Whatever really happened, Rigdon ignored any account of a heresy trial and painted a rather rosy and sympathetic picture of himself through the pen of Joseph Smith years later:

> Truth was his pursuit, and for truth he was prepared to make every sacrifice in his power. After mature deliberation, deep reflection, and solemn prayer to his heavenly Father, the resolve was made, and the important step was taken. (Aug. 1824). . .as he could no longer uphold the doctrines taught and maintained by it (Baptist Church). This announcement was like a clapp [sic] of thunder. Amazement seized the congregation, which was then collected, which at last gave way in a flood of tears. It would be in vain to attempt to describe the feelings of the church on that occasion, who were zealously attached to their beloved pastor, or the feelings of their minister. On his part it was indeed a struggle of principle over affection and kindness.[33]

The events of 1823-24 caused Walter Scott and Sidney Rigdon to form a closer relationship. Scott had been preaching at a small Sandemanian church which, unlike the Baptists, did not support their ministers financially. So Scott taught school for income. Rigdon joined Scott's church, and most of his congregation joined him in the move.[34] Needing a source of support for his family, Rigdon became a journeyman tanner for his brother-in-law, Richards Brooks. He continued to preach on weekends, endeavoring to win as many as he could to restorationist principles.

In February of 1825 Alexander Campbell began a series of thirty-two articles entitled "A Restoration of The Ancient Order of Things," which ran from February 7, 1825, through September 07, 1829, in the <u>Christian</u>

---

30 The Braden-Kelley Debate transcript (Feb. 12 - March 8, 1884), Reproduced and distributed by The Old Paths Book Club, Rosemead, California, 1955, p. 76. See also Van Wagoner, p. 29.

31 Joseph Smith, <u>History Of The Church</u>, Vol. I, p. 121. See also Van Wagoner, pp. 28-31.

32 Alexander Campbell, "Beaver Anathema, Mr. Winter, and The Star," <u>The Millennial Harbinger</u>, Vol. I, No. IV (April 5, 1830), p. 175. See also Van Wagoner, p. 31.

33 Daryl Chase, "Sidney Rigdon-Early Mormon" (Master's Thesis, University of Chicago, 1931), p. 18, quoting the <u>Journal History</u>, Vol. III, No. I, pp. 7-8.

34 Richardson, p. 99.

Baptist. In these articles Campbell further defined the organization and practices of his "Reformed Baptist" Movement. Rigdon, enamored by the restorationist theme, became an enthusiastic herald of these principles. With his lucid and dramatic eloquence, he frequently spoke to gatherings so large that those furthest from him could not hear him.[35]

Late in the fall of 1825 Rigdon was invited to become the minister of a Bainbridge, Ohio, congregation in the Western Reserve area. Leaving the pastoral care of the Pittsburgh church to Walter Scott, Sidney arrived in Geauga county in December. Even though the Bainbridge congregation officially embraced a Calvinistic creed, they allowed Rigdon to come "without being required to endorse the local articles of faith." The Grand River association, to which the Bainbridge group belonged, may not have been aware of Rigdon's unorthodoxy at this time.[36]

During his six-month ministry there, Sidney served as a circuit-riding preacher. Once a month he would preach at Mantua center in Portage county. But usually he preached at the Baptist church in Bainbridge, which began in private homes but was relocated to a school house. Mr. Joel Giles Sr., who was a member of that body and whose house was "a temporary house" for Baptist ministers, later complained bitterly that the congregation "was eventually broken up by a wolf in sheep's clothing (Sidney Rigdon, of Mormon notoriety), who entered the fold, and the sheep were scattered abroad."[37]

Rigdon's influence and persuasiveness at that time, however, was so widely recognized that he was invited to preach to the Mahoning Association, of which he was not a member, in 1826 and 1827. He was also approved to sit "in council" with them.[38] This illustrates just how open the Association was becoming to restorationist ideas. A.S. Hayden, an influential participant in the Western Reserve restoration movement, rejoiced:

> It is cheering to know that ever since the great Saxon sounded the note of liberty of conscience, every new body is more and more liberal, approaching gradually to the primitive order of the gospel of Christ. The Mahoning Association was no exception. It was far more tolerant than its ecclesiastical ancestors, the Redstone and the Wooster Association. As proof, in 1824, she admitted the church of Wellsburg, Virginia, with a statement of belief containing not one hint of the "Doctrines of Grace," commonly known as Calvinism![39]

---

35 Van Wagoner, p. 40

36 Backman, p. 354.

37 Pioneer And General History of Geauga County, Ohio—With Sketches of Some of The Pioneers and Prominent Men (Burton, Ohio: The Historical Society of Geauga County, 1880), Reproduced by Windmill Publications, Inc., Mt. Vernon, Indiana, 1990, p. 143.

38 Backman, p. 354.

39 Hayden, pp. 30-31.

In June of 1826 Rigdon was invited to preach the funeral service of Reverend Warner Goodall, the minister of the Mentor Baptist Church located thirty miles from Bainbridge. The congregation there was so impressed with him that they extended an invitation for him to become their new minister. By fall he had accepted their offer. But the first eight months of his ministry were somewhat turbulent as he faced some of the same doctrinal criticisms that he met at Pittsburgh and Bainbridge. Nonetheless harmony was soon restored as he gradually won over his detractors, by his own description, through his "consistent walk and conversation—his sociability, combined with his overwhelming eloquence."[40]

The Mentor Baptist Church had originally been constructed by a joint effort of Baptists *and Methodists*.[41] According to Rigdon's own description, it was located in an area settled by folk with good industry and management, and could boast "splendid farms, fertile fields, and stately mansions."[42] The Mentor church was a member of the more liberal Mahoning Association and through the influence of Rigdon, became the fourth congregation to join the Campbell movement—the other three being Brush Run, Wellsburg, and Pittsburgh. When the Mahoning Association met at Canfield in Trumbull county, Ohio, on August 25 through 27, Rigdon addressed the body with a sermon from the sixteenth chapter of John.[43] His messages usually left a deep impression: "The ability to persuade an audience to accept his point of view was Rigdon's greatest talent; all his associates, including Campbell, recognized his influence as an orator."[44]

While serving at Mentor, Rigdon continued to preach at Mantua once a month. Enough of a nucleus formed there to consecrate a church in that place on January 27, 1827. Historically, this church has been regarded to be the first "Church of Christ" in Ohio.[45] Though apparently the initial membership record contains only nine members, within a two-year period fifty more members were added.[46]

Rigdon's renown and influence spread rapidly. He came to be regarded as "a brilliant fellow," though "somewhat erratic and given to

---

40 Van Wagoner, p. 41, quoting Rigdon's short autobiography found in Times and Seasons, Vol. 4 (May 15, 1843, p. 194) and (June 1, 1843, pp. 209-210).

41 Mrs. Peter S. Hitchcock, "Joseph Smith and The Kirtland Temple," found in Lake County History, Bicentennial Edition (Painesville, Ohio: Painesville Publication Co. for the Lake Co. Historical Society and The Board of Lake Co. Commissioners, 1976), p. 131.

42 Van Wagoner, pp. 40-41.

43 See "Minutes of The Mahoning Baptist Association," August 27, 1826, and Richardson, Vol. II, p. 104.

44 McKiernan, p. 26.

45 Alanson Wilcox, A History of The Disciples Of Christ in Ohio (Cincinnati: Standard PublishingCo., 1918), p. 121.

46 Hinsdale, p. 16, and Shaw, p. 24.

metaphysical speculation," but nonetheless "fluent, eloquent, enthusiastic, and of great personal influence." Many even came to regard him as the greatest orator of the Mahoning Association, even "superior to Campbell as a preacher."[47]

> His fame as an orator and deep reasoner in the scriptures continued to spread far and wide and he soon gained a popularity and an elevation which has fallen to the lot of but few; consequently thousands flocked to hear his eloquent discourses.

> When it was known where he was going to preach, there might be seen long before the appointed time, persons of all classes, sects, and denominations, flocking like doves to their windows, from a considerable distance. . . .

> The churches in the different places where he preached were now no longer large enough to contain the vast assemblies which congregated from time to time, so that he had to repair to the widespread canopy of heaven, and in the woods and in the groves he addressed the multitudes which flocked to hear him.[48]

In 1827 probably the most significant meeting in the history of the Mahoning Association took place. It was held in New Lisbon, Ohio, on August 23, and Rigdon was again invited, as an outsider, to a seat. Sidney was also requested to address the association, which he did that evening from the eighth chapter of John.[49]

The subject of such strategic importance was Alexander Campbell's recommendation that a full-time evangelist be employed by the association to evangelize the Western Reserve. Forty men representing sixteen congregations considered the proposal.[50] At this point in the Restoration Movement there were still only four hundred and ninety-two total members of all the churches participating in the Mahoning Association. Statistics reported for the previous year revealed that all of the churches together could claim only thirty-four baptisms and thirteen transferred in by membership. But these forty-seven additions were offset by thirty-one subtractions at the same time—fourteen accepted dismissals, thirteen "exclusions," and four deaths.[51]

Campbell came to the meeting with a nomination for the position already in mind—Walter Scott! Whether or not Rigdon was surprised or

---

47 Shaw, p. 79.

48 Phillips, pp. 313-314, quoting the Journey History, Vol. 3, p. 11.

49 See "Minutes of The Mahoning Baptist Association," August 23, 1827, and Richardson, Vol. II, p. 174.

50 Shaw, p. 42.

51 See chart in Hayden, p. 56. (Also reproduced in Shaw, p. 43).

offended by his oversight will be discussed later. But as to *why* he was not chosen, there may be several considerations. Scott's education certainly exceeded Rigdon's, at least on a formal level. Also, Rigdon was presently involved in some significant ministries already. Then too, Van Wagoner has contributed the possibility that Campbell may have additionally been worried about pending competition from a new journal that Walter Scott was planning to edit, and this change in directions would eliminate, or at least delay, that project.[52]

But another possibility must be considered. Many of Rigdon's colleagues seemed to harbor a degree of mistrust concerning him, which even Joseph Smith admitted to later on. This may have become a barrier for him to realize some of his personal ambitions. Robert Richardson gave the following description of him:

> Captivating as a public speaker by his fluency and his exuberant fancy, he had depended upon these superficial endowments for popularity and success. In private he had been found petulant, unreliable and ungovernable in his passions, and his wayward temper, his extravagant stories and his habit of self-assertion had prevented him from obtaining influence as a religious teacher among the disciples.[53]

It must be noted, of course, that Richardson wrote this *after* Rigdon had joined the Mormons. He therefore had motive to denigrate him, though others made similar statements. Also, Richardson's evaluation was not quite accurate—unless he was referring to Rigdon's final status with the Disciples—because he *had* earlier established himself as an influential minister in that movement.

But whatever may be said of Rigdon, it cannot be seriously doubted that he was completely committed to the cause of restorationism. More than once in his life he would sacrifice a more secure occupational and financial position to follow what he believed to be the path of restoring the "true church" of Jesus Christ.

---

52 Van Wagoner, p. 43.

53 Richardson, Vol. II, p. 344.

Chapter

—7—

WALTER SCOTT AND THE DEVELOPMENT OF EVANGELISTIC RESTORATIONISM

Whereas Barton W. Stone and Thomas Campbell had initiated unity movements based upon restorationism, Alexander Campbell spent most of his time defining and organizing the movement. The activities of both Campbells focused more upon persuading people of all denominations to abandon creeds and division, and to restore the unity of the church with the Bible as their sole authority. Hence, relatively little emphasis was placed upon the evangelism of unbelievers, except by Sidney Rigdon and a few others. Wilcox has written that, between 1809 and 1827, the two Campbells and their churches at Brush Run and Wellsburg baptized probably less than two hundred people.

> Their fundamental plea was for the union of God's people. The nature of that plea determined its direction. It was not addressed primarily to the unsaved, but to those in the kingdom.[1]

The affiliation of Walter Scott with the Restoration Movement changed that direction radically. When Scott was chosen as the Mahoning Association's evangelist in 1827, he seemed a little uncomfortable with the

Figure 6. Walter Scott (1796 - 1861) (From http://www.therestorationmovement.com/scott,walter.htm)

1   Wilcox, p. 48.

appointment and unsure, at first, of his methodology. But it was not long until, as Scott's most prolific biographer William Baxter described it, one could legitimately say that, "Thomas Campbell advocated union, Alexander Campbell proposed the reconstitution of the church, and Walter Scott rediscovered the New Testament way of individual salvation, which he called 'the Gospel Restored'."[2]

Walter Scott, like the Campbells and unlike Rigdon, was from "the old country." Born on October 31, 1796—just eight years after Alexander Campbell, and a little more than a hundred miles from his birthplace— Walter Scott was named after the more famous Sir Walter Scott, a relative of his.[3] He enrolled at the University of Edinburgh at the age of 14, but did not graduate until eight years later.[4]

Raised as a Presbyterian in Scotland, Scott "had been induced to seek his fortune in the New World."[5] Arriving in New York in 1818, Scott spent a short time making acquaintances there, and then, having a strong desire to join other Scotch-Irish in the west, he journeyed to Pittsburgh. Having been trained to be a teacher, Scott found employment in an academy run by a fellow countryman named George Forrester. Forrester was not only a teacher, but also a minister who had been strongly influenced by the restorationist teachings of Robert Sandeman and the Haldanes. Scott soon became enamored with the same perspective, including the repudiation of the validity of infant baptism.

George Forrester drowned shortly after Scott submitted to immersion and became a member in his church. Consequently, Scott suddenly inherited the leadership of both the church and the academy.[6] Almost simultaneously, Scott had encountered a tract entitled On Baptism, written by Henry Errett, which had discussed the *purpose* of baptism as being for the forgiveness of sins. Since Errett lived in New York City, Scott determined to visit him and pursue this new idea.

In 1821 Scott journeyed to New York and spent three months with Errett's Scotch-Baptist Church. But he was disappointed when their efforts at reformation stifled, then aborted. He sought out other churches of similar ilk. However, one in Patterson, New Jersey, was "in a state of

---

2   W. E. Garrison, Religion Follows The Frontier, p. 119. Walter Scott later actually published a work entitled The Gospel Restored (Cincinnati: Printed by O.H. Donogh, 1836).

3   William Baxter, Life of Elder Walter Scott, With Sketches of His Fellow Laborers, William Hayden, Adamson Bentley, John Henry, and Others (Cincinnati: Bosworth, Chase & Hall, 1874), p. 29.

4   John W. Neth, Walter Scott Speaks (Berne, Indiana: Economy Printing Concern, 1967), p. 14.

5   Richardson, Vol. I, pp 502-503.

6   John Owston, "The Scotch-Baptist Influence on the Disciples of Christ," Found in Leaven, published by Pepperdine University at Malibu (Winter, 1997), p. 41.

disorganization"; another in Baltimore proved to be "in a very low condition"; a third in Rockwell had "little or nothing that could be of use in forwarding [his] designs"; and a fourth in Washington D. C. was so sunken in the mire of Calvinism, that they refused to reform." He was so discouraged that he climbed to the top of the Capitol building, meditated upon the destitute condition of the church, and then returned to Pittsburgh. It was not until his attendance at the 1826 and 1827 meetings of the Mahoning Association that his evangelistic spirit seemed to revive again significantly.[7]

It was back in Pittsburgh during the Winter of 1821-1822 that Scott met Alexander Campbell in the home of the wealthy Nathaniel Richardson. Scott had been invited to live in the home and tutor his son Robert, who was thirteen at that time. Soon Scott's abilities became so widely respected that he opened a school of his own, funded by Mr. Richardson, which eventually had more than one hundred students.[8]

During this same year Scott discovered what he regarded to be the great central truth of the Christian religion—the Messiahship of Jesus, as recognized in Peter's "Good Confession" (Matthew 16:16). This was the vital proposition "around which . . . all other truths revolve as planets around the sun."[9] If one can establish the Messiahship by reason, through the examination of evidence supplied by God's revelation to us in His Word, then everything else in the Christian system can be accepted simply because *Magister Dixit* [the Master said so]. The whole system rests upon the authority of Christ, God's Son and God Incarnate.[10] As Robert Richardson expressed it, "The best and highest reason that can be given for any action is, that God commands it."[11]

When Campbell began his journal in 1823, he was going to call it simply <u>The Christian</u>. But Scott influenced him to entitle it <u>The Christian Baptist</u> since most of their work at that time was among Baptist congregations.[12] Scott was a contributor to the journal, under the pen name

---

7   Walter Scott, "Letter 9," <u>The Evangelist</u> (Carthage, Ohio), Vol. I, No. XII (December, 1838), p. 288.

8   J. M. Powell, <u>The Cause We Plead: A Story of The Restoration Movement</u> (Nashville: 20th Century Christian, 1987), pp. 148-150. Powell erroneously gives the ages of Scott and Campbell at this time as 26 and 34, respectively. But his own book (pp. 141 and 83) shows that they were 25 and 33 when they met. W. E. Garrison, <u>Religion Follows The Frontier</u>, p. 120, lists their ages correctly. Powell also gives Robert Richardson's age for this tutorial as 14, but Richardson's own work (<u>Memories of Alexander Campbell</u>, p. 504) lists his age as 13.

9   Baxter, p. 60. Two years before he died, Scott wrote a book entitled <u>The Messiahship</u> (Cincinnati: Bosworth, Chase and Hall, 1859), which some consider to be his *magnum opus*.

10 Tristano, pp. 99. See John 1:1 and 14 for theology of incarnation.

11 Richardson, Vol. I, p. 406.

12 Owston, p. 42; Garrett, pp. 146-147; et. al.

of "Phillip," because he regarded his relationship with Alexander Campbell to be similar to that of Phillip Melanchthon's with Martin Luther.[13] In the first year of the newspaper's existence, Scott composed an article against what he labeled as the "corrupted forms of Christianity"—Roman Catholicism and the Protestant denominations:

> . . . members of a church of Christ are united to one another by the belief of a matter of fact, viz. that *"Jesus is the Christ, the Son of God,"* and not by any attribute of government, catholic or sectarian. . . . the worshiping establishments now in operation throughout christendom, increased and cemented by their respected voluminous confessions of faith and their ecclesiastical constitutions, are not churches of Jesus Christ, but the legitimate daughters of that Mother of Harlots, the Church of Rome.[14]

Thirteen years later, in a book called The Gospel Restored, he was still trumpeting the same restorationist message:

> Very unlike Romanism the primitive church engaged no arts on her side; she did not, like that harlot, seek to consecrate herself in the esteem of wordly [sic] men and the vulgar by a meretricious display of the finest specimens of sculpture, painting, music, and so forth; but marched forth to the conversion of the world, devoid of all external ornament. . . .

> Unlike Protestantism, also, she sought not to distinguish herself by an affected party prudery; but looked like a sweet, innocent virgin attired in Godly simplicity, without partiality, without hypocrisy. . . .

> Alike unacquainted with the creeds of Protestants, and the idolatrous manuals of the Papists, her only manual was the bible and her creed, for the binding together of all who obeyed her, was Jesus is the Son of God. . . .

> Let not the reader think, that Romanism, or Protestantism is primitive christianity. . . . These are institutions of priests and clergymen; guides who, if a man will follow them, will devoutly fill his soul with the most perplexing doubts and troubles concerning every matter which the author of Christianity has communicated for our faith, our hope, our obedience, and perfection in morals and religion. Reader go not after them. Seize upon the holy scriptures as a gift to you from God. Believe that you can understand them and become wiser by them, than all who live by perverting them.[15]

In 1826 Walter Scott moved to Steubenville, Ohio, to teach school. As has been previously acknowledged, the growth of the churches in the Mahoning Association had been slow and laborious. Since its inception

---

13 Hughes, Reviving The Ancient Faith, p. 50.

14 Walter Scott, "On Teaching Christianity, " The Christian Baptist, Vol. I, No. IV (November 3, 1823), pp. 66-67.

15 Walter Scott, The Gospel Restored (Cincinnati: O. H. Donogh, 1836), pp. 183-184.

in 1820, the Mahoning Association had gradually become more and more stagnated and complacent. In the corresponding letter of 1826 Adamson Bentley complained that "nothing very special has occurred amongst us during the past year," and noted that, "It is a fact that both the public teachers and the private brethren have been laboring more in the <u>doctrine</u> than in the <u>word</u>."[16] William Baxter portrayed their dejected condition:

> The monthly meetings had become cold and formal gatherings, the reading of church constitution, covenant, and articles of faith—for some had all these—had, in a measure, usurped the place of reading the Scriptures, of prayer and praise. There was but little growth in true piety, little enjoyment, and but few conversions.[17]

So in 1827 the Mahoning Association was determined to sponsor its first evangelist. The choice of Walter Scott was somewhat ironic. He was not a member of the Association; he was not really a Baptist; he was not yet a member of any church in the town where he lived; he was not located within the territory of the Mahoning Association; he was not an ordained minister; and he had no outstanding track record of evangelistic accomplishment up to that time.[18] He was not as dramatic as Rigdon, nor as analytical and rhetorical as Campbell. But he was selected, and that occasion proved to become the launching pad for an evangelistic explosion in the Stone-Campbell movement.

The context within which much of Scott's successful evangelism took place was predominately Calvinistic. Imported to America first by the Puritans and Presbyterians, Calvinism is often expressed through its five basic tenets represented in the "TULIP" acronym: 1. **T**otal depravity of man; 2. **U**nconditional election; 3. **L**imited atonement; 4. **I**rresistible grace; 5. **P**erseverance of the saints (or **P**ermanent security). Anyone giving evidence that God had given them direct unequivocal assurance of their Divine election would be granted full membership in Puritan churches. In reality, however, few were able to be so convincing and as much as two thirds of the New England population failed to qualify for church membership and, therefore, Heaven.[19] Edmund Morgan aptly portrayed the anomalies in the Calvinistic theological system:

> Puritanism required that a man devote his life to seeking salvation but told him he was helpless to do anything but evil. Puritanism required that he rest his whole hope in Christ but taught him that Christ would utterly

16   Mary Agnes Smith, "A History of the Mahoning Baptist Association" (Master's thesis, University of West Virginia, 1943), pp. 13-18.

17   Baxter, p. 89.

18   Van Wagoner, p. 44, and Smith, p. 70.

19   John C. Miller, <u>The First Frontier: Life In Colonial America</u> (New York: Dell Publishing Co., 1966), p. 54.

reject him unless before he was born God had foreordained his salvation. Puritanism required that man refrain from sin but told him he would sin anyhow. Puritanism required that he reform the world in the image of God's holy kingdom but taught him that the evil of the world was incurable and inevitable.[20]

In Presbyterian and Baptist predestinationist theology also, God's grace was irresistible for the Elect, but unattainable for those unfortunate souls who were not foreordained to eternal salvation. So there were many "seekers" in those days who agonizingly frequented the "anxious-seat" hoping to receive some sign that they were included among God's predestined Elect. Some were probably able to convince themselves that they had an experience, and others, like Rigdon, simply faked it. But many were honest with themselves and others, and came away worried, then frustrated, and finally despondent. One critic has simply abridged the Calvinistic theology with the phrase, "Don't call God; he'll call you."[21] Another antagonist, with a mixture of knowledge and misunderstanding, commiserated with frustrated suppliants when he grumbled:

> If you haven't got religion, you can't get it. If you get it, you don't know it. If you know it, you haven't got it. If you have got it, you can't lose it. If you lose it, you never had it.[22]

Scott struggled for awhile to determine what the focus of his evangelistic thrust would be. Disgruntled with religious parties and man-made creeds, he perceived that he would not be successful if his advocacy was simply another human interpretation of doctrines. He scrutinized Christianity for its most fundamental and vital metaphysical reality or truth that sustained it. He observed:

> Without an essential element, [our religion] would be like a watch without a spring or a clock without weights, ... Every system of true religion, as much as every system of physics and morals, must stand on some basis of reality. Christianity is a system of true religion, therefore Christianity must stand upon some basis of reality. It must have a creed, a master truth, an article of faith, to be offered to men for their salvation.[23]

He then concluded that, "this truth of the Christian system is enunciated in the form of a proposition—namely that Jesus Christ is the Messiah; the Son of the living God."[24]

---

20 Edmund Morgan, <u>The Puritan Dilemma — The Story of John Winthrop</u> (Boston: Little Brown and Company, 1958), pp. 7-8.

21 Daniel Schantz, <u>Walter Scott: God's Pied Piper</u> (Cincinnnati: The Standard Publishing Company, 1984), p. 5.

22 Wilcox, p. 36.

23 Walter Scott, quoted in Baxter, p. 419.

24 Ibid.

When Scott was selected as the Mahoning Association's evangelist in 1827, he was given the prerogative of calling four quarterly meetings per year. He chose the first one to meet at Braceville—where the desire for an evangelist had originated—on September 16, 1827. Adamson Bentley and Jacob Osborne, who was the minister of that church, joined him in the preaching. After only a mildly successful meeting, the three men began discussing Peter's sermon on the day of Pentecost, acknowledged by Christians as the birthday of the church. When Peter had finished his sermon and the people in the crowd asked what they needed to do to be saved, Peter responded, "Repent, and be baptized every one of you in the name of Jesus Christ for the forgiveness of your sins; and you shall receive the gift of the Holy Spirit."[25] Scott, like a man discovering a key to a treasure chest, excitedly latched on to this verse as the lynchpin of his future messages.

Previous to this time, baptism had been regarded by most churches as a rite of initiation or church membership. Scott began to advocate that this sacrament was for the remission of sins. He explained:

> By ascertaining the primitive creed of the gospel, and the blessings which originally attached to the reception of it, we obtain a rule by which all subsequent preaching can be measured and determined to be either true or false, pure or corrupted, evangelical or unevangelical. The true gospel therefore proposes to mankind as a first step, the remisssion [sic] of past sins in baptism.[26]

From this time forth he would preach a "new message" which countermanded the spiritual tyranny of predestinationism. No longer having to wait and "fret" over the revelation for their selection for salvation, people would now be told that conversion was not contingent upon a mystical experience, but that salvation was within each individual's grasp if he or she would just respond in faith to God's gift of universally offered grace. This idea was certainly antagonistic to the Calvinistic doctrine of a limited atonement. One nineteenth-century Disciple celebrated that, "Many good people were on the verge of despair. They could not find an assurance of their election. They were not certain that Christ had died for them. The new teaching assured them that Jesus tasted death for every man, ..."[27]

This emphasis helped Scott's message coalesce with a clarity of purpose that had not been there before. Instead of being a garbled mass of interpretations and confusion, the Gospel was again made simple.

---

25   The Bible, Acts 2:38 (R.S.V.). See also information in Stevenson, pp. 60-61.

26   Walter Scott, <u>The Gospel Restored</u>, p. 312.

27   B. B. Tyler, <u>Concerning The Disciples of Christ</u> (Cleveland: The Bethany C. E. Company, 1897), p. 80.

Faith, it was clear to him, was not the mystical fruit of the Spirit in the soul of one formerly depraved and incapable of believing; faith was the natural response to hearing; it was believing the evidence. Baptism was not a mere sign of an inward change of state; it was an act completing personal obedience to Christ, and remission of sins followed upon it. *Then* came Christian experience! After one had become a Christian! That was where the Holy Spirit came in . . . .[28]

A few years after 1827 Walter Scott would look back and refer to that year as the time when the Gospel was "restored" to the people. In fact, he wrote a book in 1836 entitled The Gospel Restored and proclaimed in the preface that "in 1827 the True Gospel was restored. For distinction's sake it was styled the Ancient Gospel."[29] In an 1833 issue of The Evangelist, a periodical which Scott had begun publishing the previous year, he lauded the accomplishments of the previous six years when he responded to a man's letter by saying, "The restoration of the Ancient Gospel, Sir, was a great event; it has now spread far and wide; it has carried salvation wherever it has gone; it has terrified the whole sectarian world; and has been productive of the most singular religious phenomina [sic]. . . ."[30] He then added the promise, "give me these three things, Sir, Remission of sins, the Holy Spirit, and Eternal life; and I will, under Christ, reform the old world and make a new one; . . . . [31] Scott's results for the next thirty years would seem to support his boast.

After the moderate success of his preaching campaign in Braceville, Scott decided to go home to Steubenville and see his family, as well as check on a new house he was having built nearby in Canfield. While there, Scott decided to test his revolutionary thesis on a nearby church. Despite his confidence in what he believed would be good results, his audience was, instead, stunned by the message which resulted in a combination of confusion, pity, and even scorn. One of Scott's biographers described the scene by saying, "this sounded so different from anything they had come to expect as 'gospel' that it seemed to them like a new religion.[32] Scott himself explained later:

> Now, sir, of all the things which distinguished the actual reappearance of the original gospel, the simple practice of making an immediate draught upon the faith of the auditors, . . . surprised and confused those who beheld it; to argue for a prompt acceptation of the remission of sins on the

---

28   Dwight E. Stevenson, Walter Scott: Voice of The Golden Oracle—A Biography (St. Louis, Missouri: Christian Board of Publication, 1946), p. 59.

29   Walter Scott, The Gospel Restored, preface, p. A-2.

30   Walter Scott, "On The Restoration of the Ancient Gospel," Letter No. 1, The Evangelist, Vol. 2, No. 1 (January 7, 1833), p.1.

31   Ibid. p. 2.

32   Stevenson, p. 65.

plan of the ancient gospel and to urge an immediate obedience to the divine injunction, seemed to them most extraordinary and dangerous; *extraordinary*, because they had not witnessed it before; *dangerous* because they supposed, that in this way, "all the rogues in society might get religion," . . . .[33]

Despite the rather negative results, Scott, from the perspective of six years later, confidently concluded, "You will see then, dear sir, that not only the *direct* exhibition and application of the ancient gospel, but also the *primitive mode* of separating disciples was introduced and restored at the period referred to."[34]

If there is any one date which could be regarded as a turning point in the evangelistic efforts of the Campbellite Restoration Movement, that occasion may be November 18, 1827. At New Lisbon, Ohio—in the same meeting house where Scott had been commissioned as evangelist of the Mahoning Association two months prior—Scott preached an evangelistic sermon based upon Peter's Good Confession and his sermon at Pentecost. Still realizing the revolutionary (or heretical, depending upon one's perspective) character of his proposition, Scott has been recorded to have trembled as he delivered his message.[35]

Near the end of his discourse, a man named William Amend, described by one man as "The best man in the community; an orderly member of the Presbyterian church,"[36] entered the building. In searching through the Calvinistic doctrines of the Presbyterian church, he had become "wearied" with his hopeless "wilderness" and turned to the Bible for answers. After reading the second chapter of Acts, he exulted to discover what he regarded as the *real* essence of the Gospel and remarked to his wife:

> O this is the gospel—this is the thing we wish—the remission of our sins! O that I could hear the gospel in these same words—as Peter preached it! I hope I shall someday hear it; and the first man I meet, who will preach the gospel thus, with him will I go.[37]

When Scott issued the invitation for baptism, Amend immediately came forward. "It was singular and indeed inexplicable to Mr. Scott, that the first person to respond to his call, and come forth to obey the gospel, should be a man who had not heard his sermon.[38] But this act "broke the ice" and set off much commotion in the community.

---

33 Walter Scott, "Restoration of the Ancient Gospel," Letter No. 3, The Evangelist, Vol. 2, No. 3 (March 4, 1833), p. 51.

34 Ibid.

35 Stevenson, p. 70.

36 Hayden, p. 76; and Stevenson, p. 68.

37 William Amend, correspondence, found in "On The Restoration of The Ancient Gospel," Letter No. 6, The Evangelist, Vol. 2, No. 7 (July 1, 1833), p. 161.

38 Hayden, p. 77.

An epidemic of Bible reading broke out in New Lisbon. Some read to find confirmation of Scott's unprecedented method. Many read to find ammunition with which to blast the preacher from his pulpit and drive him from the community. Arguments sprang up. Tempers flared. The church was jammed to overflowing.[39]

Hayden eloquently described the metamorphosis of Scott as well: "From that day, with this seal to his ministry, he was stronger than Ajax. To borrow one of his own expressions, 'he rushed in upon the people like an armed man!'"[40] The revival meetings lasted for a week with the whole town aroused. Others were baptized, and one man, whose mother desired to be baptized, threatened to shoot Scott if he baptized her. He baptized her anyway![41] By the following Sunday, in an atmosphere of great excitement, a total of seventeen people had been immersed into Christ.[42]

Van Wagoner contends that "There was no emotional frenzy in Scott's rhetoric as in Rigdon's. Instead he was able to calmly blend rationality and authority, appealing to common sense and to scripture."[43] While it is admitted that the basis of Scott's *theology* certainly was in the tradition of Common Sense Rationalism, the *style* of his preaching was probably not quite as Van Wagoner portrays it. Evangelists didn't then, and don't now, move people to life-changing spiritual decisions with calm appeals to reason, any more than the great generals of history could inspire their troops to fight and die using cold, matter-of-fact logic. William Baxter has probably given a more realistic description of Scott's approach:

> He usually began slowly, with simple and plain statements of his subject, rambling not unfrequently, till, warming in his subject, he broke the shackles of logic, and swept on like a swelling tide, bearing his audience away with the pathos and vehemence of his earnest and commanding oratory. On such occasions his voice became full, sonorous, and powerful. When the shower was past, the people not caring to analyze the sermon, or to trace their emotions to logical sources, were delighted and edified, and departed with marked and decided respect for the preacher, and a far higher reverence for the adorable Son of God, whom he preached and whom he served.[44]

Scott certainly did not propagate the charismatic type of revivalism participated in by Stone. He opposed both the theology behind, and manifestations of, "experimental religion," a term both he and Alexander Campbell used to describe the experiential emphasis upon the physical

---

39   Stevenson, p. 69.

40   Hayden, p. 76.

41   Baxter, p. 109, and Stevenson, p. 69.

42   Richardson, Vol. II, p. 212; and Hayden, p. 76.

43   Van Wagoner, p. 44.

44   Baxter, pp. 138-139.

manifestations of the Holy Spirit—such as conversion "exercises," speaking in tongues, faith healing, prophesying, and performing miracles.[45] Yet it would be a great misunderstanding of the *zeitgeist* of the Stone-Campbell frontier movement to suggest that it lacked emotion or enthusiasm. A description of Scott's preaching and results for the winter of 1827-1828 read, "He contended ably for the restoration of the true, original apostolic order which would restore to the church the ancient gospel as preached by the apostles. The interest became an excitement; . . . the air was thick with rumors of a 'new religion,' a 'new Bible.'"[46]

The Restoration Movement, like an adolescent entering puberty, was beginning to spurt in growth. Scott greatly enhanced his appealing message with a clever methodology that he called his "five-finger exercise." He would go to school yards or playgrounds and have children hold up their hands. He told them that each finger represented a step in the process of salvation: 1. Faith; 2. Repentance; 3. Baptism; 4. Remission of sins; 5. The gift of the Holy Spirit. Then he would inform them of the nearby location where he could tell them more about what those things meant at a meeting to be held that evening. He would then have the children close their hands into fists, tuck them into their pockets, and run home to tell their parents what they learned. Much curiosity was aroused in this manner and many people turned out to hear him.[47]

Dean Walker has written that while "The Campbells had tried to reform the Church by getting it to restore the New Testament order: Scott was restoring the church by building it anew out of the common people— sick of sin, tired of creeds, and anxious to know what God required of them to be saved."[48] Richardson added that:

> Everywhere the confusion which had involved the subject of conversion was removed; the mourning bench was abandoned; and intelligent obedience was substituted for visionary theories and a divine assurance replaced delusive frames and feelings. . . . Mr. Scott, meanwhile, fully conscious of the momentous nature of the issues he had evoked, but confident in the power of the gospel and all aflame with zeal, passed rapidly, like a meteor, throughout the Western Reserve, startling the people by the abruptness and directness of his appeals, but exciting many to inquiry and obedience.[49]

---

45 See "Philip" (Walter Scott) "Experimental Religion," The Christian Baptist, Vol. IV, No, 7 (February 5, 1827), pp. 141-143; and Richardson, Vol. II, pp. 354-361.

46 Van Wagoner, p. 44.

47 Garrett, p. 154.

48 Walker, p. 31.

49 Richardson, Vol. II, p. 218.

Powell adds that, "The Bible was read with new interest," and that, "The Mahoning River became a second Jordan, and Scott another John the Baptist."[50]

Certainly the events that transpired on the Western Reserve during this time were the beginning of what could be called a restorationist evangelism explosion. At the next meeting of the Mahoning Association in the fall of 1828, Scott was able to report around a thousand new converts to the faith.[51] Leroy Garrett claims that in his thirty-year ministry Scott baptized around thirty thousand people, "far more than anyone in his generation."[52] Whether or not those figures are accurate or exaggerated, it cannot be doubted that Scott's success was phenomenal.

The magnitude of Scott's influence began to instigate jealousies and antagonisms. A Methodist preacher, many of whose parishioners had abandoned him for Scott, spread rumors that Scott had actually drowned a few people during baptism, and had even strangled some others.[53] Some people would set loose Scott's horse while he preached, and on one occasion during a baptism someone cut off the horse's tail. Then too there was the occasion when the wife of a rather large and strong-willed Presbyterian named John Tate had attended one of Scott's meetings and resolved to be baptized. Tate was so incensed that he threatened violence against Scott and went to see him. Scott said he would baptize her even if Tate showed up sword in hand. The culmination of the whole episode saw not only Mrs. Tate baptized, but John Tate as well![54]

In January of 1828 Scott was involved in what has come to be known in Disciples' history as the "Siege of Warren." Even though the venerable Adamson Bentley preached at the large Baptist Church there, "the town lay in spiritual lethargy," according to A. S. Hayden, who was quick to acknowledge that "Bentley had preached well and lived well; but he held not the key to the heart, nor was he skilled to awaken the music of the soul."[55] Scott determined to evangelize the area believing that Bentley, who was sympathetic to the Reformed Baptist cause, would welcome him to preach to his congregation. But Bentley, somewhat skeptical at the time concerning Scott's presentation, refused to host him at first.[56] Scott came anyway, virtually without any promotion in the town, and held his first meeting in the courthouse attended by only a few old people and some boys.[57]

---

50   Powell, p. 156.

51   Hughes, Reviving The Ancient Faith, p. 52.

52   Garrett, p. 155.

53   Van Wagoner, p. 45.

54   Baxter, pp. 132-133, and Hayden, p. 99.

55   Hayden, p. 95.

56   Van Wagoner, p. 45.

57   Hayden, p. 95.

The next day, however, Bentley changed his mind, and a great crowd gathered to hear Scott at the Warren Baptist Church. Within eight days the whole Warren congregation, "with the exception of six people in two families," converted to the "Reformed Baptist" orbit.[58] A total of over fifty people were added to the Restoration Movement as a result of this meeting, "And from this period, . . . it spread like fire on a prairie all over the country, ..."[59]

In March of 1828 Sidney Rigdon visited Scott in Warren and convinced him to lead out in a revival of his own congregation at Mentor. Rigdon had come to believe that Scott had unveiled the hidden key to unlocking "the restoration of the way of bringing converts into the knowledge of pardon," and was ecstatically "transported with this discovery."[60] He implored Bentley to join them, and the three of them exceeded the impressive results of Warren. According to the Mentor church's own official history, twenty people were baptized and fifty were converted in one day, and the church soon grew to a membership of one hundred.[61]

After the great success at Mentor, Rigdon and Bentley decided to journey to the community of Kirtland, only about five miles from Mentor, to evangelize that area. Kirtland, or Kirtland Mills by its post office designation, was a community of sparsely-populated farms, located on one of the highest elevations in Ohio, and was only four miles south of the nearest stagecoach line.[62] It had been settled predominately by New Englanders and by 1830 had grown to a population of just over one thousand inhabitants.[63] Whenever Rigdon or any other circuit-riding minister visited the community, services were held in the school house, often by candlelight.[64] Rigdon and Bentley baptized twenty people during their visit, and a new church was organized there from that nucleus.[65]

These accomplishments almost immediately captured the attention of Alexander Campbell. Having heard some complaints and "exaggerated

---

58   Van Wagoner, p. 46.

59   Hayden, p. 100.

60   Ibid., p. 192.

61   The Mentor Christian Church Scrapbook (published by the church on the occasion of its sesquicentennial, 1978), pp. 5-6.

62   Eva L. Pancoast, "Mormons at Kirtland" (Master's thesis, Western Reserve University, Cleveland, May 1, 1929) p.1.

63   Max H. Parkin, "Conflict At Kirtland: A Study of The Nature and Causes of External and Internal Conflict of the Mormons In Ohio Between 1830 and 1838" (Master's thesis, Brigham Young University, 1968), p. 28.

64   Pancoast, p.2., quoting the Painesville Telegraph, Nov. 2, 1830.

65   Van Wagoner, p. 46, and Wilcox, p. 124.

rumors" about them, especially from the Regular Baptists, Alexander asked his father to investigate. After doing so, Thomas responded by letter dated April 9, 1828:

> I perceive that theory and practice in religion, as well as in other things, are matters of distinct consideration . . . . We have spoken and published many things *correctly* concerning the ancient gospel, its simplicity and perfect adaptation to the present state of mankind, for the benign and gracious purposes of its immediate relief and complete salvation; but I must confess that, in respect of the direct exhibition and application of it for that blessed purpose, I am at present, for the first time, upon the ground where the thing has appeared to be practically exhibited to the proper purpose. . . .
>
> Mr. Scott has made a bold push to accomplish this object, by simply and boldly stating the ancient gospel and insisting upon it; . . . .[66]

Thomas Campbell was so impressed with the work evangelizing the Western Reserve that he remained to help them for almost six months. By summer Alexander Campbell was able to attribute around eight hundred baptisms to Scott, Rigdon, and Bentley, "within the last six months," as well as similar results by other reformers elsewhere.[67] Members of the Mahoning Association met with excited anticipation in Warren in 1828. A. S. Hayden, who was in attendance, reported:

> The association came together purely and simply as an assembly of Christians. Though under the forms and name of a Baptist association, the creed system was abandoned and neither that denominational name, nor any other, was on its standard. . . . This great occasion was a grand demonstration of the possibility of the union of Christians on original Bible ground. It was no longer a theory. It was then an actual, accomplished fact. . . . Here were Methodists, no longer Methodists, but still Christians; Baptists surrendering the title, yet holding the Head, even Christ; Restorationists, giving up their fruitless and faulty speculations, now obedient to the faith once delivered to the saints; . . . .[68]

When Scott reported his results to the Mahoning Association, all were in agreement for his re-appointment for the next year. But a discussion broke out as to whether or not he should be allowed to evangelize *outside* the territorial limits of the Association if the need arose, and the meeting bogged down. Finally Rigdon, who had not participated in the discussion up to that point, and who was growing impatient with the lack of progress, expounded, "You are consuming too much time on this question. One of the old Jerusalem preachers would start out with his hunting shirt and moccasins, and convert

---

66   Richardson, Vol. II, p. 219, and Hayden, p. 148.

67   Alexander Campbell, ed., "Extracts of Letters," <u>The Christian Baptist</u>, Vol V, No. 11 (June 2, 1828), p. 452 of combined edition (p. 98 indiv. edition).

68   Hayden, p. 161-162.

half the world while you are discussing and settling plans!" Immediately Scott arose and vowed, "Brethren, give me my Bible, my Head, and Bro. William Hayden [a song evangelist], and we will go out and convert the world." Rigdon so moved, and his motion was seconded and passed unanimously.[69]

Perhaps because of his exodus to Mormonism, Stone-Campbell historians have not allotted Rigdon the credit he deserves for the major role he played in the evangelism of the Western Reserve. Scott is almost portrayed as having done it single-handedly. But Rigdon was dramatic and eloquent, able to persuade audiences in a way that caused Fawn Brodie to dub him, "For several years past . . . the most successful revivalist on the Western Reserve."[70] Yet as McKiernan has observed, "Disciples of Christ historians have credited Scott with Rigdon's accomplishments in the early reformation and have generally omitted Rigdon from their history."[71]

Evangelism was truly Rigdon's forte, and whenever he was convinced of his product he proved to be an excellent salesman. There is almost universal recognition among historians as to his speaking abilities. Max Parkin wrote that "His voice and manner were always imposing. He was regarded as an eloquent man at all times, ..."[72] Jedediah Grant, a bitter critic of Rigdon's, admitted that Rigdon was "truly a man of talents, possessing a gift for speaking seldom surpassed by men of this age."[73] Daryl Chase claimed that "in the type of native eloquence that was so effective among the frontier churches, he may have had no superior in the entire group [of Walter Scott, Thomas Campbell, Alexander Campbell, and Adamson Bentley]."[74] A. S. Hayden, a contemporary of Rigdon's, granted that "His action was graceful, his language copious, fluent in utterance, with articulation clear and musical," and that "His personal influence with an audience was very great," though he warned his readers that "he was an enthusiast and unstable."[75] Van Wagoner, Rigdon's most recent biographer, assessed his oratorical powers in the following manner:

> Well suited for preaching, Rigdon was blessed with a powerful and mellifluous voice, enthusiasm, and a prodigious memory for scripture. His listeners gulped his words like a gush of cool water. An avitar of eloquence who carried the flame of the visionary tradition, he could sway by the shear force of his faith, passion, and ideological fervor.[76]

---

69 Ibid., p. 174.

70 Brodie, p. 94.

71 McKiernan, p. 28.

72 Parkin, p. 40.

73 Jedediah Grant, quoted in Van Wagoner, p. 111.

74 Daryl Chase, "Sidney Rigdon — Early Mormon," (Master's thesis, University of Chicago, 1931), p. 32.

75 Hayden, p. 192.

76 Van Wagoner, Introduction, p. VIII.

When the Mahoning Association met at Austintown in 1830, there was great rejoicing as they celebrated an addition of around one thousand converts from the previous year.[77] However a lady named "Francis" wrote a letter to the <u>Millennial Harbinger</u> in October of the same year crediting Walter Scott, Sidney Rigdon, and Adamson Bentley with at least three thousand baptisms for the three years prior.[78] Sidney Ahlstrom gave this report accounting for such a phenomenon:

> What Presbyterians, Baptists, and Methodists apparently faced during these decades of Disciple expansion was a remarkable projection into the American frontier scene of a popular, down-to-earth form of eighteenth-century Christian rationalism, a movement all the more striking because it was successfully propagated in the ethos of revivalism and by an adaptation of its methods.[79]

The attractions of disciple evangelism were at least two-fold. On the one hand, as has been discussed, the universal appeal to *all* sinners proved more palatable than a limited atonement for an Elect few. Also, experientialism was still an albatross for many. One Disciple historian offered the following evaluation:

> The preaching of the Disciples made a successful appeal to a large class of persons who were too unmystical to have the kind of ecstatic religious experience which both Calvinistic Baptists and Arminian Methodists insisted upon as affording evidence of acceptance with God, and too honest to pretend to have it.[80]

The other attraction of Disciple evangelism was its simple message. It must be remembered that Scott, Rigdon, et. al. were not addressing a more sophisticated New England audience, but rather a simple and practical-minded frontier crowd. This common-sense appeal could be readily understood and believed by even the ignorant pioneer farmer.

> The people to whom the "Campbellite" preacher made his appeal had been reared in simple, Bible preaching, almost unadorned by book-learning. It must not be forgotten that among both the Baptists and the Disciples for many years following 1800 the rank and file of the church was opposed to a paid clergy — which meant that it approved and promoted a non-professional ministry. The preaching of these frontier ministers, most of whom were "raised up" from the frontier people themselves, was derived in the main from a single volume library, the Bible.[81]

---

77 Smith, p. 84.

78 Correspondence from "Francis", <u>The Millennial Harbinger</u>, Vol. I, No. 10 (October 4, 1830), p. 449 (p. 38 orig.).

79 Sidney Ahlstrom, <u>A Religious History of the American People</u>, Vol. I (Garden City, New York: Doubleday & Co., 1975) p. 547.

80 W. E. Garrison, <u>Religion Follows The Frontier</u>, p. 157.

81 Smith, p. 6.

The shear simplicity of the Restored Gospel, with its universal appeal to all who desired to be saved, caught hold "like a prairie fire." In 1830 there were said to be between 12,000 to 20,000 members in the new Disciples of Christ movement.[82] By 1840, including the additions from the 1832 Lexington meeting with Stone, there were approximately 40,000.[83] By 1850 that number had tripled to 118,000, making the Disciples of Christ the seventh largest religious body in the United States.[84] During the Civil War the Disciples continued to grow, numbering between 200,000 to 225,000 members, and elevating them to fifth place among Protestant bodies in the United States.[85] Statistics for 1870 vary between 350,000 to 375,000, 400,000 for 1875, 475,000 for 1880, 641,000 for 1890, and 1,120,000 by the turn of the century— preserving the Disciples' position as fifth among religious bodies in the United States.[86]

During the first couple decades of the nineteenth century the Campbell movement was little more than a curiosity, then a nuisance, and finally—to the Presbyterians and Baptists—a heresy. But between the years 1827 and 1830 they became a competitor and a threat, "stealing sheep from the fold" and "leading many astray." The Presbyterians, during the first decade, had already evicted the Campbellites; by the close of the 1820's the Baptists, their only allies, would do the same.

---

82 Garrison, p. 200. Statistics for the first couple decades are unreliable since there was no real organization as yet.

83 Ibid.

84 Walker, p. 45; Garrison, p. 200; and Mead, p. 107.

85 Nathan Hatch, p. 71, and Allen and Hughes, Illusions of Innocence, p. 158, give the more conservative figure. Walker, p. 45, and Garrison, p. 200, are older works and list the higher number.

86 Walker, p. 45; Garrison p. 248; and Tristano, p. 115.

Chapter
—8—

THE EVOLUTION TO ISOLATED
SECTARIAN RESTORATIONISM

Alexander Campbell's relationship with the Baptists was always rather tenuous and ambiguous. He championed their favorite minority cause of adult immersion of believers, yet he denounced their creeds, their Calvinistic beliefs, and their clergy. He gave their movement a certain level of credibility with his scholarship and his eloquence, yet he was not prone to regard himself as one of them.

> The differences between Campbell and the Baptists existed from the very beginning of the union, but they were unobserved or condoned for the sake of obtaining such a rising genius as Campbell as an adherent and advocate. There is no doubt that Campbell added very much to the prestige and favor of the Baptists among the people during all the time of his relationship with them. He was the ablest, most brilliant and versatile man they had during that period. All his influence accrued to the Baptists. The converts he made joined their churches. The victories he won in the debates with John Walker, W.L. McCalla, and Robert Owen were set down to the Baptists.[1]

Even Campbell himself seemed to waver back and forth in his affinity for them. He disdained their clergy as ignorant, authoritarian, and often self-seeking men; yet he admired the laity as a devout and Bible-loving people. As will be demonstrated in this chapter, he finally antagonized them enough to be driven out of the fold, yet he occasionally expressed regret over the event and reiterated his sincere desire for a reunification with them. Even when he was on his death bed in 1866, and was informed that there were indications of a possible reunion in various parts of the country, he rejoiced and broke down in tears, exclaiming, "This is one of the happiest moments of my life."[2]

---

1 Errett Gates, <u>The Early Relation and Separation of Baptists and Disciples</u> (Chicago: The Christian Century Co., 1904), pp. 105-106.

2 Joseph King, "A Memorial Sermon on the occasion of the Death of Alexander Campbell," delivered March 18, 1866; printed in <u>The Millennial Harbinger</u>, Vol. 37, No. 5 (May, 1866), p. 206.

But the roots that had led to the isolation of the Disciples of Christ as a movement had grown deep, and reunification was not to be. The "Reformed Baptists"—as Campbell, Rigdon, Scott, et. al. had early on come to refer to themselves—had always had a different ultimate agenda than the Presbyterians, Methodists, and Baptists. The former, being rebellious young upstarts entering somebody else's world, could afford the luxury of advocating the demolition of existing structures in favor of a spiritual renovation program. The established denominations had already put years of energy and progress into what they believed and, while perhaps open to modifications of one degree or another, were naturally unwilling to negate all their work and begin over again.

As early as the entry of the Brush Run Church into the Redstone Association, some Baptists leaders perceived inconsistencies between the Reformers and Regular Baptist doctrine. The mode and candidate for the sacrament of baptism were fully agreed upon; but there was an ever-widening disparity as to its purpose. Was it for obedience, confirmation of election, and church membership; or was it for the forgiveness of sins leading to personal salvation and the gift of the Holy Spirit? There were differences in practice as to the frequency of the celebration of the Lord's Supper, as well as the essentiality of ordination for ministerial functions. And of course, there were those disagreements over the Calvinistic elements. Then in 1816, as alluded to earlier, Alexander Campbell's "Sermon on The Law" began to awaken more Baptist leaders to the realization that Campbell may not have been their legitimate champion after all. The sermon's general theme attempted to show that Christians are no longer under the law of Moses, which had been designed only for a special purpose and for a limited time. As the twenty-eight year old continued his discourse:

> . . .the clearest thinkers among the ministers present realized that something was happening that was not in accordance with Baptist usage. Some approved, but more did not. The suspicion grew that this young man, while undoubtedly brilliant and forceful, was erratic and dangerous.[3]

One man named Pritchard attempted to halt the proceedings. When a lady in the congregation fainted, he gathered other preachers around him ostensibly to help her, but in doing so made such a commotion as to interrupt Mr. Campbell. Nonetheless undaunted, Campbell continued after the disturbance subsided. At the intermission Pritchard approached some fellow preachers and proposed having Campbell then and there condemned from the speaker's rostrum, arguing that "This will never do. This is not our doctrine. We cannot let this pass without a public protest from the Association." But one of the elders, named Estep, replied, "That would create too much excitement, and would injure us more than Mr.

---

3   W.E. Garrison, <u>Religion Follows The Frontier</u>, p. 109.

Campbell. It is better to let it pass and let the people judge for themselves."[4] So the occasion closed with no direct confrontation.

However, in the aftermath of the proceedings, many of the churches grumbled with criticism of the sermon's content. The stricture became so severe at times that Campbell was compelled to consign the sermon to print in order to be fairly evaluated. At the next regular meeting of the Redstone Association at Peter's Creek in 1817, some sought his condemnation and expulsion, but the effort was thwarted by Campbell's friends and supporters.[5]

Despite the opposition, Campbell continued to aggressively propagate what he believed to be true and important. Because he had begun to make a success of the farm deeded to him by his father-in-law, "He was now perfectly independent in fortune so that he had nothing to fear from offending the cherished beliefs of men. They could not cut off his support, for he was not dependent upon them."[6] Before 1816 Alexander Campbell had been trying to discover and define his convictions, and after 1830 he began to mollify *some* of his contentiousness; but as Richard Tristano has perceptively noticed: "The period from the delivery of the 'Sermon on The Law' in 1816 until separation from the Baptists in 1830 was distinguished by the most radical and iconoclastic Alexander Campbell who was in the process of developing his own mature thought."[7]

For the next few years, between 1817 and 1823, Campbell was busily occupied with multiple responsibilities. Besides trying to spread the principles of the Restoration Movement, he had inherited the leadership of the Brush Run Church. In 1817 Thomas Campbell decided to relocate to Kentucky for evangelistic purposes, and Alexander had to shoulder that burden until his father returned in 1819 disenchanted with the Kentucky law that prevented him from teaching the Bible to Negroes.[8] Also, in 1818, he had started the Buffalo Seminary for Boys on his farm, and his teaching demanded a great deal of his time and attention. The year 1820 was occupied with his preparation for, and debate with, John Walker. Soon after, Campbell began planning for a new journal, which he was simply going to entitle <u>The Christian</u>, but through Walter Scott's influence became <u>The Christian Baptist</u> when its first issue appeared on July 4, 1823.[9]

---

4   Richardson, Vol. I, pp. 470-473, and Alexander Campbell, "Anecdotes, Incidents, and Facts," No. II, <u>The Millennial Harbinger</u>, Vol. V, No. VI (June, 1848), pp. 348-349.

5   Gates, p. 29.

6   Ibid., p. 30.

7   Tristano, p. 93.

8   For more details, see Richardson, pp. 487-496.

9   This tradition about Scott's influence in the name comes from numerous sources, but the best and most thorough discussion may be found in Jim North's book, <u>Union In Truth</u>, pp. 129-130. (See also footnote 29).

In the meantime, Campbell discovered that he had become a target of some effective intrigue. His own description narrates some of the events:

Having for the six preceding years been engaged in teaching and in presiding over a classical and scientific seminary of learning at my present residence, I did not itinerate so extensively as before throughout the bounds of the Redstone Baptist Association. The consequence was, that the opposition to reformation in that Association was annually strengthening itself. We still had the majority on our side; but the minority, led by Elders Brownfield, Pritchard, and the Stones, was full of expedients to gain an ascendancy and to thrust myself and friends out of it. Their last effort came to my ears in August, 1823. It was as follows:—

A bill of heresies was duly made out of my printed Sermon on the Law, and from my oral sermons and lectures. Special brethren traversed the whole Association before its meeting, and very ingeniously contrived to have friends in the churches to nominate for election, as messengers to the Association, such persons as they knew of their party; and by this means had obtained what is usually called a *"packed jury,"* sure to decide against us in the Association.[10]

When Campbell learned of the maneuver, he plotted some subterfuge of his own. Calling a special meeting of the Brush Run Church, he obtained from the membership letters of honorable dismission for himself and thirty-one[11] others for the purpose of establishing a new church in Wellsburg, Virginia, where some of the members of the Brush Run Church lived. "Immediately" upon its formation three representatives were sent to the more liberal Mahoning Association to apply for membership there, since Adamson Bentley had been coaxing such a move anyhow. Campbell later wrote, "Our movements were so rapid and so private as to be wholly unknown to a single church in the Redstone Association."[12]

Then, in September, Alexander Campbell attended the Redstone Association meeting, not as a delegate, but instead as a spectator. This was a curiosity to all present, since the Brush Run Church had usually chosen him as its representative. Some of Campbell's friends proposed that he be voted to an official seat, but his enemies opposed the notion and "Much of the day was spent in this very trifling matter," until one of Campbell's opponents demanded to know why he was not chosen to represent the Brush Run

---

10   Alexander Campbell, "Anecdotes, Incidents and Facts," No. IV, The Millennial Harbinger, Vol. V, No. X (October, 1848), p. 553.

11   Campbell (Ibid., p. 554) erroneously lists the number as twenty, and Richardson (Vol. 2, p. 69.) is closer at thirty. The actual document of dismission, written and signed by Thomas Campbell on August 31, 1823, lists the names of the thirty-one who accompanied Alexander to start a new church (see Richardson, p. 69, footnote). Garrison and DeGroot, in The Disciples of Christ - A History, p. 171, correctly list the total number, *including* Alexander, at thirty-two.

12   Alexander Campbell, "Anecdotes, Incidents and Facts," (October, 1848), pp. 554-555.

Church. Probably with glee, Campbell announced that "the church of which I was now a member belongs to another Association—The Mahoning Regular Baptist Association of Ohio." The representatives were stunned, confounded, and frustrated with this revelation. Twenty-five years later Campbell, recalling the moment, gloated:

> Never did hunters, on seeing the game unexpectedly escape from their toils at the moment when its capture was sure, glare upon each other a more mortifying disappointment than that indicated by my pursuers at that instant on learning that I was out of their bailiwick, and consequently beyond their jurisdiction. A solemn stillness ensued, and for a time all parties seemed to have nothing to do.[13]

As has been mentioned in chapter six, this incident diverted the prosecutors' hostilities in another direction. Since Campbell slipped through their grasp, they then went after Rigdon, and any others who seemed friendly to the reformers. The years between 1823 and 1829 realized a further strain in the relationship between the two groups, and Campbell revealed the extent of his hostility toward them when he wrote:

> They were little men in a big office. The office did not fit them. They had a wrong idea, too, of what was wanting. They seemed to think that a change of apparel—a black coat instead of a drab—a broad rim on their hat instead of a narrow one—a prolongation of the face and a fictitious gravity—a longer and more emphatic pronunciation of certain words, rather than scriptural knowledge, humility, spirituality, zeal and Christian affection, with great devotion and great philanthropy, were the grand desiderata.[14]

From 1823 to 1830 <u>The Christian Baptist</u> became the main engine which transported Alexander Campbell's Reformed Baptist convictions to public consciousness. The Prospectus announced that the paper would "espouse the cause of no religious sect, excepting that ancient sect called 'CHRISTIANS FIRST AT ANTIOCH'." Admitting that "I am not very confident of my own reasonings," and that "I am sensible that, on many points, I have changed my opinion, and found reason to correct what I had judged formerly to be right," Campbell asked his readers to scrutinize his writings to see if they faithfully represented Scripture and sound reasoning. In a journalistic attack upon the denominations and their clergy he boldly announced his intentions:

> We now commence a periodical paper pledged to no religious sect in christendom, the express and avowed object of which is the eviction of

---

13 Ibid., p. 556. Campbell's memory may have been faulty when he stated that the Wellsburg Church "belongs to another Association." Apparently formal approval was not granted until the following year—1824. See Smith, p. 19, and Hayden, p. 31, for example.

14 Alexander Campbell, "Anecdotes, Incidents, and Facts," No. II, p. 345; and Richardson, Vol. I, p. 439.

truth and the exposure of error, as stated in the *Prospectus*. We expect to prove whether a paper perfectly independent, free from any controlling jurisdiction except the Bible, will be read; or whether it will be blasted by the poisonous breath of sectarian zeal and of an aspiring priesthood.[15]

Years later Campbell acknowledged that "The publication of the Christian Baptist was an open, formal declaration of war against all the religious sects and parties in the country.[16] When Campbell himself was accused of trying to start a new sect, he responded, "I will now show how they cannot make a sect of us. We will acknowledge *all* [italics mine] as christians who acknowledge the gospel facts, and obey Jesus Christ."[17] Richardson confirmed Campbell's purpose for The Christian Baptist by contending that he,

> . . .fearlessly began such an exposition of primitive Christianity and of existing corruptions as was well calculated to startle the entire religious community. This, indeed, was what he designed to do, for he conceived the people to be so completely under the dominion of the clergy at this time that nothing but bold and decisive measures could arouse them to proper inquiry.[18]

Campbell wrote a series of thirty-two essays entitled "A Restoration of The Ancient Order of Things," which The Christian Baptist published beginning with the February 7, 1825 issue and ending with the September 7, 1829 issue. In them he openly urged the abandonment of all things not found used by the New Testament Church—such as creeds and theological deductions or inferences—and the adoption of those things which he believed were definitely sanctioned in the "primitive practice"—such as weekly communion, the fellowship of Christian saints, the simple order of worship, and congregational independence under the sole authority of elders and deacons.[19]

In his first essay, Campbell opened with an apologetic as to why his restoration movement was not just another reformation effort. "All the famous reformations in history have rather been reformations of creeds and of clergy, than of religion," he asserted. Believing that history has pronounced a sort of judgement upon them, he eulogized, "if any of those

---

15　Alexander Campbell, "Prospectus" and "Preface," The Christian Baptist, Vol. I, No. I (July 4, 1823), pp. IV-X.

16　Hughes, Reviving The Ancient Faith, p. 24.

17　Alexander Campbell, Christianity Restored: The Principal Extras of The Millennial Harbinger Revised and Corrected (Rosemead, California: Old Paths Book Club, 1959), p. 122.

18　Richardson, Vol. II, p. 53.

19　Ibid., p. 125.

reformations began in the spirit, they have ended in the flesh." He then drew an analogy, postulating that "All reformations in religious opinions and speculations have been fated like the fashions in apparel. They have lived, and died, and revived, and died again." The gist of his proposition was eloquently summarized near the end of the article:

> Human systems, whether of philosophy or of religion, are proper subjects for reformation; but christianity cannot be reformed. Every attempt to reform christianity is like an attempt to create a new sun, or to change the revolutions of the heavenly bodies—unprofitable and vain. In a word we have had reformations enough. The very name has become as offensive as the term *"revolution"* in France.
>
> **A Restoration** *of the ancient order of things* is all that is necessary to the happiness and usefulness of Christians.[20]

These words alone would have probably proven inoffensive to the Baptist clergy. But when Campbell elaborated on his own definitions and applications of his principles, controversy arose. For example, in his articles he attacked clericalism, legislative synods and denominational associations, missionary societies, Sunday schools, and other "innovations" not directly sanctioned by Scripture. Some accused him of narrow-minded legalism. His defenders have tried to explain that he only opposed these agencies because, at the time, they were simply instruments of "sectarian spirit" whose function was more "to perpetuate the schisms of the Church than to promote the simple Gospel."[21]

Touring Virginia in 1825, Alexander Campbell met two influential Baptist leaders of that state—Andrew Broaddus and Robert Semple. Semple was impressed with Campbell's talents and graciousness in person, but critical of his caustic vituperance in print. In 1826 he wrote:

> I have known some of their party who have appeared in private conversation to be mild and gentle indeed, and every way pleasant; but when brought out in writing or speaking seemed to have another kind of temper. If you will bear with me I will suggest that this seems to me to be the case with the editor of *The Christian Baptist*.[22]

Richardson tried to defend his friend:

> Mr. Campbell has been censured by some for the severity of his strictures at this period upon the clergy and their proceedings. A milder course and

---

20 Alexander Campbell, "A Restoration of The Ancient Order of Things," No. 1, The Christian Baptist, Vol. 2, No. 7 (Feb. 7, 1825), pp. 133-136.

21 See Dean Walker, Adventuring For Christian Unity, p. 28, for example.

22 Quoted in Gates, p. 42.

gentler words, they think, would have succeeded better. It is to be remembered, however, that the milder method had already been tried. No gentler words, no kinder remonstrances, no warmer entreaties, no sounder arguments, could have been employed than those addressed to religious society, and particularly to the clergy, by Thomas Campbell and the "Christian Association." But all these well-meant efforts the clergy had treated with disdain.[23]

In May of 1827 a Baptist editor named Spencer Clack wrote Campbell a letter "Being desirous to see in our denomination *unity* of heart, of sentiment, and exertion,. . . ." In it he recognizes that Campbell has been an advocate for unity, but suggests that The Christian Baptist has produced the opposite results:

> I allude to the *effect* produced by your writings, orations, and lectures. To this fact your Christian Baptist bears testimony. Some are for you, others against you; some believe, others reject; some approve, others censure and condemn. Such is the state of affairs; such the effect produced by your writings.

He then exhorts Campbell, "Come then, my brother, come bow with me before our God, let us ask forgiveness for all the evils we have ever done;. . . ." He continues on to reason that "If creeds are unnecessary and injurious to the welfare of society; so is your Baptist; so your essays and expositions," and observes that "it appears to me you have added to the confusion of tongues;. . . ." Finally he concludes:

> What, then, is the difference between us? Simply this; We cannot agree as to what the Bible *teaches*. The Baptists think the Bible *teaches* the doctrine contained in the creeds; you think it teaches what you have written and published, and what you will hereafter write and publish.[24]

Then, in September of 1827, Robert Semple responded to a letter from someone pen-named "Querens," who challenged him to explain his charge that The Christian Baptist was promulgating mere "chimeras." Seemingly a kind man, and by his own description, "not fond of controversy, and never have been," Semple wrote a response calling Campbell "my friend," "a champion," and "a generous combatant with one who wishes nothing but fair play." But he also admitted differing with Campbell on many critical points of doctrine, stating almost matter-of-factly, "I am persuaded he is palpably on the wrong side, and it would not be a hard task to make it manifest." Maintaining that "Mr. Campbell's views are not new," he connected them directly with Sandeman, Glas, and

---

23 Richardson, Vol. II, pp. 59-60.

24 Spencer Clack, Letter to Alexander Campbell, The Christian Baptist, Vol. V, No. 1 (August 6, 1827) pp. 13-15.

the Haldanes, and pronounced that such views had been exposed and effectively refuted by a man named Fuller years earlier.[25]

In a letter to Silas M. Noel earlier that month, Semple, obviously referring Alexander Campbell, wrote, "Every '*novice*' thinks he has made discoveries overlooked by his ancients." Admitting that The Christian Baptist "has doubtless exhibited many valuable pieces and principles," he nonetheless warned:

> . . .but taken as a whole, I am persuaded it has been more mischievous than any publication I have ever known. The ability of the editor, joined to the plausibility of his plans or doctrines, has succeeded in sowing the seeds of discord among brethren to an extent in many places alarming. In my address to him a year or two ago, I said if his principles prevailed a new sect started up.[26]

Campbell had been accused of this before. His response was:

> I do intend to continue in connection with this people so long as they will permit me to say what I believe; to teach what I am assured of, and to censure what is amiss in their views or practices. I have no idea of adding to the catalogue of new sects. . . .I labor to see sectarianism abolished and all Christians of every name united upon the one foundation upon which the apostolic Church was founded. To bring Baptists and Paedobaptists to this is my supreme end. . . .And I hope I will not be accused of sectarian partiality when I avow my conviction that the Baptist society have has much liberality in their views, as much of the ancient simplicity of the Christian Church, as much of the spirit of Christianity about them, as are to be found among any other people. . . .But that there are among them some mighty *Regulars* who are as intolerant as the great pontiff of good order and regularity, no person will deny.[27]

Despite these growing hostilities, Campbell's "Reformed Baptists" remained within the orbit of the Baptist church. Errett Gates, in his The Early Relation And Separation Of Baptists And Disciples, has listed three reasons for their prolonged relationship together: (1) The lack of a central authority to organize a concerted action against the Reformers; (2) The divided opinion within the Baptists themselves in reference to Campbell; (3) The disputes among the Baptists over many of the same points Campbell was making.[28]

---

25   R.B. Semple, "A Letter...," The Christian Baptist, Vol. V, No. 5, (December 3, 1827) pp. 119-120.

26   R.B. Semple, "To Silas M. Noel," sent Sept. 3, 1827, The Christian Baptist, Vol. V, No. 9 (April 7, 1828), p. 207.

27   Alexander Campbell, quoted in Richardson, Vol. II, pp. 134-135.

28   Gates, p. 52.

The relationship between the Reformed and Regular Baptists had been fragile at best throughout the decade of the 1820's. There were irritants—like Alexander Campbell's new translation of the New Testament in 1826 in which he changed John the Baptist to John "the immerser." One writer charged him with having made at least eighty variations on Dr. George Campbell's translation in regard to baptism. In actuality, Campbell had not, it seems, made eighty "distinct and different alterations," but had instead repeated the same change every place that the same word appeared. Therefore, Campbell retorted that the writer himself "had told eighty lies in telling one truth, as if a man should say he had seen eighty pigeons when he had only seen one pigeon eighty times."[29]

By 1827 the roll call of sixteen churches constituting the Mahoning Association at that time shows that the Regular Baptist influence had virtually been purged.[30] But Campbell's influence was not the only one significant in the Association. Scott, Rigdon, and Bentley were also preponderant. There is legitimate reason to postulate that many Baptist leaders were either very patient or slow to realize what was happening. In April of 1828 Walter Scott baptized forty people in Salem, Ohio, in ten days. "The leading Baptists were delighted," wrote Gates, even though "The converts were received to baptism on the confession of their faith in the Lord Jesus Christ, without the usual routine of telling an experience and a vote of the church." But Scott apparently then crowed, "Who will now say there is a Baptist church in Salem?", and many of the old leaders who had thought he was contributing to the Baptist church until this announcement was made began to realize otherwise.[31]

Yet Campbell was still the Baptist champion one more time. In mid-April of 1829 he debated the famous British Utopian Socialist Robert Owen in Cincinnati on the topic of Christian evidences.[32] Owen came prepared with a two hundred-page manuscript containing twelve propositions espousing a mechanistic cosmology and a humanistic philosophy. Campbell responded with his advocacy of a theistic universe from a Christian perspective, addressing the audience for periods as long as twelve hours on the final day. The two verbal combatants demonstrated a remarkable amount of respect and kindness toward each other for such a potentially emotional topic. But at the conclusion of the debate Campbell put the audience to a vote. Disciples of Christ folklore, and a few histories, have recited the results of the vote in the context of who won or lost. But a more careful rendering of the results shows that Campbell asked "that all

---

29 Richardson, Vol. II, p. 148.

30 Gates, pp. 68-69.

31 Ibid., pp. 66-67.

32 For the proceedings and actual text of the debate see Charles Howard Sims, Reporter, <u>A Debate</u> <u>On The Evidences Of Christianity</u> (Bethany, VA: Published by Alexander Campbell, 1829). Robert Owen also had a transcript published in London by R. Groombridge in 1839.

the persons in this assembly who believe in the christian religion or who feel so much interest in it, as to wish to see it pervade the world, will please to signify it by standing up." Almost every one did. Then he asked "that all persons doubtful of the truth of the christian religion, or who do not believe it, and who are not friendly to its spread and prevalence over the world, will please signify by rising up. Only three stood. One cannot help but question whether this was a vote for Mr. Campbell, or rather for a faith which had very few skeptics at the time. As Owen himself rather graciously observed to the audience regarding the results, "I am much pleased with Mr. Campbell's little maneuver of the test, because I discover it pleases him and his friends. Truth requires no such support."[33]

However, as the decade began to close things came to a head. Campbell's opponents had been working hard to excommunicate the Reformers before they could do further damage to the Baptist cause. There is little doubt in this author's mind that Campbell did not want a rupture with the Baptists, and when it happened, he laid the blame solely at their feet, even though he had obviously antagonized them beyond the limits of their endurance. In his own defense Campbell wrote:

> Convinced that the greenest tree in the whole territory of christendom was decayed and decaying, we set ourselves to work at its roots to dig about it and manure it. But we found it so decayed and decaying, that little hopes to its renovation could be entertained. The keepers of the vineyard found us at work and were determined to interrupt our operations, and so the controversy began.[34]

Actual divisions began back as far as 1826, when Alexander Campbell was appointed to be the corresponding messenger from the Mahoning Association to the Redstone Association. Campbell's old enemies there had determined not to receive him, but they could not get a majority of the churches to agree with them. Therefore, the ten orthodox churches of the Redstone Association managed to ostracize the other thirteen member churches, including Brush Run, because they would not acknowledge the Philadelphia confession of faith. Most of those thirteen then formed the Washington Association in 1827, and manifested a definite sympathy with the Reformers.[35]

Other churches and associations began to follow the Redstone precedent, but probably the most significant move was made by the Beaver

---

33 Ibid., pp. 464-465.

34 Alexander Campbell, "Introductory Remarks," The Millennial Harbinger, Vol. III, No. 1 (January 2, 1832), p. 4.

35 Richardson, Vol. II, pp. 163-165. Leroy Garrett lists the year of these occurrences as 1825, and Mary Agnes Smith gives the year as 1827. But a more careful reading of Richardson, corroborated with the minutes from the Mahoning Association, confirms this year as 1826.

Association, an alliance of Calvinistic Baptists which was formed by some Regular Baptist churches in 1810 with jurisdiction over the border area of Pennsylvania and Ohio.[36] In August of 1829 the Beaver Association, at the urging of Mr. Winters from the Redstone Association, compiled a list of resolutions that has become known to history as the "Beaver Anathema." Composed of eight charges of heresy, this document constituted a formal disfellowshipping of the Mahoning Association. Most of the charges centered around disagreements regarding baptism.[37] Campbell had emphasized that the purpose of baptism was for forgiveness of sins, salvation, and the gift of the Holy Spirit. The Baptist position generally regarded baptism to be an act of confirmation, obedience, and church membership. In this discrepancy, "many of his opponents understood Campbell to be arguing that only those in his own movement were saved." But even worse than this, and "More to the point, it was not just Campbell's enemies who understood him to claim that only those in his movement were saved; many of his followers believed it as well."[38]

More associations decided to follow the Redstone example. Similar actions were taken by the North District Association in April of 1830, and the Tate's Creek Association of Kentucky in June, which mimicked the Redstone Association when an orthodox minority of ten churches expelled the other sixteen for sympathies with the Reformers.[39] Other associations— such as Sulphur Fork, Goshen, Long Run, Appomattox, and Dover— followed suit soon after, with the Dover Association adding four more charges to the heresy list.[40] Realizing the trouble being caused by such associations, the Mahoning Association *dissolved itself* in August of 1830.

On July 22, 1830, a fifty-nine year old Tennessee Baptist preacher named Garner McConnico composed a letter to some of his brethren. He began by reminding them that, as long ago as the Walker debate of 1820, "I was *doubtful* of the Scotchman," and that the McCalla debate only heightened his fears.

---

36   Van Wagoner, p. 10. For some reason, Leroy Garrett (p. 158), usually a very thorough scholar, states that a Baptist minister from Youngstown, Ohio, "persuaded some 80 members of the Mahoning Association to withdraw and *start* the Beaver Association." Since the Beaver Association was already in existence when the Mahoning Association began, this just cannot be true. Mary Agnes Smith (p. 85) acknowledges, however, that "two or three fragments" of Western Reserve churches "refused to go along with the [Mahoning] Association into the 'Reformation,'" and therefore "united themselves *with*" [italics mine] the Beaver Association (See footnote 8 in Smith for the churches involved).

37   For the specific list of charges and more detail about the occasion, see Garrison, Religion Follows The Frontier, pp. 134-135, and Gates, pp. 92-93.

38   Hughes, p. 7.

39   Garrison and DeGroot, The Disciples of Christ: A History, pp. 193-194.

     For more incidents of excommunications by churches and associations, see Gates, Ch. IX.

40   See Gates, p. 93, or Garrison, p. 135, for specific charges.

After reading Campbell's writings and holding a twelve-hour conversation with him, McConnico snorted, "consequently all the standing religious sects are wrong, and a new theory, *falsely* called the Ancient Gospel, is introduced. What a Pope!!" He then unburdened himself to his friends:

> Campbellism has carried away many whom I thought firm. These wandering stars and clouds without water, ever learning and never able to come to the knowledge of the truth, make proselytes much more the children of the devil then they were before. O Lord! hear the cries and see the tears of the Baptists; for Alexander has done them much harm. The Lord reward him according to his works. Look at the Creaths of Kentucky. Look at Anderson, Craig, and Hopwood, of Tennessee. See them dividing churches, and spreading discord, and constituting churches out of excommunicated members. Such shuffling—such lying—such slandering—such evil speaking—such dissembling—such downright hypocrisy—and all under the *false* name of reformation.[41]

In August of 1830 the Elkhorn Association of Kentucky met at Silas Church in Bourbon county and, after one especially controversial session, also decided to ostracize the Campbellites. The occasion featured, not only misunderstanding and bitterness, but irony as well. Thomas Campbell had attended the meeting and, "must have viewed the turbulent scenes of the day with pain, for he sat with his head bowed in sorrow. . . ." He finally advised those contending for the reformed position to leave. "The session ironically closed with the entire association singing the Psalm: 'Behold how good and pleasant a thing it is for brethren to dwell together in unity!'"[42]

Alexander Campbell resisted exclusion. He still felt a great affinity with the Baptist laity and many of the clergy. Also, of course, division was inconsistent with the Reformers' plea. When the Beaver Anathema appeared, he complained:

> Who is making divisions and schisms? Who is rendering the peace of the churches? Who are creating factions, swellings and tumults? We who are willing to bear and forebear, or they who are anathematizing and attempting to excommunicate?. . .
>
> **If there be a division, gentlemen, you will make it, not I** [my bold]; and the more you oppose us with the weight of your censure, like the palm tree we will grow the faster. I am for peace, for union, for harmony, for co-operation with all good men. But I fear you not; if you will fling firebrands, arrows and discords into the army of faith, you will repent it, not we. You will lose influence, not we. We covet not persecution, but we disregard it.

---

41 Letter from Garner McConnico to "Elders Clopton and Jefferies," written from Franklin, Tennessee, on July 22, 1830. Published in <u>The Millennial Harbinger</u>, Vol. I. No. 12 (December 6, 1830), pp. 540-543.

42 McAllister, pp. 211-212.

We fear nothing but error, and should you proceed to make divisions, you will find that they will reach much farther than you are aware, and that the time is past when an anathema from an association will produce any other effect than contempt from some and a smile from others.[43]

So separation came, episodically and gradually, but nonetheless completely. Campbell published the last issue of The Christian Baptist on July 5, 1830, closing out volume VII as he came to realize the inappropriateness of the title Baptist when relations were being severed.[44] In January of 1830 he had already begun a new journal entitled The Millennial Harbinger, reflecting his conviction about the imminence of the Biblically-predicted thousand-year reign of peace and prosperity. He also expressed the desire to "exhibit a milder tone" than he had with The Christian Baptist.[45] The Millennial Harbinger was then published from 1830 to 1870.[46]

In the inaugural issue of The Millennial Harbinger, Campbell seemed to be resigned to the fact that a split was coming. He therefore attempted to justify it:

> . . .no man ever achieved any great good to mankind who did not wrest it with violence through ranks of opponents—who did not fight for it with courage and perseverance, and who did not, in the conflict, sacrifice either his good name or his life. John the harbinger of the Messiah, lost his head. The Apostles were slaughtered. The Savior was crucified. The ancient confessors were slain. The reformers all have been excommunicated. I know that we shall do little good if we are not persecuted.[47]

Many Baptists were joining the Stone-Campbell Restoration Movement. Resentment grew on both sides, and some Baptists began to fear Campbell's influence so much that in 1833 a man named E.A. Mills was expelled from the Eagleville, Ohio, Baptist church because he would not quit reading The Millennial Harbinger.[48] Later in the century a

---

43 Richardson, Vol. II, pp. 323-324.

44 Tristano, p. 105. Garrison and DeGroot (p. 207) contend that Alexander Campbell also regarded the number seven, which appears often in the Bible, as somewhat sacred. Hence, "after every seventh volume of the Millennial Harbinger he began a 'New Series.'"

45 Richardson, Vol. II, p. 302.

46 Mary Agnes Smith, p. vii, footnote 5, in either an error or a misstatement claims that Campbell published The Millennial Harbinger from January 4, 1830, to December of 1870. Actually Campbell died in 1866, and J.W. Pendleton and C.L. Loos published the final years of its existence.

47 Alexander Campbell, "Prefatory Remarks," The Millennial Harbinger, Vol. I, No. 1 (January 4, 1830) p. 8.

48 Garrison, p. 137. Eighteen others were also disciplined.

Disciple named B.A. Hinsdale would romanticize that era when he articulated:

> Light broke in on all sides among the Baptists of Eastern Ohio. They were ascending the mountains of God. They obtained clearer and clearer views of truth, and one by one they burst the cocoon of the old theological and ecclesiastical wrappings. The Association protected the swelling chrysalis until, transformed, it burst its shell and flew away.[49]

Despite this chauvinistic jingoism, Campbell always, in his contemplative moments, regarded the divorce as a tragedy. There were far more points of theological and methodological agreement between the two groups than there were areas of disagreement. Even on his deathbed Campbell lamented, "There was never any sufficient reason for a separation between us and the Baptists. We ought to have remained one people, and to have labored together to restore the primitive faith and practice."[50]

But instead of being a unity movement *among* the denominational community, as the restoration pioneers had hoped, the Reformers were now censured and isolated. They continued to contend—as many still do today—that they have neither sectarian nor denominational status. But as Martin Marty has so eloquently put it, "They were not granted an exemption by their neighbors, however, and had to play the denomination game, too."[51] Richard Tristano, a Roman Catholic and therefore an "outsider" to the Restoration Movement, astutely comprehended and described its Achilles's heel:

> In throwing down the gauntlet to the bulk of American religion, Alexander Campbell rewrote the more gentle "ecumenism" espoused by his father in the *Declaration and Address*. The dialectic between "unity" and "truth," which was always present, continued, though the balance was tipped in favor of "the eviction of truth and the exposing of error." The unity motive persisted, but was transformed into a faithful remnant who would destroy the perversions of the "sects" and restore an authentic, apostolic Christianity. The unity motive, therefore, became a motive of separation as well, both between the restored and the unrestored and ultimately among those within the Restoration Movement as well.[52]

---

49   Hinsdale, p. 10.

50   Richardson, Vol. II, p. 675.

51   Martin Marty, <u>Righteous Empire: The Protestant Experience In America</u> (New York: The Dial Press, 1970), p. 71.

52   Tristano, p. 95.

THE BIRTH OF AN ALTERNATIVE EXCLUSIVISTIC RESTORATIONISM

Not all restoration movements are unity movements. Mormonism was not, but the Stone-Campbell Movement was. Because of the tragic experiences perceived by Herbert, Locke, and Thomas Campbell, division had proven to be a "horrid evil." Therefore, the Campbells viewed restorationism as a means to unity, and not simply as an end unto itself. Nevertheless, as Alexander Campbell developed and defined restorationism, it became divisive and isolated the Stone-Campbell Movement.

The question therefore presents itself as to the justification for labeling Mormonism as exclusivistic and the Disciples of Christ Movement as inclusivistic, at least originally. After all, as the Disciples of Christ developed and evolved in the nineteenth century, it certainly came to be seen by many as another denomination claiming that its position was right, and all others, to varying degrees, were wrong.

Yet I would make the following distinction as to their origins, at least. Barton W. Stone desired to unify all Christians based upon their commonly shared experiences in the Holy Spirit. Thomas Campbell wanted to unite all Christians based upon those few *essential* doctrinal tenets which they already held in common. But Mormonism made no such pretense to be a unity movement. It would only accept those who could be won or converted to believe that Joseph Smith's revelations were valid. All others were infidels. Its progenitors seemed to accept fairly early in the movement that most people would reject their special attenuation of truth.

Whereas the Campbells and Walter Scott had classical British University educations as ministers and teachers, and whereas Alexander Campbell also became a successful farmer, educator, publisher, and accepted public figure—Joseph Smith's background was very different. At first glance Joseph Smith appears to be the quintessence of frontier religious independence and rugged individualism. Calling him "a religious genius,"

Harold Bloom contends that "There was something in Smith and his vision that remains central to our country and its spirituality."[1] Fawn Brodie, referring to Smith as "purely a Yankee product," adds that "His kingdom of God upon earth was saturated with the Yankee enthusiasm for earthly blessings. No one more ingeniously than he combined Jewish and Christian mysticism with the goal of perpetual prosperity."[2]

But further analysis reveals an authoritarian revelator whose visions were directly from God and whose word was not to be questioned. He certainly tended to assuage the thirst of many for order out of religious confusion, and his followers comprise a significant part of America's frontier story.

Yet the Mormons, if they are at all faithful to the most crucial teachings of Joseph Smith and Brigham Young, no more believe in American democracy than they do in historical Christianity or in western monogamy. Smith, Young, and their followers believed in theocracy or the inspired rule of the saints, and they looked forward to each prophet in turn ruling over the Kingdom of God, as king, first here and then everywhere.[3]

Joseph Smith Jr. was born in Sharon, Vermont, on December 23, 1805, the fourth of ten children born to Joseph Sr. and Lucy [Mack] Smith, both of Scottish descent.[4] In 1816 the Smith family moved from Norwich, Vermont, to Manchester, New York, near Palmyra, because of a June snow and a cold, dry summer which produced a famine in that area.[5] They had moved numerous times while in Connecticut, and Joseph Sr., now financially destitute, looked to greener pastures. But his penchant

Figure 7. Joseph Smith (1805 - 1844) (From http://www.independentamericans.org/ We_Hold_These_Truths%20Joseph%20Smith.htm).

---

1   Bloom, p. 80.

2   Brodie, p. IX.

3   Bloom, p. 91.

4   Richard L. Bushman, <u>Joseph Smith and The Beginnings of Mormonism</u> (Urbana: University of Illinois Press, 1984), pp. 29-31; and Joseph Smith, <u>History of The Church</u>, Vol. I, p. 2. Smith was actually the fifth sibling born after a still-born son, then Alvin (1798), Hyrum (1800), and Sophronia (1803), a daughter. For more information see Lucy Mack Smith, <u>History of Joseph Smith</u> (Salt Lake City: Publisher's Press, 1979), pp. 350-351.

5   Bushman, p. 40.

was not for farming or mercantilism, which he had tried earlier and been swindled. Instead he dabbled in water-witching and treasure hunting.

Apparently the Smith family did not gain a favorable impression with many of their new neighbors and acquaintances. Eber D. Howe, a rabid anti-Mormon with an obvious desire to discredit Mormonism, gathered many of their statements together in a work published in 1834 entitled Mormonism Unvailed. In order to authenticate these testimonials, each contributor made an oath-sworn deposition in front of a judge, accompanied by statements from other citizens certifying the integrity of character of each witness. Howe syncretized their testimonies in the following manner:

> All who became intimate with them during this period [1816-1830], unite in representing the general character of old Joseph and wife, the parents of the pretended Prophet, as lazy, indolent, ignorant and superstitious — having a firm belief in ghosts and witches; the telling of fortunes; pretending to believe that the earth was filled with hidden treasures, buried there by Kid or the Spaniards.[6]

Parley Chase claimed that he had known the Smiths before their Mormon days and that the men of the family "were lazy, intemperate and worthless men, very much addicted to lying," adding that "In this they frequently boasted of their skill." David Stafford referred to Joseph Smith Sr. as "a drunkard and a liar. . . much in the habit of gambling," and continued on to say that "He and his boys were truly a lazy set of fellows, and more particularly Joseph, who very aptly followed his father's example, and in some respects was worse." G.W. Stodard maintained that "The Smith family never made any pretensions to respectability," and Roswell Nichols insisted that "For breach of contracts, for the non-payment of debts and borrowed money, and for duplicity with their neighbors, the family was notorious." Fifty-one people signed a declaration which read in part:

> We, the undersigned, have been acquainted with the Smith family, for a number of years, while they resided near this place, and we have no hesitation in saying, that we consider them destitute of that moral character, which ought to entitle them to the confidence of any community.

Eleven more signed the document declaring the family to be "lazy," "indolent," and "intemperate."[7]

Of course the Smiths had their defenders as well. But controversy surrounded them even before Mormonism appeared. Many of their neighbors were confounded by their strange superstitions; others regarded

---

6   Eber D. Howe, Mormonism Unvailed . . . (Painesville, Ohio: Published by the author, 1834), photomechanically reproduced by Jerald and Sandra Tanner (Salt Lake City: Utah Lighthouse Ministry, n.d.) p. 11.

7   Ibid., pp. 247-262.

their efforts as insincere ploys or dupes. One man related the following account concerning Joseph Smith Sr.:

> I was once plowing near the house of Joseph Smith, Sen. about noon, he requested me to walk with him a short distance from his house, for the purpose of seeing whether a mineral rod would work in my hand, saying at the same time he was confident it would. As my oxen were eating and being myself at leisure, I accepted the invitation. — When we arrived near the place at which he thought there was money, he cut a small witch hazle bush and gave me direction how to hold it. He then went off some rods, and told me to say to the rod, "work to the money," which I did, in an audible voice. He rebuked me severely for speaking it loud, and said it must be spoken in a whisper. This was rare sport for me. While the old man was standing off some rods, throwing himself into various shapes, I told him the rod did not work. He seemed much surprised at this, and said he thought he saw it move in my hand. It was now time for me to return to my labor. On my return, I picked up a small stone and was carelessly tossing it from one hand to the other. Said he, (looking very earnestly) what are you going to do with that stone? Throw it at the birds, I replied. No, said the old man, it is of great worth; and upon this I gave it to him. Now, says he, if you only knew the value there is back of my house, (and pointing to a place near) — *there*, exclaimed he, is one chest of gold and another of silver. He then put the stone which I had given him into his hat, and stooping forward, he bowed and made sundry maneuvers, quite similar to those of a stool pigeon. At length he took down his hat, and being very much exhausted, said, in a faint voice, "if you knew what I had seen, you would believe." To see the old man thus try to impose upon me, I confess, rather had a tendency to excite contempt than pity. Yet I thought it best to conceal my feelings, preferring to appear the dupe of my credulity, than to expose myself to his resentment.[8]

Testimonials about Joseph Smith Jr. were no kinder. Henry Harris, who had known the Smith family since about the year 1820, ventured that "The character of Joseph Smith, Jr. for truth and veracity was such, that I would not believe him under oath.[9] Peter Ingersoll told of an instance of Smith's youthful shenanigans:

> On our journey to Pennsylvania, we could not make the exact change at the toll gate near Ithaca. Joseph told the gate tender, that he would "hand" him the toll on his return, as he was coming back in a few days. On our return, Joseph tendered him twenty-five cents, the toll being twelve and a half. He did not recognize Smith, so he accordingly gave him back the twelve and a half cents. After we had passed the gate, I asked him if he did agree to pay double gatage on our return? No, said he, I agreed to "*hand*" it to him and I did, but he handed it back again.[10]

---

8   Ibid., pp. 232-233.

9   Ibid., p. 251.

10   Ibid., p. 235.

It became common for Smith to find and use odd shaped or strange looking stones as "peep-stones," which he claimed could reveal the location of buried treasures. In 1819, while digging a well for Clark Chase, someone found a rock that was shaped like a child's foot. Even though the Chase children wanted it, Smith took it and used it to locate the treasures. Then again in 1822, a similar circumstance involved the digging of a well for Willard Chase, who found a rock that he wished to keep "on account of its being a curiosity." But he lent it to Smith, and later to his brother Hiram, who refused to return it. These rocks were placed in a stove pipe hat and, with Smith kneeling and burying his face in the hat, were used as "peek-stones."[11]

Smith spent much time in his early years engaged in "money digging." Many of the hills in that area, he contended, were artificially made, with treasure buried in them. A local newspaper, The Palmyra Reflector, told of an instance when Smith claimed the mantel of "Walters the Magician" and "used a magic stone, a rusty sword, a stuffed toad and other articles of high validity to the superstitious, to assist in the location of buried treasure."[12] Peering into a hat, he claimed to actually see the exact location of such things as "deposited keys, barrels and hogs heads of coined silver and gold—bars of gold, golden images, brass kettles filled with gold and silver—gold candlesticks, swords, etc. etc."[13]

But these treasures could move about under the ground, or even sink deeper, depending upon such factors as charms, thunder and lightening, bad language, or even an evil thought! One account given to Frederic Mather by some "eye-witnesses" told of a dig thirty-five feet in diameter where a number of diggers "were just ready to grasp the silver, when the charm moved it three hundred feet to the northeast." Smith claimed to track it to its new location, but when the diggers were near its depth again, it moved another fifty feet. A third hole was dug fifteen of the necessary twenty feet when the treasure moved yet again. So Smith called for a black sheep to be sacrificed. None could be procured on such short notice, so a black dog was substituted. It didn't keep the treasure from moving either, so Smith finally requested that one of the diggers be the ultimate sacrifice. "None of the faithful responded to his call, and thus the magnificent scheme was abandoned."[14]

Isaac Hale, Smith's future father-in-law, had apparently boarded some of the diggers and "took stock" in this scheme. After the attempt, Smith

---

11   Frederic G. Mather, "The Early Days of Mormonism," Lippincott's Magazine of Popular Literature and Science (Philadelphia: J.B. Lippincott and Co.), Vol. 26 (December, 1880), pp. 198-199; and Howe, pp. 240-242.

12   Robert Kent Fielding, "The Growth of The Mormon Church In Kirtland, Ohio," (Ph.D. dissertation, Indiana University, 1957), p. 9.

13   Howe, p. 237.

14   Mather, pp. 199-200.

stopped at Hale's house, persuaded Emma, his second daughter, to marry him, and ran off with her. Hale threatened to shoot "the peeker" if he ever saw him again.[15]

Such testimonials and stories are easily suspect when one realizes the anti-Mormon motivations of many of the witnesses. But on March 20, 1826, Smith was brought to court and accused of many such instances of money-digging. He was found guilty of disorderly conduct.[16] According to Robert Fielding, a validated document reveals that Smith admitted the charges.[17]

However, like most people of that era, and especially in that "burned-over district" of New York, the Smith family was interested in more than just the material benefits of life. Joseph wrote in his history that, the year after they had moved to Manchester [i.e. 1817] "there was in the place where we lived an unusual excitement on the subject of religion." But while the interest was high, the confusion and competition was also.

> Some were contending for the Methodist faith, some for the Presbyterian, and some for the Baptist. For notwithstanding the great love which the converts to these different faiths expressed at the time of their conversion, and the great zeal manifested by the respective clergy, who were active in getting up and promoting this extraordinary scene of religious feeling, in order to have everybody converted, as they were pleased to call it, let them join what sect they pleased—yet when the converts began to file off, some to one party and some to another, it was seen that the seemingly good feelings of both the priests and the converts were more pretended than real; for a scene of great confusion and bad feeling ensued; priest contending against priest, and convert against convert; so that all their good feelings for one another, if they ever had any, were entirely lost in a strife of words and a contest about opinions.[18]

Marvin Hill has observed the spiritual disorder in the Smith family as well, recognizing that "In their religious as well as in their business affairs the Smiths had been restless, dissatisfied, itinerant."[19] They had an intense interest in religion, but could not settle into any denomination for long. Four of them joined the Presbyterian church for a while, and Joseph Jr.

---

15 Ibid., p. 200.

16 See Fawn Brodie, pp. 405-407, for the actual court record.

17 Fielding, p. 11. In the <u>Messenger and Advocate</u>, Vol. I, No. 3 (December, 1834), p. 40, Smith admitted to yielding to "many vices and follies" as are "common to most or all youths," and being a man "subject to passion;" but he denied "wronging or injuring any man or society of men."

18 Joseph Smith, <u>History of The Church</u>, Vol. I, pp. 2-3.

19 Marvin S. Hill, "The Role of Christian Primitivism In The Origin and Development of The Mormon Kingdom, 1830-1844" (Ph.D. dissertation, University of Chicago, 1968), p. 41.

himself felt the desire to be a Methodist. But he was unable to finally conclude "who was right and who was wrong."[20] His mother, Lucy Mack Smith, had said earlier, "If I remain a member of no church, all religious people will say I am of the world; and if I join some one of the different denominations, all the rest will say I am in error. No church will admit that I am right, except the one with which I am associated."[21]

Her quandary was common. One man named Asael Smith, expecting to die, begged his family to avoid giving their allegiance to any particular denomination, but instead to give it to "the Scriptures, and . . . sound reason."[22] Another named Asa Wild, after trying several denominations, despaired, "I was at first a Baptist, then a kind of New Light, afterward a Congregationalist; now my only creed is <u>God be merciful to me a sinner</u>." Then, receiving a revelation in which he was informed of the coming millennium, he was told by the Lord that all denominations were corrupt and that God "was now raising up an inferior class" of people with "small learning" who would preach "the everlasting gospel."[23]

This, of course, proved to become Joseph Smith and the Mormons. Smith, in his confusion about the turmoil, hypocrisy, and corruption in the religious community, found direction for solving his dilemma in James 1: 5— "If any of you lack wisdom, let him ask of God, that giveth to all men liberally, and upbraideth not; and it shall be given him" [KJV]. So he went into the woods to pray where, after an alarming encounter with a dark force, God and Jesus appeared to him in a vision. He asked them which sect was right, and which one he should therefore join.

> I was answered that I must join none of them, for they were all wrong, and the personage who addressed me said that all their creeds were an abomination in His sight: that those professors were all corrupt; that "they draw near to me with their lips, but their hearts are far from me; they teach for doctrines the commandments of men: having a form of Godliness, but they deny the power thereof."[24]

With this knowledge Joseph Smith realized that there was only one way left, and that was to *restore* the true faith. But he also believed that only God had the authority to do that. So did many others, who were convinced that God had promised that "the time would come when the true gospel would be restored." Hence, men and women began imploring God in

---

20   Joseph Smith, <u>History of The Church</u>, Vol. I, pp. 3-4.

21   Lucy Mack Smith (<u>Biographical Sketches</u>, pp. 36-37) as quoted in Bushman, p. 17.

22   Philip L. Barlow, <u>Mormons and the Bible: The Place of The Latter-Day Saints In American Religion</u> (New York: Oxford University Press, 1991), p. 10.

23   Hill, pp. 44-45.

24   Joseph Smith, <u>History of The Church</u>, Vol. I, pp. 5-6.

prayer "to restore the ancient gospel, to restore the ancient gifts, [and] to restore the ancient power. . . ."[25] This restorationist plea sought to fill a void and supply a psycho-spiritual need felt by numerous people.

> Part of the appeal of the restoration theme was the assurance it provided that one was right. This concern for *correctness* [italics mine] amid a welter of competing faiths provided the chief impulse behind the birth of Mormonism.[26]

Another explanation has been offered for the birth of Mormonism. Basing his position on the old thesis of H. Richard Neibuhr in The Social Sources of Denominationalism, Marvin Hill has suggested that Mormonism was created because economic and social factors excluded the Smiths and others from full acceptance into the denominations.

> It was this segmentation of American religious life which the Mormons most rigorously opposed—a class-oriented denominationalism which seemed to squeeze the Smiths and other economically unsuccessfuls out of any full social acceptance and comfortable participation. . . .Elmer T. Clark argues that primitive gospel ideals have tended to flourish in America among the sects of "disinherited."[27]

Whatever the explanation given for the origin of Mormonism, during the intervening years between Smith's vision of God and Christ (1820) and his visit by an angel (1823), he confessed that "I was left to all kinds of temptations," and that "I frequently fell into many foolish errors, and displayed the weakness of youth, and the foibles of human nature; which, I am sorry to say, led me into divers temptations, offensive in the sight of God."[28] But in 1823 things changed. An Angel named Moroni allegedly appeared to him, forgave his foolish sins, and told him where some golden plates were to be found which contained, not only "the fullness of the everlasting Gospel," but also a history of the inhabitants of America. With them, in the same hill called Cumorah, were to be found the Urim and Thummin of Old Testament notoriety, with which he would be able to translate the "Reformed Egyptian" language on them.[29]

The tablets were not to be found for four more years. When they were exhumed in 1827 word soon spread of a wonderful find, and stories began to circulate that aroused both excitement and curiosity, as well as

---

25   Ivan J. Barrett, Joseph Smith and the Restoration: A History of The LDS Church to 1846 (Provo, Utah: B.Y.U. Press, 1973), p. 16. Many people believed that this promise was implied in Acts 3: 20-21.

26   Allen and Hughes, Discovering Our Roots, p. 95.

27   Hill, pp. 47-48 (including first line of footnote).

28   Joseph Smith, History of The Church, Vol. I, p. 9.

29   Mather, p. 199, and Smith, pp. 11-15.

skepticism and scorn. One man, named William Stafford, scoffed, "When they found that the people of this vicinity would no longer put any faith in their schemes for digging money, they then pretended to find a gold bible, of which, they said, the book of Mormon was only an introduction."[30] Many others must have cynically reasoned that, given Smith's background and usual condition of poverty, if he really did find such plates of gold it would have been more consistent with his nature to have *sold* them. On November 8, 1833, Joseph Capron recalled:

> At length Joseph pretended to find the Gold plates. This scheme, he believed, would relieve the family from all pecuniary embarrassment. His father told me, that when the book was published, they would be enabled, from the profits of the work, to carry into successful operation the money digging business. He gave me no intimation, at that time that the book was to be of a religious character, or that it had anything to do with revelation. He declared it to be a speculation, and said he, "when it is completed, my family will be placed *on a level* above the generality of mankind!!"[31]

But others gave testimony of having actually seen "and hefted" the plates. The Book of Mormon (Ether 5: 2-4) states that *three witnesses* would be shown the plates "wherefore they shall know of a surety that these things are true." Also the Doctrine And Covenants of the revelations of Joseph Smith, prophesies—in a revelation given through Smith to Oliver Cowdery, David Whitmer, and Martin Harris in June of 1829—that "it is by your faith that you shall obtain a view of them, even by that faith which was had by the prophets of old."[32] After the supposed witnessing of the golden tablets, the three men then signed a testimony which read in part:

> Be it known unto all nations, kindreds, tongues, and people, unto whom this work shall come: That we, through the grace of God the Father, and our Lord Jesus Christ, have seen the plates which contain this record,. . . . And we also testify that we have seen the engravings which are upon the plates; and they have been shown unto us by the power of God, and not of man. And we declare with words of soberness, that an angel of God came down from heaven, and he brought and laid before our eyes, that we beheld and saw the plates, and the engravings thereon;. . . . Nevertheless the voice of the Lord commanded us that we should bear record of it;. . . .[33]

All three witnesses eventually apostacized—Cowdery being expelled in Missouri; Whitmer abandoning the Mormons and settling in Richmond,

---

30   Howe, p. 239.

31   Ibid., p. 260.

32   Joseph Smith, et. al., Book of Doctrine And Covenants, published by the R.L.D.S. Church (Independence, Missouri: Herald Publishing House, 1958), Section 15:1c.

33   Joseph Smith, trans., The Book of Mormon (Salt Lake City: The Church of Jesus Christ of Latter-day Saints, 1950), see "The Testimony of Three Witnesses" in the prefatory pages.

Missouri; and Harris returning to New York after quarreling with Joseph Smith.[34] But eight others had also added a similar testimony:

> Be it known unto all nations, kindreds, tongues, and people, unto whom this work shall come: That Joseph Smith, Jun., the translator of this work, has shown unto us the plates of which hath been spoken, which have the appearance of gold; and as many of the leaves as the said Smith has translated we did handle with our hands; and we also saw the engravings thereon, all of which has the appearance of ancient work, and of curious workmanship. And this we bear record with words of soberness, that the said Smith has shown unto us, for we have seen and hefted, and know of a surety that the said Smith has got the plates of which we have spoken. And we give our names unto the world, to witness unto the world that which we have seen. And we lie not, God bearing witness of it.[35]

Between 1827 and 1830 The Book of Mormon was translated. Since Joseph could not write, he dictated his translation at first to his wife Emma, then to Martin Harris, who had come to relieve the pregnant lady of her burdensome task. A blanket thrown over a rope served as a makeshift curtain between Smith and his scribes, and a curse forewarned that anyone attempting to see the plates or watch him translate would be struck dead.[36]

In March of 1830 the new scripture was published. Martin Harris mortgaged his farm for three thousand dollars to pay for the publication expenses, and invited the printers to his home for a celebration.[37] The book then went on sale in late March.[38] The text itself is long and laborious reading—what Mark Twain has termed "chloroform in print"—but Nathan Hatch sees in it "a document of profound social protest, an impassioned manifesto by a hostile outsider against the smug complacency of those in power and the reality of social distinctions based on wealth, class, and education."[39] He also recognizes its character as essentially populist:

> The vision of Joseph Smith is intensely populist in its rejection of the religious conventions of his day and in its hostility to the orthodox clergy, its distrust of reason as an exclusive guide, and its rage at the oppression of the poor. . . .

---

34   Mather, p. 201.

35   The Book of Mormon (same page as footnote 33), see "The Testimony of Eight Witnesses" in the prefatory pages.

36   See Fawn Brodie, ch. IV, for a full account (esp. p. 53). See also Joseph Smith, History of The Church, Vol. I, ch. 3; as well as Bushman, Joseph Smith And The Beginnings of Mormonism, ch. 3.

37   Mather, p. 205.

38   Bushman, p. 119.

39   Hatch, pp. 115-116

These populist themes resonated powerfully with Smith's earliest disciples, young men who were characteristically poor, uprooted, unschooled, and unsophisticated like himself.[40]

Almost immediately upon its release controversy arose, especially since it purported to be somewhat of a second Bible. The Ashtabula Journal scorned it as "a newly invented money speculation," while the Painesville Telegraph scoffed at it as " a pretended new revelation from God." The Cleveland Herald ridiculed both its authors and its adherents when it concluded that the "golden bible," as it came to be known, offered "new proof that all fools are not dead, and knavery in any garb may yet find votaries."[41] Alexander Campbell read the book and attacked its author for being "as ignorant and as impudent a knave as ever wrote a book," and also as an "impudent liar." Then he proceeded to satirically mock him and his work:

> This prophet Smith, through his stone spectacles, wrote on the plates of Nephi, in his book of Mormon, every error and almost every truth discussed in New York for the last ten years. He decides all the great controversies;— infant baptism, ordination, the trinity, regeneration, repentance, justification, the fall of man, the atonement, transubstantiation, fasting, penance, church government, religious experience, the call to the ministry, the general resurrection, eternal punishment, who may baptize, and even the question of free masonary, republican government, and the rights of man. All these topics are repeatedly alluded to. How much more benevolent and intelligent this American apostle than were the holy Twelve and Paul to assist them!!! He prophesied of all these topics, and of the apostacy, and infallibly decides by his authority every question. How easy to prophecy of the past or of the present time!![42]

In February of 1828 Martin Harris took a copy of some of the "Reformed Egyptian" characters, along with Smith's translation of them, to classical studies professor Charles Anthon of Columbia College, apparently one of the pre-eminent experts of his era regarding Hieroglyphics, Greek, and Latin. According to Harris, "Professor Anthon stated that the translation was correct, more so than any he had before seen translated from the Egyptian." Then, looking at characters from the untranslated portion, Anthon pronounced them "Egyptian, Chaldaic, Assyric, and Arabic; and he said they were true characters." But upon inquiring how Harris came upon this find, and being told of the angel, Joseph Smith, and the hill Cumorah—Anthon was said to have

---

40   Ibid., pp. 120-121.

41   All quoted in Parken, p. 42.

42   Alexander Campbell, "Delusions," The Millennial Harbinger, Vol. II, No. 2 (February 7, 1831), pp. 91-93.

snatched back a certificate of authenticity he gave to Harris, and then torn it up.[43]

Anthon, however, emphatically denied his alleged evaluation. In a letter dated February 17, 1831, sent to Eber D. Howe, editor of The Painesville Telegraph, Anthon wrote, "The whole story about my having pronouncd [sic] the Mormonite inscription to be 'reformed Egyptian hieroglyphics' is *perfectly false*." Then he continued, "Upon examining the paper in question, I soon came to the conclusion that it was all a trick, perhaps a *hoax*." Maintaining that the paper presented to him "had evidently been prepared by some person who had before him at the time a book containing various alphabets," Anthon claims to have pronounced it a combination of Greek, Hebrew, and Latin letters "inverted or placed sideways," ending in a circle divided into sections with symbols from a Mexican calender inscribed in them.[44]

No matter which description of the occasion is more accurate, nonetheless a new church was organized on April 6, 1830, to be simply called "The Church of Jesus Christ."[45] This was done in obedience to a commandment given through revelation.[46] Shortly after the church was founded, Joseph's wife Emma began worrying about income, "since he could not possibly prophesy all day long," and for which he received no income anyway. Then suddenly, Joseph received another vision from God, this one for Emma saying, "Emma, thou art an elect lady and thou needest not fear, for thy husband shalt support thee from the church."[47] Future visions would require church members to provide for his welfare, as well as other leaders like Sidney Rigdon. One vision said: "If ye desire the mysteries of the Kingdom, provide for him [Joseph Smith] food and raiment and

---

43 Martin Harris orally to Joseph Smith, History of The Church, Vol. I, p. 20. It is interesting to consider that Smith's infatuation with Hieroglyphics appears only about five years after the translation of the Rosetta Stone by Champollion.

44 Howe, pp. 269-272.

45 Joseph Smith, History of The Church, Vol. I, pp. 75-80. John Corrill, in his A Brief History of The Church of Jesus Christ of Latter Day Saints. . . (St. Louis: N.P., 1839) p. 12, says that "they organized the first church in the state of New York, consisting of six members only." But Dean Hughes, in The Mormon Church: A Basic History (Salt Lake City: The Deseret Book Co., 1986), p. 5, wrote that at the creation of a formal church organization there was "a group of believers—more than fifty in number" which met in Whitmer's home. However Ivan Barrett, in his Joseph Smith and The Restoration (p. 129), reconciles this seeming inconsistency by saying that, of the fifty present on that day, six men were selected as trustees for the incorporation laws of the state of New York, and he lists their names (see p. 129).

46 See especially Doctrine And Covenants (any twentieth-century edition), section 17.

47 M.R. Werner, Brigham Young (New York: Harcourt, Brace, and Co., 1925), p. 72, says that the second edition of the Doctrine And Covenants, section 24: 2d, was changed to read "thy husband shalt support thee *in* the church."

whatsoever he needeth to accomplish the work wherewith I have commanded him."[48]

Smith was reared in "a Bible-drenched society," and though an uneducated man, was familiar with Biblical characters and stories.[49] He was also strongly influenced by the prevalent attitudes of society, and the cultural ebb and flow of the day. The restorationist plea for Christian primitivism strongly appealed to him, and Smith's followers came to embrace restorationism wholeheartedly. In fact, The Book of Mormon commanded it:

> And now, my son, I have somewhat to say concerning the restoration of which has been spoken; for behold, some have wrested the scriptures, and have gone far astray because of this thing. And I perceive that thy mind has been worried also concerning this thing. But behold, I will explain it unto thee.

> I say unto thee, my son, that the plan of restoration is requisite with the justice of God; for it is requisite that all things should be restored to their proper order.[50]

Robert K. Fielding has correctly maintained that the whole basis of Mormonism is to be found in the idea of a restoration of primitive Christianity, and that this basis is used to determine all doctrines, ordinances, organizations, and authorities. The Book of Mormon, a witness to and interpreter of the Bible, facilitates the understanding of "the fullness of the Gospel," as Joseph Smith often referred to it.[51] The "true gospel," which had been lost on Earth, would now be restored through the instrument of Smith's church. Again, The Book of Mormon reveals:

> And the gospel of Jesus Christ shall be declared among them [Jews and Gentiles]; wherefore, they shall be restored unto the knowledge of their fathers, and also to the knowledge of Jesus Christ, which was had among their fathers. . . .

> And it shall come to pass that the Lord God shall commence his work among all nations, kindreds, tongues, and people, to bring about the restoration of his people upon the earth. . . .

> And now behold, I say unto you that when the Lord shall see fit, in his wisdom, that these sayings shall come unto the gentiles according to his

---

48   Quoted in Pancoast, p. 31. It is interesting to this author that the Lord always spoke to Joseph in his own tongue—English—but not his own dialect, choosing to communicate with him in the antiquated King James English instead.

49   Joel Barlow, Mormons and The Bible: The Place of The Latter-day Saints in American Religion (New York: Oxford U. Press, 1991), p. 11.

50   The Book of Mormon, Alma 41: 1-2a.

51   Fielding, p. 134.

word, then ye may know that the covenant which the Father hath made with the children of Israel, concerning their restoration to the lands of their inheritance, is already beginning to be fulfilled.[52]

Paul Conkin, in his recent study of Mormonism, attests to Smith's commitment to restorationism. Contending that "With a vengeance Smith was a restorationist," Conkin observes that "Smith seemed to be much influenced by Alexander Campbell and the Disciples."[53] Richard Bushman goes one step further, stating that the Mormons may have even borrowed the word "restoration" from the Disciples' phrase "the restoration of the ancient order of things."[54] But Allen and Hughes, both Church of Christ authors, have acknowledged that Joseph Smith was more than simply a Stone-Campbell copycat:

> Many argue that Sidney Rigdon taught Smith restoration philosophy. Yet given the pervasive appeal of the restoration idea in the early nineteenth century, it is likely that Mormonism would have adopted restoration principles regardless of any influence from either Sidney Rigdon or Alexander Campbell.[55]

There were, and are, many similarities in the restoration pleas of both the Mormon church and the Stone-Campbell Movement. Both regard the Bible as the ultimate authority on church doctrine and organization. Both look to it for the paradigm of the early church to be emulated today—a position often known as "patternism."[56] The members of both groups believe that their churches constitute the "true church." And both movements propagate a view of the process of salvation as including the acts of faith, repentance, and baptism for the remission of sins.[57]

Also, both restoration movements shared a strong anti-pluralistic perspective in regard to religious faith.[58] Spiritual pluralism, they believed, was the mother, not so much of toleration and brotherhood, as of confusion and strife. In that era truth was not relative, but concrete.

---

52   The Book of Mormon, II Nephi 30: 5 and 8; III Nephi 29: 1.

53   Paul K. Conkin, American Originals: Homemade Varieties of Christianity (Chapel Hill: U.N.C. Press, 1997), p. 176.

54   Bushman, p. 182.

55   Allen and Hughes, Discovering Our Roots, p. 95.

56   Joseph Smith once answered the question, "What constitutes a Mormon?" with the answer, "having a church organized according to the New Testament *pattern*." That word is still commonly used among the A Cappella Churches of Christ and more conservative Christian Churches today.

57   See Jan Shipps, Mormonism: The Story of a New Religious Tradition (Urbana: University of Illinois Press, 1985), p. 72.

58   See Marvin Hill, p. 4ff., and Allen and Hughes, Illusions of Innocence, p. 134ff., for further analysis of anti-pluralistic tendencies.

The Bible says that "There is one body and one Spirit,. . .one Lord, one faith, one baptism,. . . ."[59] Parley Pratt, a Mormon missionary, also foresaw a day when "through the progress of Mormon restoration, all governments, kingdoms, and tribes would be 'dissolved—destroyed—or mingled into *one—one* body politic—*one* peaceful empire—*one* Lord—*one* king—*one* interest all.'"[60]

But there were significant differences in the two movements as well, which made them incompatible at their very core. The Campbellian restoration movement was based upon the epistemology of Thomas Reid's Common Sense rationalism, which was prevalent in America in the early nineteenth century. Smith struggled against this inclination, rejecting rationalism in favor of a sort of romantic mysticism:

> Campbell's restoration movement was rational to the core, calling for the application of human reason to the biblical text and limiting authentic religion to that sphere. In doing so, the Campbell movement was as clear an expression of the spirit of Common Sense rationalism as one could hope to find in American religion in the early nineteenth century. On the other hand, Mormonism sought to transcend the cognitive and the rational and to soar with the gods in the realm of the infinite and the eternal. In this sense, Mormonism was an expression of romanticism in revolt against the constrictions of Common Sense.[61]

Another major difference between the two restoration movements had to do with the issue of authority. The Campbellian inclination, paralleling the American, and especially frontier, temper at the time, was somewhat anti-authoritarian, and therefore anti-clerical. Their congregations tended more toward egalitarianism than the established denominations. Yet the Mormon church "was founded on the basis that *authority* [italics mine] to any act in Christ's name had been restored to the earth.[62] No man had the legitimacy to restore and lead the lost New Testament church except the one given that authority directly by God himself. Joseph Smith *was* that man, referred to by some—like Parley Pratt, one of his disciples—as "Elias, the Restorer."[63] This title was in reference to one of Smith's revelations:

> Behold, this is wisdom in me; wherefore marvel not, for the hour cometh that I will drink of the fruit of the vine with you on the earth, and with Moroni, whom I have sent unto you to reveal the Book of Mormon, containing the fullness of my everlasting gospel; to whom I have committed

---

59   Ephesians 4:4-5 (R.S.V.)

60   Quoted in Allen and Hughes, Illusions of Innocence, p. 134.

61   Ibid., pp. 142-143.

62   Dean Hughes, p. 27.

63   A.T. DeGroot, The Restoration Principle, p. 127.

the keys of the record of the stick of Ephraim; and also with Elias, to whom I have committed the keys of bringing to pass the restoration of all things, or the restorer of all things spoken by the mouth of all the holy prophets since the world began, concerning the last days;. . . .[64]

Typical of restoration movements, the Mormons held that, shortly after the New Testament church period, a great apostasy occurred and Christ's original Church had vanished from Earth. With Joseph Smith and his golden tablets, this original church was now being restored. Dr. Ralph Winter—missions professor at Fuller Theological Seminary, and founder of the U.S. Center for World Mission, in Pasadena, California—has humorously dubbed this outlook as a "BOBO" theory, because the Christian faith is believed to have "blinked out" after the apostolic era, and "blinked on" again with Joseph Smith's experiences. "The result of this kind of BOBO approach," says Winter, "is that you have 'early' saints and 'latter-day' saints but no saints in the middle."[65]

> Restoration meant, above all, recovering direct communion and conversation with God himself as in biblical days. Since the apostasy had closed the heavens and stilled direct communication between God and humankind, so the first objective of the Mormon restoration was to revive direct communion with the Spirit of God. This was the heart of their restoration effort.[66]

To Smith and his Mormons, restoration came to include the rediscovery of lost material, such as the Golden Plates and the Urim and Thummin.[67] It also referred to the reappearance of gifts of the Holy Spirit— such as revelations, tongues, prophecy, healings, and miracles. Then too, restoration meant a time of the "gathering" of all God's faithful into a specific site for the new "Zion," prefacing the immanent arrival of the Millennium.

Whether or not these beliefs seem bizarre to us today, none can deny their effectiveness. John Greenleaf Whittier, a Quaker poet and a contemporary of Smith, once said of the Mormons, "I discovered, as I think, the great secret of their success in making converts. They speak to a common feeling; they minister to a universal want." He then added, "They speak a language of hope and promise to weak, weary hearts, tossed and troubled, who have wandered from sect to sect, seeking in vain for the

---

64 Doctrine and Covenants, Section 26: 2a-b.

65 Ralph D. Winter and Steven C. Hawthorne, Perspectives On The World Christian Movement-A Reader (Carlisle, U.K.: The Paternoster Press, LTD., 1981), p. 4-5.

66 Allen and Hughes, Discovering Our Roots, p. 96.

67 Van Wagoner, p. 73. In terms of the typical restoration plea to regard only the Bible as authoritative, here is where the Mormons seem to go beyond restorationism into something else.

primal manifestations of the divine power."[68] C. Leonard Allen and Richard Hughes have summarized well the restorationist attractions of Mormonism to the society in which they lived:

> Were Americans perplexed by the diversity of religions, all competing in the same free market of souls? Mormonism answered: They are all wrong, and only the restored Church of Jesus Christ is true and right.
>
> Did Americans seek to be free from the tyranny of creeds and clerics? Mormonism answered: It is possible to bypass creeds and clerics and commune directly with the Spirit of God in the restored Church of Christ.
>
> Did Americans view their nation as a new order of the ages which would launch the millennial dawn? Mormonism answered: The true, restored Church of Jesus Christ of Latter-day Saints would hasten the millennial age, and its members would reign with Christ for a thousand years.
>
> Did Americans view both their land and their government as essentially edenic, partaking of the first age before the fall? Mormonism answered: the church in this land must also be born of first times, and that is precisely the church that Joseph Smith claimed to have restored on April 6, 1830.[69]

Sidney Rigdon would prove to be one of those attracted to this new restorationist sect, and would become one of its leading proponents, as well as theological developers.

---

68   Barrett, pp. 13-14, quoting the L.D.S. Millennial Star, Vol. 10, pp. 302-303.

69   Allen and Hughes, Discovering Our Roots, pp. 97-98.

Chapter
—10—

SIDNEY RIGDON AND THE ATTRACTIONS
OF AUTHORITARIAN RESTORATIONISM

From 1827 to 1830 Rigdon, now one of the most prominent ministers in Campbell's Restoration Movement, was very successful, but he nonetheless seemed restless. He was a very popular preacher, but emotionally unstable. Both Alexander Campbell and, later on, Joseph Smith made comments acknowledging this to be true, as did others. Fawn Brodie recognized both his successes and his eccentricities when she wrote:

> For several years past, Rigdon had been the most successful revivalist on the Western Reserve. He was "gifted with very fine powers of the mind," wrote a fellow preacher, "an imagination at once fertile, glowing and wild to extravagance, with temperament tinged with sadness and bordering on credulity." He was emotional and humorless, and subject to fits of melancholy and "nervous spasms and swoonings" that he attributed to the Holy Ghost.[1]

An entry in the L.D.S. "Journal History" of September 8, 1844, articulately described the polarity of Rigdon's moods as "always either in the bottom of the cellar or up in the garret window." F. Mark McKiernan interpreted this allusion to mean that "he was usually ecstatically enthusiastic about something or totally depressed with the situation in which he found himself."[2] In the now famous Braden-Kelley Debate of 1884 between the Disciples and Reorganized Mormons, Clark Braden also credited Rigdon his abilities and debited his instabilities:

---

1 Brodie, p. 94. There is much evidence to this effect, and both major biographies of Rigdon (i.e. McKiernan's and Van Wagoner's) attempt to offer reasons for his extravagant behavior. It is known, for instance, that he was thrown from a horse as a youth and dragged with his foot in the stirrup, receiving head injuries which occasionally gave him episodic "spells" ever afterward. See McKiernan, p. 15, for example.

2 McKiernan, p. 26

From *Sidney Rigdon: The Benedict Arnold of the Restoration Movement* originally published in SCJ 6.1 (Spring, 2003). Reprinted by permission of Stone Campbell International.

As [a] Baptist and Disciple preacher he was noted for his spread eagle eloquence and ability to get up revival excitements. He had been hurt in his youth and it left him with a tendency to epileptic spells. He would often while preaching, especially in revival excitements, have such spells and see visions and swoon, have trances, etc. This tendency caused his preaching to be wild, visionary and extravagant. . . .His preaching attracted the visionary and fanatical.[3]

There have been some who have suggested that Rigdon's disillusionment with Campbell's movement began in 1827 when Walter Scott was chosen to be the evangelist of the Mahoning Association. Apparently thwarted in his hopes for recognition and influence, Rigdon, they contend, became somewhat disgruntled and reclusive. Isaac Errett, editor of The Christian Standard, later recalled:

In the year 1827, however, Walter Scott received an appointment from the Mahoning Association, which for the time seemed to bar the way to the gratification of Mr. Rigdon's ambition, and he left, nothing much being heard of him beyond the village of Mentor, and a few other points on the Western Reserve, until the year 1830, when he appeared as the front speaker and ablest defender of Joseph Smith and Mormonism.[4]

While this could have been Rigdon's *first cause*, this author is a bit skeptical of this conclusion, or at least the gravity placed upon it. First of all it must be considered that Errett and other "Campbellites" certainly had motive to denigrate Rigdon as a sort of Benedict Arnold of the Movement. Secondly, in March of 1828, Rigdon implored and convinced Scott to lead a revival in his own church at Mentor, which would probably not be the act of a jealous or resentful person. Thirdly, one should remember that it was Rigdon himself who, at the next annual meeting of the Mahoning Association in August of 1828, re-nominated Scott to continue in the same post for the next year. And finally, an examination of Rigdon's itinerary of travels and activities from 1827 to 1830 does not seem to substantiate Errett's charge of a three-year exclusivity.[5]

Whether or not Rigdon struggled with frustrated personal ambitions, the more identifiable reasons for his growing discomfort in, and eventual exodus from, the Disciples movement were rooted in their different perspectives of restorationism. One could easily argue that Campbell and

---

3　Public Discussion of The Issues Between The Reorganized Church of Jesus Christ of Latter-Day Saints and The Church of Christ [Disciples] Held in Kirtland, Ohio, Beginning February 12 and Closing March 8, 1884. . . (Reproduced and Distributed by The Old Paths Book Club, Rosemead, California, 1955), p. 357, col. 2.

4　Isaac Errett, "Pioneer Mormon Dead," The Christian Standard (Cincinnati, Standard Publishing Company, August 5, 1876), p. 252.

5　For a detailed listing of Rigdon's travels and activities during this time period see Fawn Brodie, Appendix B, pp. 431-432.

Rigdon clashed on the *interpretation* and *degree* of restoration *particulars*. Campbell, who was still concerned with the unity motive, attempted to maintain a distinction between the basic mandated essentials, and non-essential opinions which should not be the cause of division. Rigdon, on the other hand, "wanted to incorporate into Campbell's restoration every belief or practice which was a part of the New Testament church."[6] As Paul Conkin expressed it, Rigdon "thirsted for too much restoration for Alexander Campbell,"[7] even to the exclusion of a union motive.

"Clearly the most fanatical and literal-minded of the Disciples of Christ," according to Fawn Brodie, "Rigdon was obsessed with prophesies of Armageddon and was convinced his generation was doomed long before he met the Mormon prophet."[8] Alexander Campbell charged that "He became a flaming literalist of the school of *Elias* (Smith,) [sic] a millennarian of the first water;" and that "Exceedingly fond of *new ideas*, and always boasting of originality, he sought distinction by his lucubrations on the Prophecies." He prefaced his evaluation of Rigdon with a reminder and admonition:

> . . .in commencing the present reformation it was fully argued and submitted that opinions upon all subjects not revealed were private property, and that no citizen of Christ's kingdom had either a right to demand or propound them with any authority whatever. The faith is common to all and necessary to all; for all must walk by it: but no Christian is obliged to walk by the opinion of any man on earth.[9]

If Rigdon was primarily concerned with material success or fame he could have remained in the Baptist or Disciple fellowship and done well for himself. The people at Mentor were even going to provide him a house in which to live. His son Wickliffe mused later on, "The honors of the world was [sic] within his grasp, and had he continued on in the way he was going his name would have gone down to posterity as one of the great Baptists of the age in which he lived."[10] But Rigdon was wholly committed to the complete restoration of *all* things connected with the New Testament church, and he did not agree with Campbell on what should be restored. Their main areas of impasse were three: (1) divine authorization for church leadership; (2) the re-emergence of the manifestation of the gifts of the Holy Spirit; (3) the communal *koinonia* in which they "had all things in common;". . . [Acts 2:44].

---

6   McKiernan, p. 27.

7   Paul K. Conkin, <u>American Originals: Homemade Varieties of Christianity</u> (Chapel Hill, N.C.: U.N.C. Press, 1997), p. 34.

8   Brodie, p. 94, and Van Wagoner, p. 90.

9   Alexander Campbell, "Extra," <u>The Millennial Harbinger</u>, Vol. I, No. 1, New Series (December, 1837), p. 578.

10   John Wickliffe Rigdon, "Life Story of Sidney Rigdon," pp. 16-17, quoted in Van Wagoner, p. 52.

The concern for divine authority to validate one's ministry as blessed by God was not unique to Rigdon. Others, like Parley Pratt, would be attracted to Mormonism for this same reason. John Rogers, a Disciple minister, often struggled with doubts about his rightful authority to preach.[11] Samuel Rogers, his older brother, also confessed to such misgivings after Barton Stone had convinced him to minister:

> I was greatly troubled about my call. I contended that if I was called, as were the apostles, I ought to have their credentials and be able to prove my apostleship. I attempted to draw from dreams and visions and vague impressions, some superhuman aid;. . . . I thought I ought to perform miracles. My mind was often in a wretched state. About this time I got the "Christian Baptist," and found relief. . . .Stone had given me the book, but Campbell taught me how to read it in its connection.[12]

Rigdon was never blessed with such a cathartic resolution, and he continued to question his own authority until he met Joseph Smith.

In regard to his second area of conflict with Alexander Campbell, Rigdon's personal turmoil involving the restoration of the gifts of the Holy Spirit was enhanced by Campbell's denial of their validity in the modern day. Rigdon had come to believe that a truly *authorized* minister of God should be able to perform some or all of the gifts listed in I Corinthians 12—including such supernatural acts as faith healing, miracles, prophecy, and speaking in tongues. Richardson even implied that Rigdon engaged in some covert subterfuge to promote his cause: "He sought especially in private to convince certain influential persons that, along with the primitive gospel, supernatural gifts and miracles ought to be restored, ..."[13]

In the early part of the nineteenth century much of New England, and especially the "burned-over district" of New York, had been engulfed by "religious enthusiasm." Methodists, Shakers, Quakers, and others had spread this kind of emotional revivalism to the Western Reserve area as well. Some earlier Puritans had warned their contemporaries that "when the emotions are stressed at the expense of reason, 'it can't be but People should run into Disorders.'"[14] Charles Finney lamented a reaction against so much revival excitement that resulted in many people concluding that religion was a delusion.[15]

---

11 Richardson, Vol. II, p. 375. It is my opinion that many early frontier preachers, cognizant of their limited educations, may have also been expressing their psychological insecurities regarding their *abilities* to preach.

12 Ibid., Vol. II, pp. 332-333.

13 Ibid., Vol. II, p. 346, and McKiernan, p. 27.

14 Perry Miller, p. 193.

15 See Marvin Hill's Ph.D. dissertation, p. 42, especially footnote 3.

Campbell, of course, did not consider religion or Christianity to be a "delusion." But he did apply the term to *experiential* religion, or what he also referred to as "experimental religion." Reflecting his philosophical roots in Enlightenment reason, he affirmed the existence of miracles in "Biblical times," but repudiated current miracles and supernatural manifestations of the Holy Spirit. Such beliefs he attributed to the gullibility of ignorance.[16] Instead, he advocated that "Since those gifts [of the Spirit] have ceased, the Holy Spirit now operates upon the minds of men only by the word [i.e. the Bible]."[17]

In a lengthy diatribe against the growing emphasis upon experientialism, Campbell expressed his regrets about what he considered to be some misguided fanaticism:

> It is a misfortune, as far as human approbation is regarded, for any person to have to censure the times in which he lives: for in censuring the times, it is not the seasons of the year, but the people who live in the times, that are implicated. . . .

> There is no hobby which has carried his rider through all sorts of roads with more ease and respectability, than the doctrine of *metaphysical regeneration*, or *spiritual operations*. Some holy ghost is the soul of every popular sermon, and the essential point in every evangelical creed. . . .

> If salvation were proposed to mankind upon condition that they must believe that they can do nothing, and that "the Holy Ghost" will when he pleases, and not till then, fall down upon them and make them new creatures by convincing them of sin, righteousness, and judgement, these notions could not be more frequently asserted, more zealously propounded, nor more strenuously defended by those who claim to be evangelical preachers, nor more greedily devoured by their deluded admirers—I say, *deluded*; for every man who supposes he was converted to God by the literal descent of the Holy Spirit, or by its naked influence upon his spirit, is as certainly deluded as the followers of *Joseph Smith*, who believed in his Golden Bible or the plates of Nephi. Many of these visionaries are good citizens, kind friends, and benevolent neighbors, and withal pious in their way. So are the Mormonites, the Shakers, and the disciples of Jemima Wilkinson. . . .

> Peter did not order all the disciples out of the house to the basement story to "pray for the descent of the Holy Spirit upon the congregation of

---

16   For a good example of Campbell's position, as well as some fun reading, see Campbell's essay entitled "Superstitious Credulity" in <u>The Millennial Harbinger</u>, Vol. V, No. 1 (January, 1834), pp. 43-44.

17   Quoted by Allen and Hughes in <u>Discovering Our Roots</u>, p. 85. For a more complete exploration of Campbell's beliefs on this matter, see his "Address To The Readers of The Christian Baptist, No. IV," in <u>The Christian Baptist</u>, Vol. I, No. 8 (March 1, 1824), pp. 144-150.

impenitent hearers;" but he promised the gift of the Holy Spirit to all who repented and were baptized. . . .

We must occasionally notice the fanaticism of this age on the subject of *mystic impulses*; for, in our humble opinion, the constant proclamation of "the Holy Ghost" of the schoolmen, and all its influences, is the greatest delusion of this our age, and one of the most prolific causes of the infidelity, immorality, and irreligion of our contemporaries.[18]

In The Christian Baptist Campbell had written a series of essays concerning "Experimental Religion." In some of them he had to clarify his position, responding to critics who interpreted him to be denying the legitimacy of any Christian experience at all. Both he and his father Thomas had always regarded such experiences as valid evidence of sincerity and commitment. However, they objected to the use of these experiences "as substitutes for that assurance which is derived from the word of God—that simple trust in Jesus which the gospel requires," because **"feelings in religious experience are deceptive."**[19] [My bold]

Thomas Campbell, however, regretted that Alexander would make an issue of it in print. Clandestinely addressing a letter to the editor (Alexander) signed merely "T.W.", Thomas wrote "upon reading your animadversions on experimental religion, I was persuaded that it would likely give offence to many of your pious readers."[20] To some extent among the Baptist community he proved to be correct. And with Rigdon, such a stance probably initiated his theological rift with Campbell. Years later Rigdon responded to Campbell's views using Campbell's own phrase as the title of his article:

> The ancient order of things has engrossed the attention of the religious public to some extent in modern times, and has given rise to many parties and sects in the so called christian world; each one in their turn supposing that they had the ancient order of things among them, and had come to the standard of righteousness set up in the scriptures, and representing other religious denominations as having come short of the glory of God, and as not having come to the standard of truth, or else they had departed from it. . . .

---

18   Alexander Campbell, "The Times—No. IV," The Millennial Harbinger, Vol. II, No. 5 (May 4, 1831), pp. 211-215.

19   Richardson, Vol. II, p. 112. See also discussions on pp. 104, 108, and 420. A good analysis of Campbell's views on the place of religious experiences in Christianity may be found in a lecture/essay by D. Newell Williams entitled "The Gospel As The Power of God To Salvation: Alexander Campbell and Experimental Religion," printed in Lectures In Honor of The Alexander Campbell Bicentennial, 1788-1988 (Nashville: The Disciples of Christ Historical Society, 1988), pp. 127-148.

20   "T.W." [Thomas Campbell], "To The Editor of The Christian Baptist," The Christian Baptist, Vol. I, No. II (June 7, 1824), pp. 203-204.

Men may invent order after order, and scheme after scheme, but as long as their order or orders of things do not consist in having apostles, prophets, evangelists, pastors, teachers, gifts, healings, miracles, divers kinds of tongues, the interpretation of tongues, etc. their order is adverse to the order of heaven, and is not the ancient order of things as revealed in the scriptures.[21]

In a response to a letter from Olian Barr, who carried on a correspondence with Rigdon in which he politely defended the position of Campbell and questioned Rigdon's stance on numerous issues, Sidney boldly asserted:

I argue that there can be no Church of Christ unless they can prove themselves to be so by miracles, and. . .that there can be no apostles unless they can prove their mission by miracles,. . . .

That gospel [of the New Testament Church] had a priesthood attached to it, which had the power of getting revelations, and obtaining visions, as well as the ministering of angels. They had power to administer in the name of the Lord Jesus to the sick, and in his name to rebuke diseases of all kinds, they had also power to give the holy spirit by the laying on of hands, they obtained revelations, not only for their own direction in the world; but for that of the churches also that they raised   up. . . . The gospel that men preach in these days have [sic] no such ministry or priesthood: The priesthood of modern times has no such power or authority. No revelations; no ministering of angels; no heavenly visions; no ministering of the Holy Spirit by the laying on of the hands, and yet claim to be the ministers of Christ acting upon the same commission, and the same authority as they did. Surely the disparity is too great no[t] to be seen by the least discerning.[22]

Yet "the straw that broke the camel's back" precipitating the actual breach between Rigdon and Campbell centered around Rigdon's belief that true "New Testament Pattern" churches should practice communalism. Rigdon had occasional contact with the Shakers,[23] and admired their communal societies. He had informally but frequently begun to advocate a "common stock system" to those in his geographical area of influence.

Alexander Campbell, as early as 1825, had responded to a proposal for a communitarian society by asserting that, not only was such an idea a

---

21   "R" [Sidney Rigdon] "The Ancient Order Of Things," The Messenger And Advocate, Vol. I, No. 12 (Kirtland, Ohio, September, 1835), pp. 182-185.

22   Sidney Rigdon, letter to Olian Barr, The Messenger And Advocate, Vol. II, No. 5 (Kirtland, Ohio, February, 1836), pp. 261-262.

23   The rather affluent community of Shaker Heights in Cleveland, Ohio, was once a thriving Shaker community. See Weisenberger, A History of The State of Ohio - The Passing of The Frontier, Vol. III, esp. pp. 159-160, for more information.

Biblical "non-essential," but also the practice was confined only to the New Testament church *at Jerusalem*, and not the others.[24] But Campbell's debate with communal utopian socialist Robert Owen in 1829 probably brought the issue to the forefront of Rigdon's mind again.

At Austintown, Ohio, in August of 1830, the Mahoning Association met for one last time, the intended purpose of the meeting to be to dissolve itself as a body. It was there that a head-to-head confrontation occurred between Rigdon and Campbell. Rigdon took the opportunity to expound upon the text of Acts 2:45: "And they began selling their property and possessions, and were sharing them with all, as anyone might have need" (N.A.S.). He used the passage to openly advocate a communitarian society, but Campbell, who was present, took public issue with him contending that this unique verse was peculiar to one particular situation and was not meant to be a universal practice. Besides, Campbell believed such a system would encourage laziness and freeloading.

Their disagreement may also have been influenced by their own personal economic situations at the time. Alexander Campbell was one of the wealthiest men in western Virginia,[25] having made his farm very productive, whereas Rigdon still struggled financially. Quite naturally Campbell would not be very eager to dissipate his small fortune. Also Campbell had grown suspicious of Rigdon's reasons for some of his recent proposals:

> Mr. Campbell, however, never fully gave him his confidence, but looked on him as a man of restless ambition who sought to conceal his real motives under an affected zeal for reformation. Mr. C. several times told us that he never could feel that Mr. Rigdon was frank and candid with him, as a co-worker ought to be.[26]

Rigdon was embarrassed and embittered after the meeting, believing that the "Campbellite" group was willing to go only part way in its stated purpose of restoring the ancient order. On his journey back to Mentor, he stopped in Warren to complain to a friend, "I have done as much in this reformation as Campbell or Scott, and yet they get all the honor of it!"[27]

A.S. Hayden, one of his co-workers in the Disciples Movement, summarized the situation in the following manner:

---

24 Alexander Campbell, "Restoration of The Ancient Order of Things—No. VII," The Christian Baptist, Vol. III, No. 2 (September 5, 1825), p. 30.

25 This was well known back then, but Leroy Garrett so states on p. 232.

26 Isaac Errett, editorial, "The Death of Sidney Rigdon," The Christian Standard (July 29, 1876), p. 245.

27 Hayden, p. 299.

The discomfiture he experienced at the hands of Mr. Campbell at Austintown, when seeking to introduce his common property scheme, turned him away mortified, chagrined, and alienated.[28]

He would soon search out greener pastures.

Because the other Disciple churches followed Campbell in his view about communalism, etc., Rigdon supposedly removed his Mentor church from fellowship with them in early 1830.[29] He proceeded to organize a "common stock" community in February of 1830, located on Isaac Morley's large farm near Kirtland just three miles from Mentor.[30] A small minority of the Mentor congregation joined the effort, but most did not participate, fearing a loss of their farms and businesses.[31] Rigdon also convinced Lyman Wight to join eight other families in the collective experiment at Kirtland, and Wight converted five more families to start a second commune at Mayfield, about seven miles up river from Kirtland.[32] By October the group at Kirtland numbered around one hundred, all "looking for some wonderful event to take place" soon that would usher in the Millennium.[33]

In the fall of 1830 Rigdon also was anticipating the onset of the millennium. Fellow minister A.S. Hayden observed that he "was travailing with expectancy of some great event soon to be revealed to the surprise and astonishment of mankind."[34] In April of 1873 a man named Darwin Atwater wrote to Hayden recalling the events of 1830:

> Sidney Rigdon preached for us, and not withstanding his extravagantly wild freaks, he was held in high repute by many. For a few months before his professed conversion to Mormonism, it was noticed that his wild, extravagant propensities had been more marked.[35]

---

28 Ibid., p. 209.

29 This is McKiernan's opinion (p. 11), probably based upon such references as Hayden (p. 209). Van Wagoner (p. 55) disagrees that such a seclusion eventuated however. I believe it is reasonable to think that, to some extent at least, he probably did recluse, even if for no other reason than to facilitate his communal experiment.

30 See Van Wagoner, p. 87. Klaus J. Hansen, in his Mormonism and The American Experience (Chicago: University of Chicago Press, 1981), p. 127, states that *Joseph Smith* was "the originator of these [communitarian] ideas," certainly a debatable contention.

31 McKiernan, p. 29.

32 See Pancoast, p. 65, and Van Wagoner, pp. 50-51.

33 See Van Wagoner, p. 50; McKiernan, p. 29; and Pancoast, p. 20. For some reason Alanson Wilcox (p. 125) lists the number as only being seventeen! Perhaps he has confused the seventeen of their number that were re-immersed into Mormonism by Oliver Cowdery (see Howe, Mormonism Unvailed, p. 103) with the total number on the farm.

34 Hayden, p. 209.

35 Ibid., pp. 239-240.

During the previous year in 1829, Rigdon had converted Parley Pratt while on a preaching tour about thirty miles west of Cleveland.[36] Pratt—a farmer, a teacher, and apparently even a tin peddler—had been a member of the Regular Baptist Church because he believed it to be closer to the truth than any other.[37] Yet he still was dissatisfied. However, upon hearing Rigdon's testimony, he exulted, "Here was the ancient gospel in due form. Here were the very principles which I had discovered years before; but could find no one to minister in."[38]

Pratt decided that he would also enter the ministry. By the summer of 1830 he had sold his farm and headed back to his original home in New York state to preach.[39] Yet his mind was still perturbed by the incessant question regarding the modern-day origin of apostolic authority and power:

> But still one great link was wanting to complete the chain of the ancient order of things; and that was, the authority to minister in holy things— the apostleship, the power which should accompany the form. This thought occurred to me as soon as I heard Mr. Rigdon make proclamation of the gospel. Peter proclaimed this gospel, and baptized for remission of sins, and promised the gift of the Holy Ghost, because he was commissioned so to do by a crucified and risen Saviour. But who is Mr. Rigdon? Who is Mr. Campbell? Who commissioned them? [40]

It was at Newark, near Buffalo, that Pratt first encountered <u>The Book of Mormon</u> and the claims of Joseph Smith. Convinced that he finally had come across the "full truth," Pratt was baptized into the Mormon faith and anxiously desired to return to his family and friends to tell his story.[41] Rigdon, naturally, was one of them—not only because they were friends, but because he was a man of influence and eloquence.

In early October, 1830, Joseph Smith commissioned four men—Parley Pratt, Ziba Peterson, Oliver Cowdery, and Peter Whitmer—as missionaries to the Indians ["Lamanites"] west of the Missouri river. Leaving Palmyra

---

36 McKiernan, p. 29. Clark Braden, at the end of his seventh speech (p. 77) in the Braden-Kelly Debate, gives a chronology that shows Pratt's conversion by Rigdon to be in 1828, but the confluence of events following Pratt's conversion indicates that Braden's year is too early.

37 Fielding, p. 26; the Braden-Kelly Debate, p. 77; and Pancoast, p.18.

38 Parley Parker Pratt, <u>Autobiography of Parley Parker Pratt. . .</u> (Chicago: Law, King and Law, 1888), p. 32.

39 Fielding, p. 27.

40 Pratt, p. 32. See also comments in Hatch, p. 168, and Bushman, p. 180.

41 Fielding, p. 27.

around October 15 with copies of The Book of Mormon, these men arrived at the home of Sidney Rigdon sometime in late October.[42]

Presenting themselves as emissaries of a latter-day prophet, a truly restored Church, and a companion book to the Bible, "They professed to be special messengers of the Living God, sent to preach the Gospel in its purity, as it was anciently preached by the Apostles."[43] Rigdon's immediate reaction was to doubt their supernatural claims about the youthful Joseph Smith and The Book of Mormon. When the representatives attempted to debate their assertion, Rigdon stifled their efforts, saying, "No, young gentlemen, you must not argue with me on this subject; but I will read the book, and see what claims it has upon my faith, and will endeavor to ascertain whether it be a revelation from God or not."[44]

When the visitors requested the opportunity to address Rigdon's congregation, however, Sidney either "readily consented," as Joseph Smith claimed, or condescended. Whatever his deportment, once Oliver Cowdery and Parley Pratt had finished, Rigdon arose and cautioned his flock. . .

> that the information they had that evening received was of an extraordinary character, and certainly demanded their most serious consideration; and as the Apostle advised his brethren to "prove all things, and hold fast to that which is good," so he would exhort his brethren to do likewise, and give the matter a careful investigation, and not turn against it without being fully convinced of its being an imposition, lest they should, possibly, resist the truth.[45]

The following Wednesday the visitors held a meeting at the Methodist meeting house in town. They read excerpts from The Book of Mormon and exhorted those in attendance to be *re-baptized* for remission of their sins because their first baptism "was of no avail, for there was no legal administrator, neither had there been for fourteen hundred years, until God had called them to the office, ..."[46] That evening seventeen people were

---

42 Barrett, pp. 150-151; "Mormonism," article in The Telegraph, edited by Eber D. Howe (Painesville, Ohio), Vol. II, No. 35 (February 15, 1831), p. 1; Parkin, p. 344; et. al. A.S. Hayden (p. 210) lists their arrival "about the middle of November," which is undoubtedly too late for the timing of subsequent events. On the other hand Walter Scott's Evangelist (Carthage, Ohio) New Series, Vol. IX, No. 6 (June 1, 1841), p. 133, printed an 1831 letter from Josiah Jones remembering their arrival "about the 6th. of October last." Most reliable sources give the late October time, however. Joseph Smith's History of The Church, Vol. I, pp. 120-125, gives a full accounting of the story with extensive footnotes, including corroboration from Sidney's oldest daughter Athalia, who was present at the occasion and still living when the history was completed.

43 Both McKiernan (p. 30) and Van Wagoner (p. 59) quote this line from John Corrill's history (p. 7).

44 Joseph Smith, History of The Church, Vol. I, p. 124.

45 Ibid.

46 Josiah Jones, The Evangelist (June 1, 1841), p. 133. For a Christian, the implications of this belief are staggering—ie. that **no one's** sins were forgiven for 1400 years!

re-immersed by Oliver Cowdery. When Rigdon learned of it he was, at first, incensed, charging "that what they had done was entirely without precedent in the holy scriptures—for they had immersed those persons that they might work miracles. . . ." He then demanded proof for their book and their mission, to which they responded that they prayed for a sign and an angel gave them one. Rigdon concluded the discussion by warning them of Satan's deceptions.[47]

In the meantime, he had been studying The Book of Mormon on his own for two weeks. His son Wickliffe later described the intensity of his scrutiny by saying, "He got so engaged in it that it was hard for him to quit long enough to eat his meals. He read it both day and night."[48] Two days after his confrontation with the men, Rigdon decided to "tempt" God for a sign, and he received one. This convinced him of the truth of Mormonism and, recognizing the new course that was before him, he asked his wife Phebe, "My dear, you have followed me once into poverty, are you willing to do the same again?" She responded "I have counted the cost, and I am perfectly satisfied to follow you; it is my desire to do the will of God, come life or come death."[49] She and Sidney were baptized the following Monday, November 14, 1830, by Oliver Cowdery.[50]

Alexander Campbell was mortified when he heard the news. When informed of Rigdon's vision of an angel, he scoffed, "He who sets out to find signs and omens will soon find enough of them. He that expects visits from angels will find them as abundant as he who in the age of witchcraft found a witch in every unseemly old woman."[51]

The following weekend Rigdon and the four Mormon apostles journeyed to Kirtland to hold a three-day meeting with "The Big Family." But when he arose to address the congregation there, he was so overcome by emotion that he could barely speak. A.S. Hayden reported the occasion with a different perspective:

> He attempted to preach; but with the awful blasphemy in his heart, and the guilt of so shameless an apostasy on his conscience, how could he open his mouth in the name of the insulted Jesus? The eloquent lips which never stammered before, soon became speechless, and his tongue was dumb.

47 The [Painesville] Telegraph (February 15, 1831), p. 1.

48 John W. Rigdon, "Lecture On The Early History of The Church," typescript, p. 7.

49 Quoted in Mather, "The Early Days of Mormonism," pp. 206-207.

50 The [Painesville] Telegraph (February 15, 1831), p. 1; Republished in The Western Reserve Chronicle (Warren, Ohio: Hapgood and Crowell, pub.), Vol. XV, No. 753 (March 3, 1831), p. 4. Further information in Daryl Chase, p. 75.

51 Alexander Campbell, "Sidney Rigdon," The Millennial Harbinger, Vol. II, No. 2 (February 7, 1831), p. 101.

The faithless watchman, covered with the shame of his fall, surrendered his pulpit and congregation to the prey of wolves.[52]

The reactionary criticisms from his ex-brethren in the Disciples Movement had only just begun. After his baptism and trip to Kirtland, Sidney and Phebe returned to their Mentor congregation. Years later, their son Wickliffe recalled the scene [errors not mine]:

> When they got back and his congregation heard of what he had done they were furious at him and said to him if he had remained a campbelite and continued to preach the Gospel of which he had helped to create, he might have gone down to the Grave as one of the great divines of the age. But now he had gone and thrown it all away and was agoing to fool himself away and was agoing to follow a fool of a boy. . . . It was nonscenes and a man of his knowledge ought to have known better than to have had any thing to do with such impostures.[53]

The Mentor congregation refused to let the Rigdons move into the new house they had built for them, and declined to have anything more to do with them. So Sidney moved his family and few belongings to live with some recently baptized Mormons at Hiram, a community about two and a half miles from Kirtland.[54] Dr. Robert Richardson, a close friend and personal physician of Alexander Campbell, dictated[55] a comprehensive[56] biography of Campbell to his daughter in his later years in which he rather unkindly eulogized Rigdon's exit from the Disciples Movement:

> He was ambitious of distinction, without the energy and industry necessary to secure it, and jealous of the reputation of others, without the ability to compete with them. Floating upon the tide of popular excitement, he was disposed to catch at anything which, without demanding labor, might serve for his advancement, and was naturally led to seek in deception the success which he found denied to indolence.[57]

Another man who was upset with Rigdon was John Corrill, who eventually converted to the Mormon faith. Expecting Rigdon to confound his visitors with his Scriptural knowledge, Corrill was astonished to hear of Rigdon's defection. He decided to pay the men a visit. Feeling "indignant,"

---

52 Hayden, pp. 212-213, places this event on the first Sunday after the arrival of the four Mormon missionaries, and also places the baptisms of the Rigdons as being on "that day." But Josiah Jones, The Evangelist (June 1, 1841), p. 133, who claims to have actually been present at the first Sunday meeting "in Euclid," associates this event at Kirtland with the second Sunday.

53 John W. Rigdon, "Lecture On The Early History of The Church," typescript, p. 8.

54 Ibid.

55 By this time in his life he had gone blind.

56 A work of almost 1200 pages.

57 Richardson, Vol. II, p. 344.

he desired an argument with Cowdery, who refused. He managed to quarrel with Ziba Peterson for a short time. Then after supper he was finally able to see Rigdon. However, when he attempted to question—or more probably, *debate*—Rigdon on his newly-found faith, "He [Rigdon] observed that he was now beyond the land of contention, and had got into the land of peace."[58]

But Rigdon may not have at the time been as secure in his new commitment as he had implied to Corrill. In early December, about three weeks after his baptism, Rigdon journeyed to New York to meet Joseph Smith. Corrill stated that Sidney made the trip because "he was afraid that he had been deceived."[59] True or not, upon his arrival in December of 1830, Rigdon was not disappointed. Smith, who was then twenty-four, had received a new vision from God for the thirty-seven year old pilgrim:

> Behold, verily, verily I say unto my servant Sidney, I have looked upon thee and thy works. I have heard thy prayers and prepared thee for a greater work.

> Thou art blessed, for thou shalt do great things. Behold, thou wast sent forth even as John, to prepare the way before me, and before Elijah which should come, and thou knew it not.

> Thou didst baptize by water unto repentance, but they received not the Holy Ghost; but now I give unto thee a commandment, that thou shalt baptize by water, and they shall receive the Holy Ghost by the laying on of the hands, even as the apostles of old.[60]

Rigdon remained with Smith through most of January. During his absence, though, the doctrine of restored power to do miracles preached by "the Lamanite missionaries" generated excitement and anticipation among the new converts. Oliver Cowdery wrote, "Every thing said in the scriptures about the thousand years of Christ's reign on earth, . . . most clearly sets forth that it is to be a time of miracles."[61] Even Joseph Smith, in the December, 1830, revelation about Sidney Rigdon, reenforced the concept of modern-day miracles:

> . . . for I am God and mine arm is not shortened, and I will show miracles, signs and wonders, unto all those who believe on my name.

---

58 John Corrill, A Brief History of The Church of Christ of Latter Day Saints (commonly called Mormons) Including An Account of Their Doctrine And Discipline with the Reasons of the Author For Leaving The Church (St. Louis: N.P., 1839), pp. 7-8.

59 Ibid., p. 16.

60 Doctrine and Covenants, Section 34: 2a, b, and c.

61 Oliver Cowdery, "Millennium No. XIV," The Messenger and Advocate, Vol. I, No. 8 (May, 1835), p. 116.

And whoso shall ask it in my name, in faith, they shall cast out devils; they shall heal the sick; they shall cause the blind to receive their sight, and the deaf to hear, and the dumb to speak, and the lame to walk: and the time speedily cometh that great things are to be shown forth unto the children of men; . . . .[62]

However, in their enthusiasm to witness or perform miracles, young Mormons began engaging in "outrageous behavior." Bizarre and fanatical scenes ensued in the name of the Holy Spirit. Anti-Mormon Eber D. Howe reported:

Immediately after Mr. R. and the four pretended prophets left Kirtland, a scene of the wildest enthusiasm was exhibited, chiefly, however, among the young people: they would fall, as without strength, roll upon the floor, and, so mad were they that even the females were seen in a cold winter day, lying under the bare canopy of heaven, with no couch or pillow but fleecy snow. At other times they exhibited all the apish actions imaginable, making grimaces both horrid and ridiculous, creeping upon their hands and feet, etc. Sometimes, in these exercises, the young men would rise and play before the people, going through all the Indian manoeuvres of knocking down, scalping, ripping open, and taking out the bowels. At other times, they would start and run several furlongs, then get upon stumps and preach to *imagined* congregations, baptize ghosts, etc. At other times they are taken with a fit of jabbering that which they neither understood themselves nor any body else, and this they called speaking foreign languages by divine inspiration. Again the young men are seen running over the hills in pursuit, they say, of balls of fire which they see flying through the air.[63]

John Whitmer, commissioned by God in a revelation to "write and keep a regular history" of the Mormon church,[64] wrote that "Some had visions and could not tell what they saw. Some would fancy to themselves that they had the sword of Laban, and would wield it as expert as a light dragon; some would act like an Indian in the act of scalping; some would slide or scoot on the floor with the rapidity of a serpent, which they termed sailing in the boat of the Lamanites, preaching the gospel."[65] Others claimed they witnessed letters written by angels falling like snowflakes from Heaven.[66] And still others propagated wondrous ideas which included that many of them would never die if they had adequate faith, or that the ten lost tribes of Israel had recently been discovered frozen in the ice at the

---

62 Doctrine and Covenants, Section 34: 3b, c, d.

63 "Mormonism," The [Painesville]Telegraph, (February 15, 1831), p. 1.

64 Doctrine and Covenants, Section 47: 1.

65 John Whitmer's History, republished by Utah Lighthouse Ministry. (Salt Lake City, n.d.), p. 4.

66 Fielding, p. 35.

North Pole, and that they would soon (when the ice melted) come with huge amounts of gold and silver.[67]

When news of these manifestations reached Parley Pratt, he called them "disgusting, rather than edifying."[68] When he reported back to Joseph Smith about them, Smith recognized that such wild and uncontrolled spiritual exercises might bring disgrace and ridicule upon his infant church. Rigdon preceded Smith back to Kirtland, but when Smith arrived in early February he was astonished at many of the scenes among his proselytes. These he condemned as, not the manifestations of the Holy Spirit, but the works of Satan. By August he had a revelation to reenforce his convictions:

> Verily, I say unto you, there are those among you who seek signs, and there have been such even from the beginning; but, behold, faith cometh not by signs, but signs follow those that believe. . . .

> Wherefore, I, the Lord, am not pleased with those among you, who have sought after signs and wonders for faith, and not for the good of men unto my glory; nevertheless, I gave commandments and many have turned away from my commandments and have not kept them.[69]

Apparently Smith and his revelation were effective in drastically reducing such abuses. It was now time to get to the task of building up the "stake"[70] in Kirtland. Back in January David Whitmer had announced in Kirtland that it was to be the eastern border of "the Promised Land," with the western border being the Pacific Ocean[71]—an idea that foreshadowed the "Manifest Destiny" spirit of America in the next decade. Rigdon, now freed of the restraining hand of Campbell and the Disciples, proceeded on to pursue "the fullness of the Gospel" as he interpreted it. Later he gratefully rejoiced, "One thing has been done by the coming forth of the book of Mormon; it has puked the Campbellites effectually; no emetic could do half so well."[72]

Since Rigdon had renounced his former affiliation with the Disciples, he now felt free to unburden himself regarding his doubts and unsettled state of mind while he was with them. Walter Scott, who worked closely

---

67   Howe, <u>Mormonism Unvailed</u>, pp. 124 and 128.

68   Pratt, p. 61.

69   <u>Doctrine and Covenants</u>, Section 63: 3a and 4a.

70   A "stake" was a supportive community facilitating the eventual establishment of the new Zion, where the ultimate "Gathering" would take place.

71   <u>The [Painesville] Telegraph</u>, Vol. II, No. 3 (January 18, 1831), p. 3.

72   Sidney Rigdon, "Persecution," <u>The Messenger And Advocate</u>, Vol. III, No. 4 (January, 1837), p. 438. McKiernan (p. 36) quoted William Lynn, <u>The Story of The Mormons</u> (New York: N.P., 1902), p. 62, probably not realizing where this comment originated (he also slightly misquoted it).

with Rigdon since 1827, printed a letter claiming that Rigdon, "like a true wolf in sheep's clothing," had confessed in a schoolhouse meeting "that for two years past his preaching had been of no use to us; it was more to please our fancy and tickle our ears, than to effect our hearts."[73] Alexander Campbell seemed to be at a loss at this renunciation, perhaps recalling almost ten years earlier when Rigdon had so rejoiced at finally discovering "the true Gospel." Campbell repined:

> It was with mingled emotions of regret and surprise that we have learned that Sidney Rigdon has renounced the ancient gospel, and declared that he was not sincere in his profession of it: . . . . His instability I was induced to ascribe to a peculiar mental and corporeal malady, to which he has been subject for some years. Fits of melancholy succeeded by fits of enthusiasm accompanied by some kind of nervous spasms and swoonings which he has, since his defection, interpreted into the agency of the Holy Spirit, or the recovery of spiritual gifts, produced a versatility in his genius and deportment which has been increasing for some time. I was willing to have ascribed his apostacy to this cause, . . . had he not declared that he was hypocritical in his profession of the faith which he has for some time proclaimed. Perhaps this profession of hypocrisy may be attributed to the same cause. This is the only hope I have in his case.[74]

A.S. Hayden agreed that Rigdon had been "an enthusiast and unstable"; but he made an attempt, at least, to be fair, saying, "Whatever may be justly said of him after he had surrendered himself a victim and a leader of the Mormon delusion, it would scarcely be just to deny sincerity and candor to him, ..."[75] Thomas Campbell, not willing to give up so easily—or perhaps hoping to stunt Rigdon's future influence upon others—accepted Rigdon's open challenge for anyone to debate him. Mailing Rigdon a lengthy letter previewing the positions he would defend, Thomas was generally courteous in tone. But when Rigdon arrived at one line that portrayed the verbal combatants as Thomas Campbell saw them—i.e. "you, as a professed disciple and public teacher of the infernal book of Mormon; and I as a professed disciple and public teacher of the supernal book of the Old and New Testaments of our Lord and Saviour Jesus Christ"—he quit reading and threw the letter in the fire. Campbell tried to explain publicly that by "infernal" he did not mean "from Hell," but rather "dug up from the ground," as were the Golden Tablets.[76] But the disclaimer was of no avail. Rigdon's break with the Campbell Restoration Movement was now complete!

---

73 Walter Scott, The Evangelist, Vol. IX, No. 6 (June 1, 1841), pp. 134 and 136.

74 Alexander Campbell, "Sidney Rigdon," The Millennial Harbinger, Vol. II, No. 2 (February 7, 1831), p. 100.

75 Hayden, p. 192.

76 Both letters may be found printed in The [Painesville] Telegraph, Vol. II, No. 35 (February 15, 1831), p. 2.

Chapter

—11—

QUARRELSOME RESTORATIONISM: CONTENTIONS BETWEEN THE TWO MOVEMENTS

Rigdon believed that he was finally free to begin the restoration of "the fullness of the Gospel." He had left the confinement of a "false" restoration movement upon finding the "true" one. In accepting Mormonism "Rigdon got rid of the restraining hand of Alexander Campbell; he could move about with greater freedom of speech for the Mormons did not limit their 'Restoration' ideas to the New Testament as had been the case with Campbell."[1]

At least he had a promising start. McKiernan has argued that "Rigdon was much more to Mormonism than an efficient aid to the Prophet; he was intimately involved in directing every major endeavor of Mormonism during its first decade."[2] This contention is certainly justifiable. He influenced Smith to move the whole church to Kirtland. He helped Smith with his translation work, shared in some visions, and was chosen to the highest offices in the church. He even "gave Mormonism an intellectual respectability of which it could not boast up to that time."[3]

Yet in a few years he would experience an even more oppressive dominance by Joseph Smith. Campbell was an organizer and theologian, but Smith was *the revelator* through whom God Himself spoke. Campbell could be questioned, or even argued with, but not Smith. As John Lee was to say later, Rigdon eventually evolved to being "the mouthpiece of Joseph Smith, as Aaron was of Moses in olden time."[4]

---

1   Chase, p. 38.

2   McKiernan, p. 12.

3   Chase, p. 74.

4   John Lee, <u>Mormonism Unveiled</u> (St. Louis: Pease-Taylor Publishers, 1891), p. 61.

Smith arrived in Kirtland in the way one might expect him to—in dramatic fashion! Having claimed that he had seen a vision of Newel K. Whitney, a financially successful merchant in Kirtland, Smith arrived with Rigdon, Edward Partridge, and his wife Emma for a visit:

> About the first of February, 1831, a sleigh containing four persons drove through the streets of Kirtland and drew up in front of the store of Gilbert and Whitney. One of the men, a young and stalwart personage alighted, and springing up the steps walked into the store to where the junior partner was standing. "Newell K. Whitney! Thou art the man!" he exclaimed, extending his hand cordially, as if to an old and familiar acquaintance. "You have the advantage of me," replied the merchant, as he mechanically took the proffered hand. "I could not call you by name as you have me." "I am Joseph the prophet," said the stranger smiling. "You've prayed me here, now what do you want of me?"[5]

He and Emma then lived with the Whitneys for "several weeks."

The popularity of the Mormon message was contested, then protested, but not stifled. Even before "the four Lamanite missionaries" had continued on their journey westward from Kirtland, about half of Rigdon's Kirtland congregation had followed him into Mormonism, and the missionaries had baptized around 130 new converts in the Western Reserve.[6] Their restorationist, anti-Calvinistic plea appealed to many in the same way the Stone-Campbell Movement had.

Yet there was also significant resistance to their message. Most congregationalists, Presbyterians, Baptists, and even Methodists, held to their own church creeds as the proper expression of faith.[7] Also, the great majority of people in the Western Reserve were offended by The Book of Mormon, a modern-day prophet with exclusive rights to revelations, and the Mormon community's exclusive and communal postures. Even the Disciples of Christ, after the first "shock-wave" from the inroads of Mormonism, scurried to reenforce their churches against the incursions of the great "delusion." Both Campbells, Scott, Bentley, and others, traveled widely to combat its spread, until men like A.S. Hayden would claim, "After its first approach, it boasted of few converts from any of our churches." Whether this claim was actually true or not, Hayden went on to support his opinion:

> The reason the delusion made little progress among the Disciples, save only at Kirtland, where the way for it was paved by the common-stock principle,

---

5   Joseph Smith, History of The Church, Vol. I, p. 145-146.

6   Richardson, Vol. II, p. 346, and Backman, p. 347. Parley Pratt, in his Autobiography, published in 1888, claims 127 baptisms "in two or three weeks" (p. 48).

7   Backman, p. 349.

is to be found in the cardinal principle every-where taught and accepted among them, that *faith is founded on testimony.*[8]

Yet numerous conversions *did* take place among the Disciples, and even among some Methodists, in the towns of Hiram, Mantua, and adjoining towns. Because of the similarities in their positions, the Mormons were more successful proselytizing Disciples of Christ than any other denomination. B.A. Hinsdale would later muse, "How many Disciples were seduced from the faith and were joined to the new idols, probably can not now be determined; but so many were, that for the time it seemed as though the Church would be broken up."[9] Many in other denominations were unsympathetic to the Campbellite attrition. Hinsdale wrote:

> Strenuous opponent[s] of the Campbells and their work, at once exclaimed: "See what deserting the old standards leads to!" "We told you so." My father, who then passed his majority, tells me that the first he ever saw or heard of Mormonism was an article in a newspaper published in Hudson, Ohio, entitled "Campbellism Gone to Seed."[10]

Men like Adamson Bentley at Warren and M.S. Clapp at Mentor, Rigdon's old church, helped keep their congregations in the Stone-Campbell orbit. Yet there were many people in the 1830's who believed in the immanence of the Millennium, and Mormonism's emphasis upon that—as well as on a restoration of spiritual gifts, preached by the mouths of eloquent men—made Mormonism almost irresistible.

A lawyer named Vernem Card joined Willoughby deputy sheriff John Barr on a horseback trip to Mayfield on one occasion to hear Cowdery and Rigdon preach about the revelations of Mormonism. The road was crowded with people who also were going to hear them. From the context of Barr's statement it seems apparent that the two men went mainly out of curiosity. What happened surprised them both:

> Standing in the water, Rigdon gave one of his most powerful exhortations. The assembly became greatly effected. As he proceeded he called for the converts to step forward. They came through the crowd in rapid succession to the number of thirty, and were immersed, with no intermission in the discourse on the part of Rigdon. Mr. Card was apparently the most stoical of men—of a clear, unexcitable temperament, with unorthodox and vague religious ideas. He afterward became prosecuting attorney for Cuyahoga County. While the exciting scene was transpiring below us in the valley and in the pool, the faces of the crowd expressing the most intense emotion, Mr. Card suddenly seized my arm and said, "Take me away!" Taking his arm, I

---

8   Hayden, pp. 215-216.

9   Hinsdale, p. 19.

10   Ibid., p. 20.

saw that his face was so pale that he seemed to be about to faint. His frame trembled as we walked away and mounted our horses. We rode a mile toward Willoughby before a word was said. Rising the hill out of the valley, he seemed to recover, and said, "Mr. Barr, if you had not been there I certainly should have gone into the water." He said the impulse was irresistible.[11]

What was **not** irresistible, however, to most people was the Kirtland communal experiment. While this era was a time when numerous such efforts were attempted, the vast majority of people had no interest in such an undertaking. They charged that it was simply an effort to gather their property into a common fund and allow certain privileged and lazy people to live without working.[12]

Not only did the Mormons receive external criticism for their effort, but internal dissensions began to arise as well. In his history of the Mormon church, John Whitmer reported that "There were some of the Disciples who were flattered into this church because they thought that all things were to be common, therefore they thought to glut themselves upon the labors of others."[13] He also observed:

> The Disciples had all things common and were going to destruction very fast as to temporal things, for they considered from reading the scripture that what belonged to one brother, belonged to any of the brethren, therefore they would take each others clothes and other property and use it without leave, which brought on confusion and disappointments, for they did not understand the scripture.[14]

The journal of Levi Hancock, a Latter-Day Saint, who visited the commune, illustrated the developing problem:

> While I was in the room at "Father Morley's", as we all called him, Herman Bassett came to me and took my watch out of my pocket and walked off as though it was his. I thought he would bring it back soon but was disappointed as he sold it. I asked him what he meant by selling my watch. "O," said he, "I thought it was all in the family." I told him I did not like such family doings and I would not bear it.[15]

When Smith realized the transgressions happening at the farm, he abandoned the common-stock experiment for an economic system that became known as The Law of Consecration and Stewardship. Of course, a

---

11   John Barr, quoted in Mather, p. 207.

12   Wilcox, p. 126.

13   Whitmer, p. 3.

14   Ibid., p. 2.

15   Van Wagoner, p. 84, and Parkin, p. 98, both quote this selection from the journal of Levi Hancock (p. 45), which may be found in the Special Collections section of Lee Library at Brigham Young University in Provo, Utah.

revelation[16] supported this decision. Rigdon protested the cessation, but acquiesced to the will of the Prophet. In future days he would repeatedly urge a restoration of the effort, but to no avail. Smith "commanded his missionaries to destroy the notion abroad that the church had ever been a common-stock concern."[17]

But the dismantling of the common-stock system had little effect upon the growth of Mormonism. Latter-Day Saint evangelism was not buttressed by this world's economics, but by other-worldly miracles. As Robert Kent Fielding has asserted, "These marvelous manifestations of apparently supernatural power were one of the chief means of spreading the fame of Mormonism abroad. People flocked to Kirtland by the thousands."[18]

Many people believed that Joseph Smith could perform miracles. According to Parley Pratt the number of baptized saints in the area around Kirtland "soon increased to one thousand."[19] And the numbers continued to swell as more and more reports of miracles were given.

In February of 1832 Joseph and Sidney both supposedly shared in a vision with around twelve witnesses present. The vision displayed a trinity of kingdoms—the celestial, terrestrial, and telestial worlds—into which all people would be sorted at the day of judgment.[20] According to Philo Dibble, who was one of the twelve witnesses, he could not see the vision, but he could see the glory and feel the power all around him.[21] As the two men were entranced, sporadically Joseph would marvel and say, "What do I see?" Then he would describe the scene and Rigdon, also transfixed, would respond, "I see the same." This scene kept repeating at intervals for over an hour. At its conclusion Rigdon was exhausted, but Smith seemed to be rejuvenated. When questioned about the disparity in the demeanors of both men, Smith grinned and quipped, "Sidney is not as used to it as I am."[22]

There are many who advocate that the greatest miracle Smith performed at Kirtland was the healing of a Hiram woman with a rheumatic arm. After commanding her to "be whole," Smith left the room and, allegedly, the woman raised her arm above her head with no more pain.

---

16 See Doctrine and Covenants, Section 42. Also Max Parkin has a good explanation and elaboration of the transition to the new system on p. 99, especially footnote 33.

17 Brodie, pp. 141-142.

18 Fielding, p. 43.

19 Pratt, Autobiography, p. 48.

20 One can read the text of the revelation in Doctrine and Covenants, Section 76, and a description of the event in The Evening and Morning Star (December, 1833).

21 Barrett, p. 204, quoting The Juvenile Instructor, Vol. 27 (May 15, 1892), pp. 303-304.

22 Brodie, p. 118. Also quoted in Barrett, p. 204, and Bushman, pp. 23-24.

The next day she washed her clothes "unassisted," and shortly afterward, joined the Mormon church.[23]

Such instances only increased Smith's notoriety. According to the Lake County Historical Association:

> Claims of the prophet's spectacular healing miracles among his sick followers, with news of strange and wondrous new languages and manifestations from the Lord, brought wagon loads of both converts and curiosity seekers to our Kirtland hills. Soon the Mormon colony numbered three thousand people. This rapid increase alarmed their neighbors.[24]

This heightened apprehension spawned rumors, criticism, and condemnation among the general public. Many anti-Mormon stories circulated regularly, whether they were true or not. Of course, some were based upon the truth, some were half-truths, and others were distorted or embellished beyond recognition, or even fabricated. It has been contended that the Mormons themselves even circulated incredible anti-Mormon tales in an effort to make the other side look ridiculous. Often the other side didn't even need their help![25]

Yet the Mormons themselves regularly plowed and fertilized the ground into which these seeds of dissension fell. They made claims and prophesied supernatural events that, when unfulfilled, required some creative explanations. When the sick were not healed it was because they lacked faith, or because it was their "appointed" time: "He that has faith in me to be healed *and is not appointed unto death* [italics mine], shall be healed."[26] Apparently Oliver Cowdery tried to heal a young female confined to her bed for two years. He commanded her to rise up and walk, which she did for a few steps and then fainted. He failed, and she remained confined to her bed. Again there were explanations:

> . . .the Mormonites have endeavored to save the credit of their prophets, by declaring that they never pronounced these people whole but only prayed for them—but when confronted by one of the disciples in Kirtland upon the instance just mentioned, as it was so public they could not deny it, one of them said that he did not know but Cowdery did command her to arise, but if he did it was in a laughing, jesting way!!!—Another of the Mormonites said Cowdery did not command her to rise, but merely asked her why she did not arise.[27]

---

23 For a more complete description of the event, see Fielding, p. 42.

24 The Lake County Historical Society, Here is Lake County, Ohio (Cleveland: Howard Allen Inc., Publishers, 1964), p. 62.

25 For full accounts of many of these anti-Mormon tales, see Pancoast, pp. 83-93, and Parkin, pp. 235-247.

26 Pancoast, p. 84, quoting The Evening And Morning Star (July, 1832), p. 31.

27 "Mormonism," The [Painesville] Telegraph (February 15, 1831), p. 1.

In foretelling the future the Mormons often fared no better. Martin Harris predicted that Christ would return within fifteen years and that anyone not accepting The Book of Mormon by that time would be destroyed. Even more specifically, he prophesied that—within four years of September, 1832—there would not be one wicked person left in the United States; there would be no more presidents over the nation; and every Christian would have become a Mormon. He then upped the ante to his claim by saying, "If these things do not take place, I will hearby consent to have my hand separated from my body."[28] Of course, he kept his hand. Richard S. Van Wagoner, a Utah Mormon, has honestly conceded, "In presenting their colorful history to the world, twentieth-century Mormons overlook or are unaware of the fact that many of the divine predictions of Joseph Smith, Brigham Young, Parley P. Pratt, Willford Woodruff, and other church leaders did not materialize."[29]

It is human nature to seek verification of truth claims, especially supernatural ones. A Campbellite minister challenged Joseph Smith to perform a miracle for him, promising that if he could do so the minister would convert to Mormonism and bring his congregation of "several hundreds" with him into the fold. However, he likewise threatened Smith that if he could not perform a miracle, he would become his "worst and bitterest enemy." Smith accepted the challenge and offered the minister his choice of four miracles: to be struck blind, made dumb, rendered paralyzed, or have a withered hand. The preacher declined any of these, perhaps fearing that Smith or God just might do it. So Smith retorted, "Then, Sir, I can perform none. I am not going to bring any trouble upon anybody else, Sir, [just] to convince you."[30]

Sometimes the Mormons themselves needed reenforcement and failed to get it. When an old Mormon named John Morse died, someone hurriedly sent for Smith to revive him. Viewing the lifeless body, Smith refused, claiming it would be unkind to reanimate him just to have him suffer from rheumatism and die again so soon anyway.[31]

The Mormon belief in miracles and continual revelation engendered a considerable amount of ridicule—and sometimes even apostasy—on the early Western Reserve. Ezra Booth, a respected and "celebrated" Methodist preacher from Mantua, had converted to Mormonism in May of 1831 when he witnessed Joseph Smith's healing of "Mrs. Johnson's" lame arm.[32] Yet he

---

28   Howe, Mormonism Unvailed, pp. 14-15.

29   Van Wagoner, p. 457.

30   Werner, pp. 81-82. Also found in Pancoast, p. 85.

31   This story is told (retold? No footnotes) in Mather's The Early Days of Mormonism, p. 203.

32   Hayden, pp. 250-251.

apostatized just five months later. Believing he had been deceived, he wrote a series of nine articles in <u>The Ohio Star</u>, which were also reprinted in <u>The [Painesville] Telegraph</u>. In a personal note to the editor, he listed his reasons for doing so:

> 1st. To discharge a duty which I owe to God and the public. 2d. To rescue, if possible, the honest and contentious who are involved in it. 3d. To prevent others from falling into it. 4th. To comply with the request of a number who have solicited an exposure to Mormonism.[33]

That which precipitated his apostasy involved Joseph Smith's declaration on June third that God would choose twenty-eight elders for a journey to "the Promised Land" in Missouri where He had been building up a wonderful "City of Zion." He then endowed them with miraculous gifts and supernatural powers to preach in tongues, raise the dead, heal the sick, and cast out demons. When they departed they informed the rest of "the flock" that few, if any, would be returning, and that they would summon the rest when all was ready.[34]

Ezra Booth was one who made the thousand-mile journey. Upon arrival he experienced a great disappointment. "We expected to find a large church," he lamented, "which Smith said, was revealed to him in a vision, Oliver had raised up there. This large church was found to consist of four females."[35] He also expected to see miracles performed, and none were! Eventually complaining that "revelations which come from him [Joseph Smith] are something short of infallible,"[36] Booth alluded to his whole experience as a lesson for others:

> It has taught me quite beyond my knowledge, the imbecility of human nature, and especially my own weakness. It has unfolded in its proper character, a delusion to which I had fallen a victim. . . .
>
> If God be a God of consistency and wisdom, I now know Mormonism to be a delusion. . . .but thanks be to God, the spell is dissipated. . . .when I embraced Mormonism I conscientiously believed it to be of God. The impressions of my mind were deep and powerful. . . .

---

33   Ezra Booth, letter to <u>The Ohio Star</u> (Ravenna, Portage County, Ohio), Vol. II, No. 42 (October 20, 1831), p. 3.

34   <u>The [Painesville] Telegraph</u> (Painesville, Geauga County, Ohio), Vol. II, No. 52 (June 14, 1831), p. 3. According to another article in <u>The [Painesville] Telegraph</u>, Vol. III, No. 2 (June 28, 1831), p. 3, the Mormon leaders had by then departed for Missouri, but before doing so, had ordered around twenty families from Thompson Township to leave with them or "be deprived of all the blessings of Mormonism." Most of them obeyed, "leaving their spring crops all upon the ground."

35   Ezra Booth, "Mormonism # 5," <u>The [Painesville] Telegraph</u>, Vol. III, No. 23 (November 22, 1831), p. 2. See also <u>The Ohio Star</u> (November 7, 1831).

36   Ezra Booth, "Mormonism # 7," <u>The [Painesville] Telegraph</u>, Vol. III, No. 25 (December 6, 1831), p. 1. See also <u>The Ohio Star</u>, (November 21, 1831).

On our arrival in the western part of the state of Missouri, the place of our destination, we discovered that prophesy and visions had failed, or rather had proved false. This fact was so notorious, and the evidence so clear that no one could mistake it—so much so that Mr. Rigdon himself said that "Joseph's *vision* was a bad thing." This was glossed over, apparently, to the satisfaction of most persons present; but not fully to my own.[37]

Yet tales about the Latter-Day Saints were told and re-told, especially from such anti-Mormon sources as the Disciples. Parkin judiciously observed that "When such reports were reprinted at places distant from their Ohio source, they found a credulous audience; one senses that twice told tales began to invite unrealistic embellishments."[38] In many cases it now seems impossible to sort out the truth or fiction in them. Two widely-published stories were re-published by the Mormon Messenger And Advocate in Kirtland with the intention of exposing their folly and refuting them.

The first appeared in numerous sources, but perhaps first in the New York Mercury on June 25, 1835. Entitled "An Angel Caught," it claimed that Joseph Smith "sought to give additional solemnity to the baptismal rite, by affirming that on each occasion an angel would appear on the opposite side of the stream, and there remain till the conclusion of the ceremony." Then, at each baptismal event, a figure dressed in white *was* present on the opposite bank until its conclusion, which bolstered the faith of all present. But on one occasion some suspicious young "unbelievers" concealed themselves until the angel appeared, and then charged out forcing it into the stream. Even though "its efforts at escape were powerful," they managed to get him out of the stream only to discover that it was the Prophet himself in disguise![39]

The second commonly-told tale likewise appeared in multiple sources, and it had many variations, unless a similar circumstance happened on numerous occasions. In one version two disciples named J.J. Moss and Isaac Moore feigned interest in Mormonism in order to infiltrate it and expose it vulnerabilities. Moss wrote in his diary that it was common to witness an angel walking on water at night baptisms, as if to give divine approval. During daylight hours Moss and Moore found a two-inch plank just below the water's surface. They sawed it almost in half and the next night, when the angel walked on water, the plank broke "causing a mighty splash and a very un-angelic shriek!"[40] Another version identifies the angel as a Mormon elder,[41] while a third version—reprinted by the Mormons—

---

37   Ezra Booth, "Mormonism # 1," The [Painesville] Telegraph, Vol. III, No. 19 (October 25, 1831), p. 1. See also The Ohio Star (October 13, 1831), p. 3.

38   Parkin, p. 238.

39   Oliver Cowdery, ed., "Slanderous," The Messenger And Advocate (Kirtland), Vol. I, No. 10 (July, 1835), pp. 148-149.

40   Shaw, p. 84, quoting M.M. Moss (Ed.), "Autobiography of a Pioneer Preacher," The Christian Standard (January 15, 1938).

41   Parkin, p. 242.

identifies the angel as a Mormon preacher who *drowned* as a result of the prank![42] A fourth perspective was given by Lucia Goldsmith, who claimed she was present "with an equestrian party of eight" in the fall of 1835 when Joseph Smith supposedly healed a man. She then added:

> Perhaps you have read of the Prophet's attempt to walk on the water (?). There was a shallow place in the river there, where he was to perform <u>the miracle</u>. A moon light eve was chosen, a crowd had collected. Smith started boldly out for a few feet—when his <u>faith</u>—<u>or something</u>, failed, and down he sank. Some wicked (?) one had removed the support at the place of the plank he had placed just under the surface of the water. He never made the attempt again here—but any way, he had <u>his final baptism</u> in Kirtland.[43]

Such stories alienated the Mormons even further from the mainstream society around them. As Max Parkin has stated, "The active tongue of the story-teller multiplied the abuse amassed upon the Saints of the Latter-days and particularly their leader and Prophet."[44] Sidney Rigdon would also find himself embroiled in the controversies, although he was more interested in winning new converts than striving with old associates.

Contentions between both restoration movements escalated during their eight-year cohabitation on the Western Reserve. Campbellites suffered more losses of membership and leadership to the Mormons than any other religious group in Ohio.[45] A.S. Hayden reported that "It caused a great shock" among their community, and he dramatized the extent of this alarm with the simile, "The force of this shock was like an *earthquake*."[46] A Portage County man observed in 1832 that "The Mormonites in some places, seem to be swallowing Campbellites. . . ."[47]

An examination of the major denominational publications of the era has revealed that the Disciples of Christ issued more anti-Mormon books and tracts than any other denomination in the nineteenth century.[48] The Mormons often responded in kind with equally vituperative rejoinders. In Alexander Campbell's February, 1831, twelve-page essay entitled "Delusions," Campbell began with the statement, "Every age of the world has produced

---

42   W.W. Phelps, "Thou Shalt Not Lie," <u>The Messenger And Advocate</u>, Vol. II, No. 3 (December, 1835), pp. 230-231, quoting the story entitled "Tragical Event" from <u>The Philadelphia Saturday Courier</u>.

43   Lucia Goldsmith, "Sidney Rigdon, The First Mormon Elder," found in the papers of Lucia A. Goldsmith, Manuscripts Collection, The Western Reserve Historical Society, Cleveland, Ohio.

44   Parkin, p. 247.

45   Ibid., p. 226.

46   Hayden, p. 240.

47   Parkin, p. 227, quoting from <u>The Battleboro Messenger</u> (Battleboro, Vermont), Vol. XI, No. 9 (March 24, 1832), p. 1.

48   Ibid., p 235. See especially footnote 27 for source reference.

impostors and delusions," and proceeded on to identify Joseph Smith as an "impious fraud."[49] Sidney Rigdon later responded to him with a boast:

> "Delusion," said Mr. A. Campbell, in 1831, soon after the church of the Saints began to be established in this place; but unfortunately for his purposes, if a purpose he had, his cry was unheard, the cause still progressed, and *continues* to progress.[50]

In July of 1831 Campbell wrote in his <u>Millennial Harbinger</u> that Sidney Rigdon had confided in him that "were Joseph to be proved a liar, or say himself that he never found The Book of Mormon as he has reported, still he would believe it, and believe that all who did not believe it shall be damned."[51] He then continued on for many years to attack Mormonism itself as an "imposture." In one article he wrote:

> This meanest, vilest, and most diabolical of frauds ever practiced in the encyclopedia of delusions and impostures, has grown up to such an enormous stature of impudence, arrogance, and malignity, as to call forth the attention, remonstrance, and abhorrence of all well-meaning men, religious, moral, and political. Its arrogance and impiety are daily growing more and more obnoxious to the reprobation of all sorts and degrees of philanthropists.[52]

His numerous printed criticisms eventually drew a response from Joseph Smith:

> I have, of late, been perusing Mr. A. Campbell's "Millennial Harbinger." I never have rejoiced to see men of corrupt hearts step forward and assume the authority and pretend to teach the ways of God—this is, and always has been a matter of grief, therefore I cannot but be thankful, that I have been instrumental in the providence of our heavenly father in drawing forth, before the eyes of the world, the <u>spirits</u> by which certain ones, who profess to be "Reformers, and Restorers of ancient principles," are actuated! I have always had the satisfaction of seeing the truth triumph over error, and darkness give way before light, when such men were provoked to expose the corruption of their own hearts, by crying delusion, deception, and false prophets, accusing the innocent, and condemning the guiltless, and exalting themselves to the stations of gods, to lead blind fold men to perdition![53]

---

49 Alexander Campbell, "Delusions," <u>The Millennial Harbinger</u>, Vol. II, No. 2 (February 7, 1831), pp. 85 and 91.

50 Sidney Rigdon, "Delusion," <u>The Messenger And Advocate</u>, Vol. I, no. 6 (March, 1835), p. 90.

51 Alexander Campbell, "Mormonism," <u>The Millennial Harbinger</u>, Vol. II, No. 7 (July 4, 1831) p. 332.

52 Alexander Campbell, "Mormonism In An Agony," <u>The Millennial Harbinger</u>, New Series, Vol. VI, No. VIII (August, 1842), pp. 358-359.

53 Parkin, Appendix D, p. 370, reprinting a letter from Joseph Smith (dated September 24, 1834) to Oliver Cowdery, editor of <u>The Evening And Morning Star</u>.

Disputes between these restoration cousins (Disciples and Mormons) continued well beyond the deaths of Smith and Campbell. In 1884 a more formal and polite public debate was held in Kirtland, Ohio, between a Mormon named Kelley and a Disciple named Braden. But vicious verbal assaults continued to be launched as well. In 1887 a deputy U.S. Marshal said the following regarding the Latter-Day Saints:

> As their creed is different from any other, "thou shalt not bear false witness," from what I have seen, must read in their catechism, "thou shalt lie when it suits thy purpose;" for, of all the square, single-handed liars on earth Mormons stand out pre-eminent. . . . they are taught to lie from their cradles.[54]

But of all the controversies between the Disciples Of Christ and the Mormons, the one which has probably received the most print and attention was the Spalding Controversy. Originating in 1834, this thesis struck at the very heart of the Mormon faith—The Book of Mormon itself. The attempt endeavored to prove that the book was nothing more than an elaborate plagiarism and conspiracy, with Sidney Rigdon at the center of it.

THE SPALDING CONTROVERSY

Of all the quarrels between the two restoration movements, the Spalding Controversy lasted the longest and has probably produced the most literature. Since the arguments involve the integrity of The Book of Mormon itself, "literally hundreds of articles and books have been written purporting to prove the fraudulent character of the book, or to confound those who thus sought to disprove its divine origin."[55] Even though this debate seems finally to be resolved, some discussion of it is appropriate here for two reasons. First, it was the most significant dispute between the Disciples and Mormons, lasting well into the twentieth century. And second, Sidney Rigdon was the central character implicated in the authorship of The Book of Mormon. However, a simple overview and cursory discussion will serve the purposes of this work, especially since the topic has been thoroughly analyzed in other works.[56]

---

54   Fred E. Bennett, Fred Bennett, The Mormon Detective; or Adventures In The Wild West. Mormonism Unmasked (Chicago: Laird and Lee, 1887), micropublished in Western Americana; Frontier History of The Trans-Mississippi West, 1550-1900 (New Haven, Conn.: Research Publications, Inc., 1975), p. 25. Filmed from the holdings of Yale University's Beinecke Library.

55   Pancoast, p. 11.

56   For a much more extensive and thorough analysis of the Spalding Controversy, see Jerald and Sandra Tanner, Did Spalding Write The Book of Mormon? (Salt Lake City: Utah Lighthouse Ministries, 1977), which includes a 1910 copy of Solomon Spalding's Manuscript Found story. Also Daryl Chase, in Sidney Rigdon - Early Mormon, and Fawn Brodie, in No Man Knows My History (Appendix B, pp. 419-433), have prolonged analyses of the Spalding Thesis. For the affidavits of the eight witnesses affirming Smith's plagiarism of Spalding, see Eber D. Howe's Mormonism Unvailed, Ch. 19 (pp. 278-290).

In February of 1831, shortly after the publication of The Book of Mormon, Alexander Campbell affirmed his opinion as to its authorship, insisting that "there never was a book more evidently written by one set of fingers, nor more certainly conceived in one cranium. . . ." He then identified the author: "And as Joseph Smith is a very *ignorant* man and is called *the author* on the title page, I cannot doubt for a single moment but that he is the sole author and proprietor of it."[57] Fawn Brodie has contended that the Mormon church, rather than contest this identification of Joseph Smith with ignorance, has even *exaggerated* his superficiality "since the more meager his learning, the more divine must be his book."[58]

However in 1834 a work was published which caused many to question the book's authorship, and Campbell to change his opinion. Entitled Mormonism Unvailed, and supposedly written and published by Eber D. Howe, editor of The [Painesville] Telegraph, the thesis of the book was that The Book of Mormon was nothing more than a clever conspiracy and a treacherous plagiarism concocted by Sidney Rigdon and Joseph Smith to dupe the public, and perhaps gain money and positions of significant influence. Howe, who was apparently prodded to produce the volume by a man named Doctor Philastus Hurlbut,[59] claimed the altruistic high ground for his effort:

Figure 8. Eber D. Howe (1798 - 1885) (From http://www.solomonspalding.com/NEWSP/HOWE/Ex02a.htm.)

> The following work was undertaken with reluctance, at the earnest solicitation of a great number of friends, who had, with the author, long looked upon the subject of which it treats, with mingled feelings of abhorrence and pity—the Impostors and their victims of delusion, were viewed through these two different media.[60]

After referring to the Mormons as "designing knaves," "impostors," "false prophets," "false Messiahs," and "fanatics,"[61] he resolutely states:

---

57   Alexander Campbell, "Delusions," The Millennial Harbinger, Vol. II, no. 2 (February 7, 1831), p. 93.

58   Brodie, p. 69.

59   "Doctor" was apparently his *given* name, and not a title or earned degree (see Dean Hughes, The Mormon Church - A Basic History, p. 54). Also, many sources spell (or misspell) his last name as "Hurlburt," but the most reliable sources spell it as I use it.

60   Eber D. Howe, "Advertisement," found as a preface to Mormonism Unvailed.

61   Ibid., pp. V-IX.

We anticipate the bitter vituperation and sneers of the Mormon leaders and their influence over their already numerous followers, and do not expect to accomplish a reformation amongst them; but if we shall serve to enlighten *any*, who are not already the slaves of Mormon madness, alias the Devil, we will feel richly compensated.[62]

In Mormonism Unvailed Howe postulates that The Book of Mormon is, in essence, a religiously amended copy of an earlier work entitled Manuscript Found, written by a minister named Solomon Spalding. Spalding had been a Connecticut soldier during the American Revolution and, after that, a Dartmouth college graduate in 1785.[63] But subsequently his life appears to have been a series of failures. As a minister he lost his faith; as a merchant his trade failed; as an industrialist his iron foundry became bankrupt; and as an author his works went unpublished.[64]

In an effort to raise money to live on, he composed a romantic work about aboriginal America which he called The Manuscript Story, or Manuscript Found.[65] According to a number of witnesses, Spalding read passages of the book to them while he was composing it. Solomon's brother John Spalding later testified to the following:

> He then told me [he had] been writing a book, which he intended to have printed, the avails of which he thought would enable him to pay all his debts. The book was entitled the "Manuscript Found," of which he read to me many passages.—It was an historical romance of the first settlers of America, endeavoring to show that the American Indians are the descendants of the Jews, or the lost tribes.[66]

According to Matilda Davison, Spalding's wife, who remarried after his death in 1816, he completed his work around 1812.[67] Then Henry Lake, Spalding's business partner, encouraged him to have it published:

> Spalding left here [Conneaut, Ohio] in 1812, and I furnished him with the means to carry him to Pittsburgh, where he said he would get the book printed, and pay me. But I never heard any more from him or his writings, till I saw them in The Book of Mormon.[68]

---

62   Ibid., p. 94.

63   Mathes, p. 205.

64   McKiernan, p. 37.

65   These may be referring to the same document, or two documents, one amending the other. This possible discrepancy will be discussed later.

66   Howe, Mormonism Unvailed, p. 279.

67   Matilda Davison, "The Mormon Bible," The Millennial Harbinger, New Series, Vol. III, No. 6 (June, 1839), p. 266.

68   Howe, p. 282.

In Pittsburgh Spalding submitted his <u>Manuscript Found</u> story to the printing office of Patterson and Lambdin for publication. Patterson allegedly requested that Spalding write a title page and preface for the book,[69] but his wife said, "This Mr. S. refused to do, for reasons which I cannot now state,"[70] and the book languished on the shelf of the printing office. Spalding died in 1816, and the printing establishment was dissolved and broken up. Mr. Patterson supposedly reported that Spalding's written work "remained upon their shelves for years, without being printed, or even examined."[71]

Mr. Lambdin, having failed in business, came into contact with Sidney Rigdon, as the tale goes, who had begun a three year residency in Pittsburgh in 1822, and he gave Rigdon the manuscript "to be embellished, altered, and added to" as he saw fit.[72] But when Lambdin died, Rigdon despaired of ever getting the work published, until he came into contact with Joseph Smith, as early as 1827 according to some witnesses.[73] Then he and Smith connived a scheme in which <u>Manuscript Found</u>, with many additions and changes, evolved into <u>The Book of Mormon</u>.

Many connections were made between Rigdon and the printing office. Some asserted that he had even worked there. Walter Scott, Rigdon's cohort in Pittsburgh, could not confirm his employment at the office, but he did affirm the following:

> That Rigdon was ever connected with the printing office of Mr. Patterson or that this gentlemen ever possessed a printing office in Pittsburgh, is unknown to me, although I lived there, and also know Mr. Patterson very well, who is a book seller. But Rigdon was a Baptist minister in Pittsburgh, and I knew him to be perfectly known to Mr. Robert Patterson.[74]

Rigdon was even accused of *stealing* the article from the office. James M. Mathes wrote that Spalding's story "was purloined; and Rigdon was blamed with the theft." He then added that "In 1823, while pastor of the

---

69 Charles A. Shook, <u>The True Origin of The Book of Mormon</u> (Cincinnati: The Standard Publishing Co., 1914), p. 119.

70 Davison, "The Mormon Bible," p. 266.

71 Quoted in D.P. Kidder, <u>Mormonism and The Mormons</u> (New York: G. Lane and C.P. Trippett for the Methodist Episcopal Church, 1844), p. 36.

72 Ibid., p. 48.

73 James H, Snowden, <u>The Truth About Mormonism</u> (New York: George Doran Co., 1926), pp. 89-91, says that "several neighbors of the Smiths in Palmyra testify that they had personal knowledge of visits of Rigdon with Smith before 1830," and proceeds to list four of them by name with their comments. These three pages make interesting reading, especially when compared to Fawn Brodie, pp. 430-432.

74 Walter Scott, "The Mormon Bible," <u>The Evangelist</u>, Vol. VII, No. 7 (July 1, 1839), pp. 160-161. Hans Rollman, in his <u>The Early Baptist Career of Sidney Rigdon in Warren Ohio</u> (pp. 41-42), discusses the possibility that Rigdon also knew Solomon Spalding, which he doubts. Spalding died in 1816. However, since Rigdon grew up at Peter's Creek, near Pittsburgh, it is still possible.

Baptist church in Pittsburgh, Rigdon showed to Dr. Winter, one of the most reliable citizens of Pittsburgh, Spalding's M.S. [Manuscript Story]."[75]

Others added more pieces to the puzzle. Matilda Davison, Spalding's widow, boldly asserted that:

> Sidney Rigdon, who had figured so largely in the history of the Mormons, was at this time connected with the printing office of Mr. Patterson, as is well known in that region, and as Rigdon himself has frequently stated. Here he had ample opportunity to become acquainted with Mr. Spalding's manuscript, and to copy it if he chose.[76]

Rigdon immediately responded with a written refutation of her charges in The Boston Recorder on May 27, 1839, and proposed that "If I were to say that I ever heard of the Rev. Solomon Spalding and his hopeful wife, until Dr. P. Hurlbut wrote his lie about me, I should be a liar like unto themselves."[77]

But the accusations continued anyway. Darwin Atwater recalled:

> That he knew before of the coming of The Book of Mormon is to me certain, from what he said the first of his visits at my father's, some years before. He gave a *wonderful description* of the *mounds* and other antiquities found in some parts of America, and said that they must have been made by the Aborigines. He said *there was a book to be published containing* an account of those things.[78]

Adamson Bentley, Rigdon's brother-in-law wrote, "I know that Sydney [sic] Rigdon told me there was a book coming out (the manuscript of which had been found engraved on gold plates), as much as two years before the Mormon book made its appearance in this country or had been heard of by me." He then concluded that "It was got up to deceive the people and obtain their property, and was a wicked contrivance with Sidney Rigdon and Joseph Smith, Jr."[79] Robert Richardson also accused Rigdon of entering into a clandestined conspiracy:

> Having copied or obtained possession of this manuscript, Rigdon seems to have secretly occupied himself during several years in altering and arranging it to suit his purposes; and discovering, at Palmyra, New York, as early as 1827, a suitable coadjutor in the person of Joseph Smith.[80]

---

75 Mathes, p. 144.

76 Davison, "The Mormon Bible," p. 267.

77 Quoted in Brodie, p. 427.

78 Darwin Atwater letter, reproduced in Hayden, pp. 239-240.

79 Adamson Bentley, "Mistakes Touching The Book of Mormon," The Millennial Harbinger, Third Series, Vol. I, No. 1 (January, 1844), pp. 38-39.

80 Richardson, Vol. II, p. 345.

Smith and Rigdon vehemently denied these accusations, insisting that they had not even met until 1830. Furthermore, Rigdon always maintained that he never saw The Book of Mormon until the four Lamanite missionaries presented it to him that October day in 1830. His daughter Nancy corroborated his story remembering that, as an eight-year-old, "I saw them hand him the book and am as positive as can be that he never saw it before. . . ."[81]

His son John (Wickliffe), having returned from a trip to Salt Lake City in 1865, and having become disillusioned with the bad behavior of the Mormons there, wanted to know from his father if "it was all a humbug." Sidney, very near the end of his life, responded as sincerely as he could, "My son I will swear before God that what I have told you about The Book of Mormon is true. I did not write or have anything to do with its production and if Joseph Smith ever got that other [than] from which he always told me. . . Smith guarded his secret well for he never let me know by mood or action that he got them differently."[82] Almost twenty years later Clark Braden, suspicious because for the rest of his life "He [Rigdon] lived in ease, with no visible means of support," leveled the accusation that "Rigdon lived on Mormon money, paid to keep him silent."[83] Nonetheless, Rigdon swore allegiance to The Book of Mormon to his dying day.

But Hurlbut had spent much of 1833 voraciously assembling affidavits from more than a hundred people who knew Smith or Spalding,[84] and the sheer volume of testimonies seemed overwhelming. Many claimed to have read or heard the story of Manuscript Found, and all of those said they recognized its substance, expressions, and even characters in The Book of Mormon when they encountered it. John Spalding, Solomon's brother, testified:

> I have recently read The Book of Mormon, and to my great surprise I find nearly the same historical matter, names, etc. as they were in my brother's writings. I well remember that he wrote in the old style, and commenced about every sentence with "and it came to pass," or "now it came to pass," the same as in The Book of Mormon, and according to the best of my recollection and belief, it is the same as my brother Solomon wrote, with the exception of the religious matter.—By what means it has fallen into the hands of Joseph Smith, Jr. I am unable to determine.[85]

---

81 Quoted by Thomas Lee Scott, Jr., p. 10.

82 John Wickliffe Rigdon, "Lecture Written By John M. Rigdon On The Early History Of The Mormon Church," (BYU, Harold B. Lee Library, "Special Collections"), pp. 27-28.

83 Braden-Kelley Debate, "Mr. Braden's Sixth Speech," Col. 1, p. 357.

84 Brodie, p. 143.

85 John Spalding's testimony; see Howe, p. 280.

Henry Lake, Solomon's business partner, also said that, upon examining The Book of Mormon, he had "no hesitation in saying that the historical part of it is principally, if not wholly taken from the 'Manuscript Found.'"[86] Isaac Hale, Smith's father-in-law, called The Book of Mormon "a silly fabrication of falsehood and wickedness, got up for speculation, and with a design to dupe the credulous and unwary—and in order that its fabricators may live upon the spoils of those who swallow the deception."[87] And Lucy Harris, the wife of Martin Harris—one of "the three witnesses" to the authenticity of The Book of Mormon—testified that the "whole object was to make money by it."[88] In light of these and many more similar testimonies, Howe concluded:

> We therefore, must hold out Sidney Rigdon to the world as being the original "author and proprietor" of the whole Mormon conspiracy, until further light is elicited upon the lost writings of Solomon Spalding.[89]

As convincing as the Spalding thesis sounds—and the more testimonials one reads the more persuasive the thesis becomes, at least at the initial exposure—there are many inconsistent or even contradictory factors that defy credibility. For example, as Fawn Brodie has noticed, all of the witnesses seem to have remembered an unbelievable number of details about Manuscript Found, considering it had been twenty years since they had heard it read.[90] Furthermore, they all tended to "remember" the *same* items in which the Manuscript Found resembled The Book of Mormon, and even tended to phrase their observations in the same way. One is suspicious that Hurlbut *prompted* the memories of his interviewees, especially when *both* John Spalding's and Martha Spalding's *separate* testimonies contained the same explanatory line—"by land and sea, till they arrived in America"—matching each other word for word![91] Also, that Hurlbut was the ghostwriter for each affidavit can be clearly evidenced by the uniformity of penmanship style.[92]

Then, too, there was the question of motives. Howe and Hurlbut could hardly be regarded as impartial and objective. Howe, it was said, had a prolonged grudge against the Mormons because his wife had joined their church,[93] and he had been very critical of them in The [Painesville] Telegraph

---

86   Henry Lake's testimony; Ibid., p. 282.

87   Isaac Hale's testimony; Ibid., p. 265-266.

88   Lucy Harris' testimony; Ibid., p. 255.

89   Howe, p. 290.

90   Brodie, p. 143.

91   Compare both testimonies in Howe, pp. 279-280.

92   Brodie, p. 423.

93   McKiernan, p. 37.

ever since 1831. But Hurlbut apparently had even more motivation for resentment. He had been excommunicated from the Mormon church in June of 1833 on charges of adultery and threatening the life of Joseph Smith.[94] There were many Mormon, and even some Gentile, sources which identified Hurlbut as the real author of Mormonism Unvailed.[95] Joseph Smith was one of these plaintiffs, maintaining that Howe had to claim its authorship "as Mr. Hurlbut, about this time, was bound over to court, for threatening life."[96] He elaborated his conviction three years later:

> While Hurlburt [sic] was held in bounds by the church, and made to behave himself, he was denounced by the priests as one of the worst of men, but no sooner was he excluded from the church for adultery, than instantly he became one of the finest men in the world, old deacon Clapp of Mentor ran and took him and his family into the house with himself, and so exceedingly was he pleased with him, that purely out of respect to him, he went to bed with his wife. This great kindness and respect, Hurlburt did not feel just so well about but the pious old deacon gave him a hundred dollars and a yoke of oxen, and all was well again.
>
> This is the Hurlburt, that was the author of a book which bears the name of E.D. Howe, but it was this said Hurlburt that was the author of it; but after the affair of Hurlburt's wife and the pious old deacon, the persecutors thought it better to put some other name as author to their book than Hurlburt, so E.D. Howe substituted his name.[97]

Nonetheless Mormonism Unvailed was quite convincing to those with a propensity to distrust Mormon origins. Alexander Campbell changed his mind about Joseph Smith being the author of The Book of Mormon. He admitted that "Since reading 'Mormonism Unvailed' we had but little doubt that Sidney Rigdon is the leading conjuror in this diabolical affair; . . . ."[98] Oliver Cowdery, reacting to Campbell's altered opinion, melodramatically wrote in his Messenger And Advocate:

> He has recently begun to howl most prodigiously; calling upon the people in great agony to read Mr. How's [sic] book, as a sure antidote against delusion. As this is all that Mr. Campbell can do, or dare do, we do not wish to deprive him of this privilege.

---

94 Scott H. Fauling, ed., An American Prophet's Record: The Diaries And Journals of Joseph Smith (Salt Lake City: Signature Books, 1989), pp. 19-20.

95 See Pancoast, Appendix I.

96 Joseph Smith, "To The Elders of The Church of The Latter-Day Saints," The Messenger And Advocate, Vol. II, No. 3 (December, 1835), p. 228.

97 Joseph Smith, ed., "Argument To Argument Where I Find It; Ridicule To Ridicule; and Scorn To Scorn," The Elders Journal, Vol. I, No. 4 (August, 1838), pp. 59-60.

98 Quoted by Walter Scott in "The Mormon Bible," The Evangelist, Vol. VII, No. 7 (July 1, 1839), p. 160.

. . .Mr. Campbell has been invited to show himself a man of principle—after repeated insults to the church of the "Latter Day Saints," and to exchange papers and cut a quill like a man; but seeing he dare not do it, . . . we consider this effort of his in the same point of light which we do a whipet spannel [sic], when he is afraid to face his enemy, he turns his hind parts and barks—so bark on Alexander.[99]

But Campbell continued to believe Rigdon to be a conspiratorial author of The Book of Mormon for the rest of his life. In July of 1839 Walter Scott identified many elements of Mormon theology as those he had developed earlier, and claimed that Mormonism was using the simplicity of the Restoration (Disciples) plea as a host for its parasitic evangelistic success. He clearly charged "that Rigdon filched from us that elementary method of stating the gospel which has so completely brought it within the grasp of everyone who hears it."[100] Campbell concurred. Then in 1844 Campbell reasserted his conviction "that Sidney Rigdon had a hand in the manufacture of the religious part of The Book of Mormon is clearly established from this fact, and from other expressions in that book, as certainly 'stolen' from our brethren as that he once was amongst them."[101] And once again in 1856 he reaffirmed his opinion that "The real high-Priest of Joe Smith, he certainly was, and the available author of The Book of Mormon, as I have, at least to myself, evidences ample and satisfactory."[102]

After the publication of Mormonism Unvailed, Mormon refutations were printed in volumes almost equal to the assertions of their detractors. In 1838 Parley Pratt replied with Mormonism _Unveiled_ [italics mine], and in 1840 Benjamin Winchester released his exposé The Origin of The Spalding Story. So Hurlbut decided to go for the jugular. He visited Matilda Davison in Massachusetts and secured permission to publish Manuscript Found, offering her half of the profits. But the document he obtained did not bear a resemblance to The Book of Mormon, and Spalding's neighbors denied that it was the Manuscript Found with which they were familiar.[103]

Eber D. Howe wrote to Robert Patterson inquiring about Manuscript Found, and Patterson responded by saying that "he had no recollection" of any such manuscript, and that he and Lambdin did not form their

---

99   Oliver Cowdery, ed., "A Summary," The Messenger And Advocate, Vol. I, No. 5 (February, 1835), pp. 76-77.

100 Walter Scott, "The Mormon Bible," p. 160.

101 Alexander Campbell, "Mistakes Touching The Book of Mormon," The Millennial Harbinger, Third Series, Vol. I, No. 1 (January, 1844), p. 40

102 Alexander Campbell, "Millennium," The Millennial Harbinger, Fourth Series, Vol. VI, No. 12 (December, 1856), p. 698.

103 Brodie, pp. 427 and 424.

partnership until 1818, which was two years *after* the death of Solomon Spalding.[104] Apparently seeing no advantage in the version of Manuscript Found in their custody, Howe and Hurlbut smothered it to public awareness,[105] and eventually its whereabouts was unknown. However in 1884 it was rediscovered by L.L. Rice, the successor of Howe as editor of The [Painesville] Telegraph, in a trunk of Howe's old papers in Honolulu, Hawaii! Labeled in pencil "Manuscript Story—Conneaut Creek," the document was copied and given to President J.H. Fairchild of Oberlin College, who carefully perused it and pronounced that it was definitely not the precursor to The Book of Mormon.[106] The 1910 publication of Manuscript Found has a Publishers' Preface which states that "Mr. Spalding's 'Manuscript Story' no more resembles The Book of Mormon than 'Gulliver's Travels' is like the Gospel of Saint Matthew."[107]

Although the publication of Manuscript Found resolved the controversy for most people, a few retained the conviction that there had been *two* manuscripts, not one, written by Spalding. Howe had postulated way back in 1834 that Spalding "had altered his first plan of writing, by going farther back with dates, and writing in the old scriptural style, in order that it might appear more ancient." Howe also stated that some of the witnesses were shown the older manuscript and recognized it as Spalding's, though they added that it bore no resemblance to the newer manuscript.[108] The latter is the one purported to have been used by Rigdon and Smith. Charles Shook has identified the Oberlin holding as the earlier effort, "Manuscript Story," but the true "Manuscript Found," he contends, remains undiscovered.[109]

However, even non-Mormons who have carefully scrutinized the matter see no substantial evidence for the Spalding thesis. John Corrill, who apostacized from the Mormon church, admitted, "As to the origin of the Book, I made very diligent inquiry, and from all I could learn, I became satisfied that Smith was the author, and I never have been able to trace it to

---

104 Ibid., p. 425.

105 The "Publishers' Preface" to the 1910 edition of the original of the "Manuscript Story," p. IV., claims that Hurlburt, "discovering that it would, if published, prove fateful to his assumptions, he suppressed it." See Jerald and Sandra Tanner, Did Spalding Write The Book of Mormon?, Part 2, p. IV.

106 Ibid. See also Van Wagoner, p. 139, footnote 21; and Joseph H. Fairchild, "Solomon Spalding and The Book of Mormon," Western Reserve Historical Society Tract No. 77, Vol. III (March 23, 1886),   pp. 197-198.

107 See "Publishers' Preface" (re. footnote 104), p. iii; although this preface erroneously spells it Mormonism Unveiled (like Pratt's spelling), and gives a wrong publication date of 1836 instead of 1834.

108 Howe, p. 288.

109 See Shook, especially pp. 184-187, for details and arguments. Snowden (The Truth About Mormonism, p. 90) is another author who accepts this two-manuscript thesis.

any other source."[110]   And Jerald and Sandra Tanner, two modern-day avid anti-Mormon researchers and publishers, have carefully investigated the whole matter and concluded that there is no legitimate foundation for the Spalding theory, or for the idea of two manuscripts.[111]

Recently, in June of 1977, three California researchers and handwriting experts caused a stir with an assertion that twelve pages of the Mormon Book of <u>First Nephi</u> appear to have been written by Solomon Spalding. William Kaye, one of the men, stated in a letter dated September 8, 1977, "It is my considered opinion and conclusion. . . that the questioned handwriting in the above named Mormon documents and the known handwriting in the above named Spalding documents undoubtedly have all been executed by the same person."[112] Again, after deliberate consideration of the evidence, the Tanners "had to state the case as we saw it":

> For a number of years we have published material critical of the Mormon Church, and for this reason we were deluged with requests for information on this new discovery. Under the circumstances it was almost impossible to keep out of the controversy. Since we do not believe in the divine authenticity of the Book of Mormon, nothing could have pleased us more than to have seen the conclusions of the California researchers verified. Nevertheless, we had grave doubts about the new find, and after an examination of the documents we were forced to the conclusion that the discovery would not stand up under rigorous examination.[113]

Joseph Smith, just one year after <u>Mormonism Unvailed</u> was released to the public, seems to have been prophetic when he gloated that <u>The Book of Mormon,</u> "like an impenetrable, immoveable rock in the midst of the mighty deep, exposed [to the] storms and tempests of satan [sic], . . .has, thus far, remained steadfast and is still braving the mountain waves of opposition. . . ."[114] This confidence in its authenticity was not confined to the Prophet, either. In 1835 <u>Mormonism Unvailed</u> sold for eighteen and three quarter cents per copy, while <u>The Book of Mormon</u> retailed for two dollars. Elders Orson Hyde and W.E. McLellin literally issued a dare to non-Mormons, challenging them to "Tell everybody to buy and read

---

110 John Corrill, <u>A Brief History of The Church of Christ of Latter Day Saints, (commonly called Mormons;) Including An Account of Their Doctrine and Discipline With The Reasons of The Author For Leaving The Church</u> (St. Louis: "Printed For The Author," 1839), p. 11.

111 Jerald and Sandra Tanner, <u>Did Spalding Write The Book of Mormon?</u>, pp. 1-33 (see specifically pp. 16-17 for comments regarding the two manuscript theory).

112 Ibid., p. 18. For the original article see Russell Chandler, "Trio Challenges Authenticity of Mormon Book," <u>The Los Angeles Times</u> (June 25, 1977).

113 Ibid., p. 5 and 1.

114 Joseph Smith, "To The Elders of The Church of the Latter Day Saints," p. 227.

'Mormonism Unveiled' if they wish, for we are convinced of Paul's statement, where he says, 'Ye can do nothing against the truth but for the truth.'"[115] From the Mormon perspective, this controversy was well summarized by M.R. Werner:

> The whole Spalding story is an instance of the feverish efforts of Anti-Mormons to prove that Joseph Smith was incapable of writing the Book of Mormon without the aid of God, and they refused to admit for a moment that he did so with the aid of God.[116]

---

115 Orson Hyde and W.E.McLellin, "For The Messenger And Advocate," <u>The Messenger And Advocate</u>, Vol. I, No. 8 (May, 1835), p. 116.

116 Werner, p. 60.

Chapter
—12—

PERSECUTING RESTORATIONISM: VIOLENCE BETWEEN THE TWO MOVEMENTS

Quarrels over religious opinions are one thing, but threats to one's political, social, or material condition are quite another. Somehow the latter seem to pose a more personal, or at least a more immediate, menace to one's welfare, and he or she is more apt to respond forcefully to the perceived danger. As the Mormon influence grew, and as its rather radical message spread amongst ever-widening circles, a correspondent reaction paralleled its growth.

When Mormonism was first introduced into the Western Reserve, many regarded it as a curiosity. Some scorned it as an amusement, while a few considered it to be a nuisance, a con, or even a heresy. But once established in the Kirtland area, Mormonism began to grow and be perceived as a threat to the established society and denominations. In 1831 church membership quadrupled.[1] By 1832, in some places, like Portage County for instance, "the Mormons seemed to be engulfing the Campbellites and other religious groups."[2] The incumbent Protestant denominations and the dominant Anglo-Saxon culture resisted various incursions into their "Righteous Empire," even though at the core of its democratic philosophical foundation "America was a pluralistic society. . . . Her charter did not permit religious monopolies, did not establish hosts to welcome (or shun) guests, did not license empires within the republic."[3]

---

1   Roger D. Launius, "The Latter Day Saints And The "House Of The Lord' At Kirtland, Ohio," The Lake County Historical Society Quarterly (Mentor, Ohio), Vol. XXI, No. 4 (December, 1979), p. 2.

2   H.F. Lupold, The Latch String Is Out - A Pioneer History of Lake County, Ohio (Mentor, Ohio: Lakeland Community College Press, 1974), p. 108.

3   Martin Marty, Righteous Empire: The Protestant Experience In America, p. 123.

Without doubt many Mormons contributed to, rather than alleviated, the natural tensions produced by unknown or misunderstood newcomers invading someone else's territory. Some of the first missionary elders, in boldness and lack of tact, had a knack for stirring up beehives of resentment. Joel Johnson, for example, audaciously informed his Amherst, Ohio, audience that, since the Roman Catholic Church was widely regarded as the "Mother of Harlots," the Protestant denominations must be her daughters.[4] James Carroll, graciously invited by a Baptist preacher to preach in his pulpit, began his sermon with the terse remark, "You have a pretty meeting-house, and good buildings and farms; but do you know that the 'Mormons' are coming here to possess the whole of them?"[5] And Joseph Smith himself, when he was once asked, "Will everybody be damned but Mormons?" answered, "Yes, and a great portion of them, unless they repent and work righteousness."[6]

Fears intensified whenever evidence would be produced that designs on personal property, for instance, were not just the ravings of a few maverick preachers, but official Mormon policy instead. In 1832, when many of the Hiram Latter-day Saints traveled to Missouri to lay the foundation of the temple of Zion, they apparently left some papers behind "which revealed to [the townfolk] the horrid fact that a plot was laid to take their property from them and place it under the control of Joseph Smith the prophet."[7] Max Parkin, after sighting numerous instances of such abrasive agitations, marveled and proclaimed, "Perhaps, the real wonder is that the message of the Mormon elders continued to find interested hearers in [the] face of all of their problems."[8]

Feelings were also injured whenever a prominent Disciple, Baptist, or Methodist was converted to Mormonism, but animosities increased whenever one of them would "apostacize" back out of the movement. Whitmer's history of the Latter-day Saints states, "There was much trouble and unbelief among those who call themselves disciples of Christ. Some apostacized and became enemies to the cause of God, and persecuted the Saints."[9]

One of these was Simonds Ryder, a prominent Hiram Disciple who was "the most important accession that the Hiram Church has ever had,"

---

4   Parkin, p. 158, quoting the personal journal of Joel Hills Johnson (June, 1831), a copy of which may be found in the Special Collections Library at Brigham Young University.

5   Ibid., p. 160, quoting The Journal of Discourses, IV, p. 305.

6   Joseph Smith, ed., The Elders' Journal (Far West, MO.), Vol. I, No. 3 (July, 1838), p. 42.

7   Hayden, p. 221.

8   Parkin, p. 162. See chapter VII in Parkin's "Conflict at Kirtland" for a listing and analysis of the political and economic factors which contributed to the Mormon conflicts there.

9   Whitmer, p. 6.

and "perhaps the most influential man in the township."[10] At first exposure, Ryder rejected Mormon Restorationism because he did not believe that the gifts of the Holy Spirit were legitimately manifested in the modern day.[11] But after reading about a devastating earthquake that hit Peking in China, and remembering that a young Mormon girl had predicted the event just six weeks earlier, he converted and became an ordained Mormon elder in June of 1831.[12] However, Ryder quickly recanted his conversion after a special revelation to Joseph Smith erroneously spelled Ryder's name "Rider," because Ryder had the conviction that God would not misspell any name in a true revelation.[13]

From that time forward Ryder became one of the Western Reserve's most avid persecutors of the Mormons. The conflict began verbally, with Ryder and Ezra Booth preaching and writing attacks upon the Saints. Rigdon finally challenged both to public debates, but Ryder declined and Booth didn't show up as scheduled. Inflammatory words led to militant action on a dark night in March (24th) of 1832. A mob of infuriated—and apparently somewhat inebriated—Disciples, Baptists, and Methodists,[14] allegedly led by Simonds Ryder, stormed the homes of Rigdon and Smith, and pulled them outside. Rigdon's head was beating on the floor as they dragged him out of the house, and someone tried to throw nitric acid in his face, but missed as he turned his head.[15] Due to a concussion he lost consciousness. He was then stripped naked, tarred and feathered, and left on the ground.

Smith, who had been babysitting with his twins, both sick with the measles, put up more of a fight than Rigdon. Dragged from his bed by the hair, clothes, and limbs, Smith—with Emma screaming in the background—managed to free one leg and kick one of the men in the face, sending him sprawling to the ground. This man, Warren Waste, reputed to be the strongest man in the Western Reserve, had previously bragged to his compatriots that he could handle Joseph Smith all by himself, and in a fury

---

10 Hinsdale, p. 17. For a brief background on Simonds Ryder see Richardson, Vol. II, pp. 257-258.

11 Pancoast, p. 40.

12 See Hayden, p. 251; Joseph Smith's History Of The Church, Vol. I, p. 158 (including the footnote); McKiernan, p. 52; and VanWagoner, p. 109.

13 McKiernan, p. 52. See Joseph Smith, Doctrine And Covenants, Section 52:8c, for misspelling.

14 Ivan Barrett (p. 205) numbers the mob at forty men, while Dean Hughes (p. 46) tallies it at fifty. Joseph Smith's History Of The Church (Vol. I, p. 264) tells of a man "who gave the mob a barrel of whiskey to raise their spirits," which Fawn Brodie (p. 119) and Van Wagoner (p. 115) then reiterate. M.R. Werner (p. 77) constitutes the mob as being from the Disciples, Baptists, and Methodists.

15 Van Wagoner, p. 115. Many sources tell of this event, but Van Wagoner gained access to the "Manuscript Minutes" of April 6, 1844, which gave more specific details of the occasion.

he got back up and, shouting "God damn ye, I'll fix ye," choked Smith into unconsciousness.[16]

He soon revived, however, and as the mob dragged him past Rigdon, he thought Sidney was dead. Smith began to beg for his life, and someone in the mob responded, "God damn ye, call on yer God for help, we'll show ye no mercy." But after conferring together, the mob determined to tar and feather Joseph as well. When they attempted to push the tar paddle into Smith's mouth, Smith turned his head and again they shouted, "God damn ye, hold up yer head and let us giv ye some tar." Someone else tried to force a glass vial allegedly containing poison into his mouth, but the vile broke in his teeth. Another man clawed his naked body with his fingernails "like a mad cat" muttering while he did so, "God damn ye, that's the way the Holy Ghost falls on folks!"[17] Eli Johnson attempted to then have Smith castrated for supposed indiscretions with his sister, but the mob apparently lost its resolve when it beheld the pitiful condition of the two men.[18]

The mob left both men lying on the ground—naked, bleeding, dazed, and in Rigdon's case, still unconscious. Smith arose, pulled the tar away from his lips so he could breathe better, and made his way to "Father Johnson's." "When I came to the door I was naked, and the tar made me look as if I were covered with blood," he reported, "and when my wife saw me she thought I was all crushed to pieces, and fainted."[19] His friends spent most of the night scraping and peeling the tar off his body, and the next morning being Sunday, incredibly he still preached to his congregation—which that morning also included Simonds Ryder and other members of the mob![20]

Rigdon was not so durable. His son Wickliffe described the events that followed [errors not mine]:

> My father must have lain on the ground when the mob left him for some time. At last he got up in a dozed condition did not know where he was nor where to go but at last got his face turned toward his home more by accident than design and went realing along the road not knowing where he was and would have past his house but my mother was out the door watching for him and went out as he came along and got him in the house. She got the tar and feathers off from him as best she could and got him to bed. In the morning J. Smith came over to see him but he was crazy. He wanted him to get him his razor. J. Smith wanted to know what he wanted

---

16   Joseph Smith, <u>History Of The Church</u>, Vol. I, pp. 261-262; and Barrett, p. 205.

17   Ibid., p. 262-263.

18   Brodie, p. 119.

19   Joseph Smith, <u>History Of The Church</u>, Vol. I, p. 263.

20   Ibid., p. 264.

it for he said he wanted to kill his wife. J. Smith soothe him as best he could and left him. In a few days my father regained his mind.[21]

Max Parkin has listed three factors as motivating the violent events of March 24, 1832: (1) the Mormon Law of Consecration, which some feared would interfere with private property rights; (2) the increase in Mormon converts in the Hiram area, leading to anxieties of becoming a major Mormon center; (3) resentment due to the conversion of family members.[22] But from the Mormon perspective the reason was simpler. Eva Pancoast has contended that "All Mormon accounts of this tarring and feathering, as well as of later persecutions, attempt to make the ground of attack the hostility to the Mormon's religious beliefs, presenting them entirely in the light of outrages on liberty of opinions."[23] Reflecting back on the episode at Hiram four years later, as well as problems in the meantime, Sidney Rigdon charged that men like Simonds Ryder "as well as others, of the smaller animals of this species (I mean the Campbellites). . . ," were simply puppets "held in bondage, whose minds are too limited to exercise one independent thought for themselves, and only think as they are permitted by their masters." Portraying Disciple leaders as theological tyrants, he complained about their stooges:

> They are not at liberty to believe what the bible says, unless they first find it in the Evangelist, or Harbinger, and then, and not till then dare they believe it; but if they find it in the Evangelist, or Harbinger, it matters not whether it is in the bible or whether it is not in it, of course, in their estimation it is true; because brother Campbell, or brother Scott, has said it, that is enough: bible or no bible.

> We feel in the mean time at liberty to say, that we have all the evidence necessary to satisfy our mind, that Messrs.. Campbell, and Scott, the leaders of that brotherhood, are not honest in their religion. . . .[24]

A year later he attempted to identify the root of the Saints' persecution problems. As Pancoast has suggested, the cause was said to be intolerance. In an article entitled Persecution, Rigdon wrote:

> There is no country, perhaps, in the world, which boasts more of its liberties, than our own; . . .and yet, wonderful to tell, after all our pretensions, a man is not at liberty to worship according to the dictates of his own conscience.

---

21 John Wickliffe Rigdon, typescript, p. 9. See also Joseph Smith's description in his History Of The Church, Vol. I, p. 265.

22 Parkin, p. 255.

23 Pancoast, p. 45.

24 Sidney Rigdon, "For The Messenger And Advocate" (a letter to "Br. O. Cowdery"), The Messenger And Advocate, Vol. II, No. 7 (April, 1836), pp. 297-298.

. . .there is not a State in this UNION, where a man is at liberty to worship God according to the dictates of his conscience; . . . .

Included in the article was his forecast of doom:

. . .millions and tens of millions of the human race will make their bed in hell for persecuting and reviling men on account of their religion.[25]

The Latter-day Saints encountered a similar persecution at their new "Zion" established in Jackson County, Missouri. "The troubles of 1833, which led to their expulsion from the county, were originated by these fanatics making boasts that they intended to possess the entire county, saying that God had promised it to them and they were going to have it," reported Colonel Pitcher, one of the protagonists in the action. He then added, "This of course caused ill feeling toward them, which continued to grow more and more bitter, until the final uprising."[26] Joseph Smith added fuel to the fire when, in that same year, he predicted "by the authority of Jesus Christ, that not many years shall pass away before the United States shall present such a scene of *bloodshed* as has not a parallel in the history of our nation."[27]

Even though the Mormons held steadfast to their claim that they were being persecuted solely for their unorthodox religious beliefs, their detractors were often more offended by their lack of tact or aggressive demeanors. They apparently stirred up fear and anger wherever they went. In 1834 Eber D. Howe wrote:

Their first salutations to every community that does not believe their book and pretensions, are, that destruction awaits them for their unbelief. . . , and all that do not come to him [Joseph Smith] for power and instructions will be damned. Add to this, some among them frequently boast of their increasing strength, and that consequently they will soon be enabled to possess themselves of all the secular power of the country, as they already have of the spiritual. This they calculate to accomplish by concentrating their forces in particular neighborhoods. We have been credibly informed that Rigdon has given it as his opinion that the Mormons will be able to elect a member of congress in five years, and that in three years they would take the offices in the town of Kirtland. They say that when they get the secular power into their hands, every thing will be performed by immediate revelations from God. We shall then have Pope Joseph *the First* and his hierarchy.[28]

25 Sidney Rigdon, "Persecution," The Messenger And Advocate, Vol. III, No. 4 (January, 1837), p. 436.

26 Van Wagoner, p. 145, quoting R. Etzenhouser, From Palmyra, New York, 1830 to Independence, Missouri, 1894 (Independence: Ensign Publishing House, 1894), p. 323.

27 Joseph Smith, History Of The Church, Vol. I, p. 315.

28 Howe, Mormonism Unvailed, p. 145.

The people of Jackson county responded in anger. Calling the Latter-Day Saints deluded fanatics, weak and designing knaves, lazy and vicious vagabonds, slave stealers, blasphemers, and land thieves—they composed a letter of complaint on July 15, 1833, expressing their intention "to rid ourselves [of the Mormons], peaceably if we can and forcibly if we must, . . .believing as we do, that the arm of civil law does not afford us a guarantee, or at least not a sufficient one against the evils which are now inflicted upon us. . . ."[29] Numerous instances of persecution ensued, such as the destruction of homes and the whipping of men. The Mormons attempted to form a self-defense force, but it was inadequately armed. In early November, 1833, an incident took place which left three or four people killed, others wounded, the printing office destroyed, and two Mormon leaders tarred and feathered. The Saints, under compulsion, agreed to vacate Jackson county by January 1, 1834.[30]

Marvin Hill has argued that it was the Mormon exclusiveness with its "projected totality" that alienated the mob, because they thought it was "anti-democratic and dangerous." Their counter-force was organized, not against aberrant religious convictions, but to offset a perceived economic and political threat presented by the Mormons. He concluded:

> It seems then, that the non-Mormons were largely correct in maintaining that the main reason for their antagonism toward the Saints was not religious. Or, to put it another way, the persecution of the Mormons was religious only in the sense that, from the Gentile point of view, the Latter-day Saint religion included too much.[31]

In 1833 tensions also rose around Kirtland, and it became increasingly necessary to protect the lives of men like Smith and Rigdon from a recurrence of the Hiram episode in 1832. Observing the tragic events in Jackson county, Whitmer proclaimed, "That this is a religious persecution is notorious throughout the country."[32] He also described the deprivations and trials of the Missouri Saints, hoping to win sympathy for their plight, and perhaps to herald similar potential disasters for other unprepared Mormons:

> The situation of our brethern [sic] after leaving their homes in Jackson in the most distressing circumstances, in the cold month of November, found it difficult to preserve life in many instances. Some fled with but few clothes, leaving their beds and bedding; others taking with them what they could carry and running for their lives; women losing some of their children

---

29   Whitmer, p. 29.

30   Corrill, p. 20, and Van Wagoner, p. 146.

31   Hill, p. 5.

32   Whitmer, p. 12.

33   Ibid., p. 11.

while fleeing for their lives; and thus you may judge how the poor Saints have suffered, after having given only a few hints of the distress.[33]

Smith responded to the need. Late in February of 1834 Parley Pratt and Lyman Wight arrived in Kirtland from Missouri eager to avenge their brethren and regain their lost property. Smith was inspired to raise a volunteer "army" of five hundred men, but less than two hundred responded. Nonetheless by May Rigdon had blessed the army, designated as "Zions camp," with an address, and by June they were at the border of Jackson county. However, anticipated support from Governor Dunklin did not materialize, and "Zions camp" experienced some exhaustion and sickness. When the Governor threatened to call the state militia to oppose them, the crusade was abandoned and, on July 9, Smith started back to Kirtland with his men.[34]

Back in the Western Reserve persecution continued. In April of 1835 Smith was brought to trial in Painesville, in the Court of Common Pleas, for "assaulting" (four or five blows to the head) his brother-in-law Calvin Stoddard in a dispute over the possible location of water on a certain plot of land. The case was dismissed.[35] Also in 1835, Grandison Newell, a Kirtland land speculator, took Rigdon to court in Geauga County, charging him with issuing unauthorized bank notes. Then, claiming that the Latter-day Saints had cost him more than one thousand dollars, he led a mob which stoned Orson Pratt when the Mormon elder tried to preach in Mentor.[36] In the same town, when Parley Pratt, Orson's brother, attempted to preach in the fall of 1835, a large group of fifty men marched around playing musical instruments and drowning out his sermon. They also tossed eggs at him. Eventually a Chardon, Ohio, Common Pleas Court convicted Newell and he was fined forty-seven dollars in damages.[37]

Rigdon did not let these torments pass unnoticed. In January of 1836 he attacked the character of Simonds Ryder who, it should be recalled, led the mob that attacked Smith and Rigdon in Hiram, yet did not seem to have the courage to face Rigdon in a public debate. Sidney wrote, "Let me here mention Simonds Rider as another instance of the same kind, [sic] he could blow like a porpoise when there was no person to oppose him; but when called upon to be as bold in the presence of those whom he envied, as in their absence, he had recourse to the same

---

34 For a detailed account of these events, see Brodie, Ch. X.

35 See Parkin, pp. 131-133.

36 Elizabeth G. Hitchcock, "Grandison Newell: A Born Trader," <u>Lake County History-The Bicentennial Edition</u> (Painesville, Ohio: Published by the Lake County Historical Society and The Board of Lake County Commissioners, 1976), p. 181.

37 H.F. Lupold, <u>The Latch String Is Out: A Pioneer History of Lake County, Ohio</u>, p. 108. See also <u>The Chardon Spectator</u>, Vol. V, No. 18. (October 30, 1835) n.p. given; and Parley P. Pratt, <u>Autobiography</u>, p. 128.

means of slander and abuse. . . ."[38] In June, Ryder announced that he was going to sue Sidney for slander, and Rigdon satirically responded, ". . . O! I do not want to be sued for the terrible crime of telling the truth about a man."[39] And in November, Rigdon again vilified those who persecuted the Latter-day Saints. Listing the various points of doctrine upon which many of the denominations disagreed with the Mormons, Rigdon concluded:

> It is in relation to these things that the church of the Latter-Day Saints has been so shamefully abused and belied, by all these parties both Jews and gentiles, reformers and non-reformers, (not even excepting the pious A. Campbell and old Clapp, his Sanco Panza, and the *will-making* A. Bently[sic], one of his flunkies:). . . .[40]

> For believing these things, and acting accordingly, the saints have been made to feel the hand of persecution from this ungodly generation which is fast ripening for the damnation of hell; for the saints have began [sic] to gather together. . . .[41]

A few disgruntled apostates could not have wrought the havoc on the Saints that actually resulted. There was much anti-Mormon feeling among the communities where their number became significant. Then, when "They began to make their boasts that in a short time they would control all the county offices and elect a member of Congress from their own ranks,"[42] people were scared into action. Fear of being outvoted is one thing; but word went around the community that the Mormons had boasted that, once established in power, this country would be governed by Joseph Smith and his revelations. Eber D. Howe attempted to justify the vigilante actions when he wrote, "when they attempt to rob the people of this country of their political rights. . . it is time for the community to be alarmed."[43]

Rigdon, however, kept insisting that the persecution had its basis in theology, and not in politics. In January of 1837 he again identified his old restoration colleagues as the catalysts of oppression:

---

38 Sidney Rigdon, letter to John Whitmer, <u>The Messenger And Advocate</u>, Vol. II, No. 4 (January, 1836), p. 242.

39 Sidney Rigdon, letter to Oliver Cowdery, <u>The Messenger And Advocate</u>, Vol. II, No. 9 (June, 1836), p. 334.

40 See Ibid., p. 335, and McKiernan, p. 28. Adamson Bentley had successfully influenced old Mr. Brooks to cut Phebe and Sidney out of his will, thus excluding them from a share in the family estate.

41 "S.R." [Sidney Rigdon], "The Latter Day Glory," <u>The Messenger And Advocate</u>, Vol. III, No. 2 (November, 1836), pp. 403-404.

42 Parkin, p. 192, quoting Eber D. Howe's <u>Autobiography and Recollections of A Pioneer Printer</u>, p. 44.

43 Eber D. Howe, ed., <u>The [Painesville] Telegraph</u>, Vol. IV, No. 4 (January 27, 1837), n.p.

The spirit of persecution has prevailed in every age of the world, to the great disgrace of the human race, and if there is justice in heaven, to the condemnation of millions; . . . .

In our own vicinity we have a most striking proof of the spirit of persecution in a religious society which made as great a boast of liberty and the blessings of freedom, as any other. I mean the Campbellites.

One of the great cries of this horde of iniquity against the saints, was, that they were trying to get people's property into their hands, and to cheat them out of their just rights.

It will be hard to persuade us. . . that nine-tenths of all the lies put in circulation against the saints, did not originate with the before mentioned gang.[44]

Persecution increased in the spring of 1837. There were some occasions when Smith and Rigdon actually had to escape the wrath of the mob by hiding in the woods for as much as three days at a time.[45] Smith even left Kirtland for a while. In mid-July he went on a five-week missionary tour of Canada hoping to diffuse much of the hostility that had amassed against him. But the troubles resumed when he returned.

Rigdon, for his part, assaulted the Presbyterians, Methodists, Episcopalians, Baptists, and Disciples, in The Messenger And Advocate, accusing them of knowing little about "the Father and the Son," and of serving Beelzebub instead.[46] But he always saved the harshest words for his old cronies, the Disciples. In January he had prophesied their demise:

There is perhaps no people now living, who have said more about the rights of conscience, than this brood of persecuting Campbellites: . . . . What have the saints done to enrage the malice, and excite the wrath of this gang of persecuting Campbellits [sic]?

The book of Mormon, then, has revealed the secrets of Campbellism, and unfolded the end of the system. Every eye may see, and every heart understand; for the public may depend upon it, that the vomit which it has received, is too severe for it; it has spewed itself to death, and in a very short time it will have fled the Lake shore, to appear no more forever.[47]

There were many instances of troubles and persecutions visited upon the Saints of the Western Reserve during the years 1831-1838. Historian

---

44 Sidney Rigdon, "Persecution," The Messenger And Advocate, Vol. III, No. 4 (January, 1837), pp. 436-437.

45 Parkin, p. 310.

46 Sidney Rigdon, "Persecution," The Messenger And Advocate, Vol. III, No. 6 (March, 1837), pp. 478-479.

47 Sidney Rigdon, "Persecution," The Messenger And Advocate, Vol. III, No. 4 (January, 1837), p. 438.

George Smith has calculated that there were around fifty law suits leveled at Smith during his lifetime,[48] and many of these were during that period. Rigdon was also brought to court numerous times.

But the proverbial straw that broke the camel's back relating to the influence of Smith and Rigdon in the Kirtland community—and the whole Western Reserve for that matter—was the creation of the Kirtland Safety Society Bank. Organized on November 2, 1836, supposedly with the minimum capital of four million dollars, the bank was directed by Sidney Rigdon as its President and Joseph Smith as it cashier.[49] Even from the bank's inception, many people doubted the amounts claimed as backing. James Mathes was one of them:

> On Sunday Smith announced that it was the will of the Lord, that all Saints who had coin or current bank bills, no matter how much, or how little, should bring it to the Lord's bank, and exchange it for the Lord's money—bills of "The Kirtland Safety Bank." To induce them to do so, he announced that the bank had a paid up stock of one hundred thousand dollars. He had paid in thousands; so had others. The faithful obeyed the will of the Lord, of course. The coin was spread over the piglead in the boxes, and some of it and the currency displayed in the windows, and the Lord's bank began business with several thousand dollars, that had been lied out of the dupes through religious fanaticisms.[50]

Immediately upon its establishment, the bank dispatched Oliver Cowdery to Philadelphia to procure plates to print money, and Orson Hyde to Columbus for recognition of incorporation. Cowdery returned with the plates, but Hyde failed in his task, the Mormons claiming that, "because we were 'Mormons' the legislature raised some frivolous excuse on which they refused to grant us those banking privileges they so freely granted to others.[51] In actuality, this refusal does not necessarily seem to be a case of discrimination. In 1836 there were thirty-four petitions for additional banks in Ohio, and only one was approved—the bank of Manhattan in the newly established town of Toledo. "Wildcat" banks had become a problem with their insecure bank notes, and the Ohio legislature was being careful about expanding upon the thirty-one financially-sound banks already chartered by 1835.[52]

---

48 Parkin, p. 265, quoting The Journal of Discourses, Vol. VIII, p. 104. See Parkin's footnote 40 for elaboration.

49 Brodie, p. 194. James Mathes, in The Christian Record (p. 146), wrote that "in the winter beginning 1837, Smith and Rigdon *conceived* [italics mine] the idea of starting a bank." That date is too late. See Smith's History Of The Church, Vol. II, p. 467.

50 Mathes, pp. 146-7.

51 Joseph Smith, History Of The Church, Vol. II, p. 468.

52 Weisenberger, The Passing Of The Frontier, Vol. III, p.311.

There was a significant amount of initial apprehension about such a venture, both outside and even *inside* Mormon ranks. Rigdon, who usually supported Smith's ideas, was one who was apparently dubious. Wickliffe later asserted, "My father opposed it. He said it would not be legal as they had no charter and did not wish to have anything to do with it but J. S. thought differntly [sic] and persuaded father to sign bills as President and Joseph signed them as cashier."[53]

When the Ohio legislature refused to recognize the bank on January 1, 1837, the Prophet called a special meeting of the Kirtland Safety Society for the next day. On January 2, with Rigdon presiding, the society circumvented legalities by re-organizing as the Kirtland Safety Society *Anti-Banking Company*.[54] Having already gathered wealthy investors and printed the bank notes, the new company simply rubber-stamped the prefix "anti" and suffixes "ing" and "company" on each note and then circulated them.[55]

The bank was still operating illegally by an 1836 Ohio statute, and the name change did little to inspire the confidence of outsiders. The Cleveland Weekly Gazette reacted with indignation at what it considered to be a gross fraud, claiming that the bank's bills were backed only by *spiritual* collateral, and that this was the "kind of radicalism that would flourish better in Michigan than Ohio."[56] The newspaper also worried "that Rigdon, a notorious hypocrite and knave, is at the head of the concern[;] for ourselves, we are anxious to see some guaranty [sic] that there is good faith and property in this banking matter. . . ."[57]

But the Saints, confident in Joseph Smith's assertions that the bank had Divine blessings, optimistically invested their money into it. Not only did they believe it would flourish, but Smith believed his bank would eliminate all of its competition. In February of 1838, Warren Parrish, one of the bank's officers who later apostacized, wrote:

> I have listened to him with feelings of no ordinary kind, when he declared that the audible voice of God, instructed him to establish a Banking-Anti Banking institution, who like Aaron's rod shall swallow up all other banks (the Bank of Monroe excepted,) and grow and flourish and spread from the rivers to the ends of the earth, and survive when all others should be laid in ruins.[58]

---

53 John W. Rigdon typescript, p. 11.

54 Joseph Smith, History Of The Church, Vol. II, pp. 470-471.

55 Brodie, p. 196.

56 Fielding, p. 186, quoting The Cleveland Weekly Gazette, Vol. I, No. 3 (January 18, 1837) n.p.

57 Parkin, p. 219, quoting the same issue above. See also Van Wagoner, p. 185.

58 Ibid., p. 297, quoting The Painesville Telegraph, Vol. II, No. 15 (February 22, 1838), n.p. Eva Pancoast, in her Mormons At Kirtland (p. 180) refers to Eber D. Howe's offer in The Painesville Telegraph (April 7, 1837) to prove in court that Smith made this boast on an even earlier occasion as well.

The bank printed a large quantity of unsecured notes, and inflation ran rampant. Mathes wrote, "Of course, there was lots of money in Kirtland. Every man was lousy with it. . . .Everybody was rushing to Kirtland to sell anything and everything for enormous prices," he claimed. "Property of all kinds was changing hands at enormous figures and was continually going up higher. Everybody's pockets were bursting with money, and everything booming." One old citizen of Kirtland complained to Mathes, "They stole the country bare as far as they could travel and get back in a night's journey."[59]

Soon the bank began to be in crisis. It simply didn't have the backing it claimed, and it also kept printing too much money. On March 24, 1837, Rigdon, now treasurer, and Smith were sued by Samuel D. Rounds, a non-Mormon, and fined one thousand dollars plus court costs. Warren Parrish, having become the bank cashier, resigned and began to openly reveal questionable banking procedures by the Prophet:

> I have been astonished to hear him declare that we had sixty thousand dollars in specie in our vaults and six hundred thousand dollars at our command, when we had not to exceed six thousand dollars and could not command any more; also that we had but about ten thousand dollars of our bills in circulation when he, as cashier of that institution, knew that there was at least one hundred and fifty thousand dollars.[60]

Over-extended credit and real-estate speculation soared.[61] Suddenly reality hit and people tried to salvage their financial positions. They began exchanging the wildcat money for "sound money" at rates as high as five or ten dollars for one.[62] By May the panic of 1837 was being felt. In one month alone eight hundred other wildcat banks in America suspended operations. But the Kirtland bank actually kept issuing notes until June 29, when Rigdon was subpoenaed for printing worthless money.[63]

Joseph Smith claimed to have advised the bank officers on sound banking policies, but the officers would not harken to his financially inexperienced counsel. By the end of June, 1837, both Smith and Rigdon had resigned their positions at the bank. Smith claimed that the bank officers would not listen to the voice of God. Others alleged that the failure of the bank was due to bad business conditions in 1837. But Robert K. Fielding has expressed his opinion that "The Saints were not the victims of the folly of others, but of their own folly."[64] Van Wagoner

---

59 Mathes, pp. 147-149.

60 Brodie, p. 197, quoting his letter to <u>Zion's Watchman</u> (March 24, 1838).

61 For examples and details, see Parkin, p. 294.

62 Mathes, p. 147.

63 Brodie, p. 198.

64 Fielding, p. 203.

attributes much of the responsibility for the bank failure to Rigdon and Smith:

> Neither Joseph Smith nor Sidney Rigdon demonstrated at any time during their careers the financial acumen that became the hallmark of millionaire Brigham Young's thirty-year administration in the Rocky Mountain Basin. Joseph's and Sidney's fiscal ventures—first in Kirtland and later in Nauvoo, where both ultimately filed for bankruptcy—proved disastrous forays into high finance and real-estate management, areas in which they had little knowledge and less expertise. Rigdon's and Smith's implications that God devised their financial plans left no room for mistakes in the minds of followers who became disillusioned and antagonistic.[65]

Smith and Rigdon soon became *personae non grata* in the Western Reserve, not only with the population at large, but also with many of the Mormons themselves.[66] The year 1837 had been an exceedingly turbulent one for the Prophet and his "Mouthpiece." In June of 1837 Grandison Newell had taken Smith to court on a charge of hiring two men to kill him. Even though Smith was acquitted of the charge, the two men—named Denton and Davis—said they actually showed up to do the deed but Newell was not home. Nevertheless Smith had made a permanent enemy out of the saw mill and chair factory capitalist:

> Known as the "Mormon Persecutor," Newell did much to force the Mormons to leave Kirtland in 1838. He "blacklisted" them in his factories, and once accused Joseph Smith, Jr., the Mormon Prophet-leader, of attempted assassination. Grandison Newell confessed in his own papers that it cost him $1,000 to rid Geauga county of the "Mormon Menace."[67]

The year 1837 also saw the rise of a significant apostate mob which threatened the lives of Smith and Rigdon. Angry creditors besieged Smith with subpoenas, and Grandison Newell secured a warrant for Smith's arrest on the charge of banking fraud. Mormon dissenters seized control of the Kirtland temple, and the impending violence that loomed caused Joseph to conclude that it was unsafe to remain in Kirtland any longer. Carefully planning his exodus, he confidently comforted his worried friends and relatives, "one thing, brethren, is certain, I shall see you again, let what will happen, for I have a promise of life five years, and they cannot kill me until that time is expired."[68]

---

65 Van Wagoner, p. 177. For in depth analyses of the bank fiasco see Parkin, Ch. X; Brodie, Ch. XIV; Fielding, Ch. VIII; and Chase, Ch. IV.

66 The internal troubles of the Mormons will be discussed in the next chapter.

67 Harry F. Lupold, "Origin of Mentor Township" (a speech given to the Mentor Bicentennial Community Presentation Ceremony on June 4, 1975), published in The Historical Society Quarterly (Lake County, Ohio), Vol. 17, No. 3 (August, 1975), p. 3.

68 See Barrett, p. 355; Brodie, p. 207; and Lucy Mack Smith, pp. 247-248.

On the evening of January 12, 1838, a former friend of Joseph Smith's, who had joined the apostates, repented of his waywardness and warned Smith of a mob plot to assassinate him and Rigdon.[69] When the mob arrived at his home, Joseph had been nailed into a box, placed upon an ox cart, and spirited off into the woods where a friend of his waited with "Old Charlie," Smith's favorite horse. He and Rigdon then rode sixty miles to Norton Township in Medina County and waited for their families to join them.[70]

Many years later Rigdon's son John (Wickliffe) recalled the events of that night for posterity:

> I was attending school in [the] upper part [of the] temple when we left. On coming home from school in [the] afternoon of [the] day we left I saw considerable commotion about my fathers home. I inquired of my mother what was [the] reason. She said "Nothing that concerned me." In [the] evening I saw several men come to our house and whisper a time (?) and go away. I wanted to know of mother what was the trouble but could get no reply; and was at last ordered to bed. And I and brother Sidney went to bed. Along in [the] night [I] was awakened by [a] man trying [a] pair [of] shoes on my feet. I asked what he was doing. He said he had gotten me [a] new pair [of] shoes. I said that was all right, but had he not better wait till morning then I could try them on better. He said, "You go to sleep and don't ask questions." I did so. Not long after that my brother and I were awakened and told to dress as we were going away. I asked where we were going, and he said to a land flowing with milk and honey that I had heard talked so much about. Well, I thought if I was going to that land which was flowing with milk and honey it was a pretty good place for me to go. And I wanted to go.[71]

Riding in an open lumber wagon all night long, the family stopped for breakfast at a hotel near Akron, according to Wickliffe's memory. After meeting up with his father and Smith, they then journeyed to Dublin, Indiana.

But the trip was not without peril. Their enemies pursued them for two hundred miles, determined to over take them. Smith later recorded their harrowing close calls:

> The weather was extremely cold, we were obliged to secrete ourselves in our wagons, sometimes to elude the grasp of our pursuers, who continued their pursuit of us more than two hundred miles from Kirtland, armed

---

69 Barrett (p. 355), among others, gives this account, but Joseph's mother, Lucy (p. 248) prefers a more theological version of the occasion, claiming that Joseph "was warned by the Spirit to make his escape."

70 Ibid. See also Van Wagoner, p. 211, and Fielding, p. 282.

71 John Wickliffe Rigdon typescript, p. 12.

with pistols and guns, seeking our lives. They frequently crossed our track, twice they were in the houses where we stopped, once we tarried all night in the same house with them, with only a partition between us and them; and heard their oaths and imprecations, and threats concerning us, if they could catch us; and late in the evening they came into our room and examined us, but decided we were not the men. At other times we passed them in the streets, and gazed upon them, and they on us, but they knew us not.[72]

Smith and Rigdon would never return to the Western Reserve. Instead, they journeyed to Caldwell County, Missouri, where they attempted to relocate their "stake" in a settlement called "Far West." Persecution would follow them there, as well. But external dangers were not the only troubles they faced. Internal dissension was beginning to threaten the essential fabric of the Church.

---

72   Joseph Smith, <u>History of The Church</u>, Vol. III, p. 2-3.

Chapter
—13—

DISENCHANTED RESTORATIONISM - DISILLUSIONMENT AND INTERNAL DISSENSIONS

It may be legitimately argued that the threat of destruction to the Mormon restoration movement crested in the years from 1836 through 1844. It was hard enough fending off the ominous attacks from outside the ranks. But when *internal* dissensions began to appear in significant numbers, the perpetuation of Mormonism became even more precarious.

At least three main issues were responsible for the creation of disgruntled followers during this period: 1) The idea and practice of "plural marriage;" 2) the failures of the Kirtland banking effort; 3) the increasingly authoritarian posture of Joseph Smith. Without doubt, this author admits that there were other issues that alienated some. But the most extensive reactions seemed to have rooted in one or all of these three.

The idea of plural marriage—which was openly promulgated by Brigham Young, who had twenty-seven wives and fifty-six children—was originated and secretly practiced by Joseph Smith.[1] Back in August of 1831 Smith had responded to instances of sexual immorality among the Saints with a vision, part of which read:

> And verily I say unto you, as I have said before, he that looketh on a woman to lust after her, or if any shall commit adultery in their hearts,

---

1   Back in 1968 Max Parkin in his <u>Conflict At Kirtland</u> (p. 174) rather timidly offered his opinion that "It *appears* [italics mine] that polygamy was a secret practice in Kirtland in the 1830's. . . ." But by 1994, with a greater coalescence of Mormon primary sources, Richard S. Van Wagoner (p. 293) could confidently assert, "A multitude of Mormon records provides irrefutable evidence for Smith's prerogative with an array of women, many of them just a few years older than his own children." For a listing of "The Plural Wives of Joseph Smith," see Fawn Brodie, Appendix C (pp. 434-465).

they shall not have the Spirit, but shall deny the faith and shall fear: wherefore, I, the Lord, have said that. . . whosoever loveth and maketh a lie, and the whoremonger, . . .shall have their part in that lake which burneth with fire and brimstone, which is the second death.[2]

Yet Smith's covert sexual escapades became so well known by some of the leaders that open opposition fomented among a few of them. During the lifetime of "the Prophet" many charges of "extra-marital romantic liaisons" were leveled at him. His celeritous departure from Harmony, Pennsylvania, in 1830, was attributed to sexual overtures he allegedly made to a local girl named Eliza Winters.[3] But one of the more infamous of such episodes occurred in 1834 with a young lady named Fanny Ward Alger. While evidence and testimonials from Miss Alger, a young lady named Fanny Brewer, Martin Harris, and even Emma Smith herself, seemed to substantiate the validity of the occurrence, Oliver Cowdery in 1837, openly charged Smith with adulteress relations with her—a complaint which seems to have facilitated Cowdery's excommunication in 1838.[4]

In a letter to Oliver Cowdery written in 1834, Joseph Smith openly admitted that "I do not, nor never have, pretended to be any other than a man 'subject to passion,' and liable, without the assisting grace of the Savior, to deviate from that perfect path in which all men are commanded to walk!"[5] But privately Smith believed that polygamous relationships were sanctioned by the Old Testament and through personal revelation. He once confessed to Brigham Young that if he were to reveal all that the Lord had revealed to him his followers would all desert him.[6]

This tension perpetrated a sort of double life for Smith. His public posture was to oppose polygamy. As editor of the Elders' Journal in 1838, Smith responded to the question, "Do the Mormons believe in having more wives than one?", with the answer, "No, not at the same time."[7] And again, in 1843, Joseph forbade the practice of plural marriage with the injunction that "No man shall have more than one wife."[8]

---

2   Joseph Smith, Doctrine and Covenants, Section 63: 5 a & b.

3   Van Wagoner, p. 291. For a more thorough discussion of this topic, read all of chapter 21, entitled "Between Family and Friends."

4   See Parkin's description, p. 166. See also Fawn Brodie, p. 182, for Fanny Alger's statement.

5   Joseph Smith, Messenger And Advocate, Vol. I, No. 3 (December, 1834), p. 40.

6   Max Parkin, p. 166, applies this reference in the Journal of Discourses, No. IX, p. 294, to Smith's perspective on plural marriage.

7   Joseph Smith, The Elders' Journal (Far West, Missouri), Vol. I, No. III (July, 1838), p. 43.

8   Faulring, p. 417. According to Van Wagoner, pp. 303 and 304 (footnote 17), under Brigham Young's direction at a later date the church altered Smith's statement deleting ten words and adding forty-nine others. As the statement now reads, Smith supposedly qualified his response to read, "No man shall have more than one wife, *unless the Lord directs otherwise.*" [italics mine].

Yet the actual practices of his private life engendered resentment. Gossip circulated widely about a proposition Joseph Smith made to Sidney Rigdon's sixteen-year-old daughter Nancy, a rumor given much credence by Nancy's and Sidney's reactions, which will be discussed later in this chapter. And in 1843, Smith apparently promised Helen Mar Kimball, the fifteen-year-old daughter of Mormon Apostle Heber C. Kimball, that, if she "sealed" with him, her eternal salvation would be assured, along with those of all her relatives. In a letter to be opened only after her death, she admitted, "I willingly gave myself to purchase so glorious a reward."[9] Mr. Van Wagoner has acknowledged the skill with which Smith, by then living in Nauvoo, Illinois, was concealing his hypocrisy:

> And while the Prophet now stands astride the Mormon world like a colossus, in Nauvoo he maneuvered within the charisma of his own mystique to defy both church, Nauvoo City, and Illinois marriage laws, as well as to conceal his behavior from his wife Emma. This equivocal deportment, secreted by a deferential and circumspect group of men and women, created two cultures in Nauvoo—one where monogamy and fidelity prevailed—the other where Eros and duplicity seemed to subvert the highest moral values, and where exonerating the "Lord's Anointed" became more important than telling the truth.[10]

The second area which spawned a large amount of resentment involved the operation of the bank in Kirtland, which left a legacy of destitution and bitterness among many of the Saints in Kirtland. One who was especially hurt, angry, and eventually outspoken, was Parley Pratt, the man who had led Rigdon to Mormonism. On May 23, 1837, Pratt wrote a letter to Smith chastising him for his foolish property speculation and accusing him of impropriety. A rather long, but expressive and revealing, excerpt reads:

> Having long pondered the path in which we as a people, have been led in regard to our temporal management, I have at length become fully convinced that the whole scheme of speculation in which we have been engaged, is of the devil. I allude to the covetous, extortionary speculating spirit which has reigned in this place for the last season; which has given rise to lying, deceiving and taking advantage of one's neighbor, and in short, every evil work.

---

9   Van Wagoner, p. 293, quoting Helen Mar Kimball. See p. 306, footnote 31.

10 Van Wagoner, p. 293. Eva Pancoast (p. 111) states that "Legally, Kirtland saints and Joseph Smith never practiced it [polygamy]. Historically they undoubtedly did." Paul Conkin (pp. 196 and 198) observed that "Smith seemed. . . .to let sexual lust take control of his life," and that Emma was "very distressed and angry" with him for his affairs with other women. Barrett (p. 526) tells of Emma's sharp reaction to Joseph's revelation regarding "celestial marriage;" and Van Wagoner (p. 306) relates a discussion in which Emma years later, after finding out that her husband had not ended his liaisons as she had thought, snapped at Joseph W. Coolidge, "Then he was worthy of the death he died."

And being as fully convinced that you, and President Rigdon, both by precept and example, have been the principle means in leading this people astray, in these particulars, and having myself been led astray and caught in the same snare by your example, and by false prophesying and preaching, from your own mouths, yea, having done many things wrong and plunged myself and family, and others, well nigh into destruction, I have awoke to an awful sense of my situation, and now resolve to retrace my steps and get out of this snare, and make restitution as far as I can.

And now dear brother, if you are still determined to pursue this wicked course, until yourself and the church shall sink down to hell, I beseech you at least, to have mercy on me and my family, and others who are bound with me for those three lots (of land) which you sold to me at the extortionary price of 2000 dollars, which never cost you 100 dollars. For if it stands against me it will ruin me and my helpless family, ... [11]

The letter was obtained by and published in the Zion's Watchman, much to Pratt's chagrin. He had intended the letter, it seems, to remain private. Such severe and open criticism by one of the Saints, could not, of course, be tolerated. In August of 1838, under pressure from both church and private conscience, Pratt published a penitent retraction of his attack on Smith and Rigdon. After contending that the printed letter was not a true copy of the one he wrote, and that he was unduly severe and harsh in his censorship due to his heightened state of emotions, Pratt expressed his entire confidence in the Latter-day Saints' faith, and insisted:

I did not however believe at the time and never have believed at any time before, or since, that these men were dishonest or had wrong motives or intentions, in any of their undertakings, either temporal or spiritual; I have ever esteemed them from my first acquaintance, as men of God, and as mighty instruments in his hands to bring forth, establish, and roll on the kingdom of God. But I considered them like other men, and as the prophet and apostles of old liable to errors, and mistakes, in things which were not inspired from heaven; but managed by their own judgment. . . .

I no longer censure them for any thing that is past, but I censure myself for rashness, excitement, imprudence, and many faults which I would to God, that I had avoided. But this much I can say that the time past can only teach us to be more wise for the future. I close this communication by saying that from 1830 until now, I have had full confidence in the book of Mormon, the Revelations of God to Joseph Smith Jr., and I still esteem both him and President Rigdon, as men of the highest integrity, the most exalted principles of virtue and honor, and men who will yet be instruments in the Lord's hand to accomplish a work in which I shall esteem it the highest honor and the greatest blessing to bear some humble part.[12]

11   A copy of this letter, printed originally in the Zion's Watchman, may be found in Parkin, Appendix E, p. 372; and also in Van Wagoner, p. 195.

12   Parley Pratt, "To The Public," The Elders' Journal, Vol. I, No. 4 (August, 1838), pp. 50-51.

However, Pratt was not the only plaintiff. Warren Parrish—the bank's teller, and later cashier—was also vocal in his public charges, as were such other significant leaders as Fredrick Williams, Orson Pratt, Lymon Johnson, and David Whitmer. For a short time Smith was so upset that he was physically incapacitated. Rigdon tried to deflect some of the blame toward himself, but soon both circled the wagons and readied a counter-offensive, blaming especially Parrish and Williams for the bank failure. The church council could not determine whom to proceed against, and so it adjourned in confusion.

The third arena of contention involved the personal authority of Joseph Smith himself. In the earlier years Smith was still, of course, the Revelator. But political power was somewhat diffused among the First Presidency and the Council of Elders. One might successfully argue that the power structure did not change essentially during Smith's later years. But there were those that disagreed, or at least came to believe that he had too much power. Most adherents, of course, seemed to believe that no one had the right to question his prophecies or his decisions. He was, after all, directly responsible only to God. But eventually a large minority began to question his fallibility, and even, as in the case of Rigdon later, his ascendency.

Many instances of Smith's authoritarian comportment could be cited here, but a few should suffice to make the point. In July of 1837, Warren Cowdery, Oliver's brother, who by then had become the editor of the Latter-day Saints' <u>Messenger and Advocate</u>, shocked many with a critical essay concerning the bank and those who controlled and operated it. After rehearsing a history of the bank and its failures, he proceeded to discuss the reasons for inequality and oppression among people. In a semi-veiled allusion to the Prophet, he warned his readers:

> If we give all our privileges to one man, we virtually give him our money and our liberties, and make him a monarch, absolute and despotic, and ourselves abject slaves or fawning sycophants. . . whenever a people have unlimited confidence in a civil or eclesiastical [sic] ruler or rulers, who are but men like themselves, and begin to think they can do no wrong, they increase their tyrany [sic], and oppression, establish a principle that man, poor frail lump of mortality like themselves, is infallible. Who does not see a principle of popery and religious tyranny involved in such [an] order of things? Who is worthy [of] the name of a freeman, who thus tamely surrenders, the rights and privileges, and immunities of an indepebdant [sic] citizen?[13]

The article proved to be the death knell of the <u>Messenger and Advocate</u>. In the next issue, Rigdon announced that the journal would

---

13   Warren Cowdery, ed., <u>Messenger and Advocate</u>, Vol. III, No. 10 (July, 1837), p. 538.

terminate with the September issue, and that it would be supplanted by a new periodical edited by Joseph Smith himself. It was to be called the Elders' Journal, with a subscription price of two dollars a year.[14]

In March of 1831 Joseph Smith was given a revelation in which God willed that John Whitmer keep a history of the Latter-day Saints.[15] Whitmer preferred not to do it, but relented to the desire of God.[16] In November of the same year the Lord reaffirmed his wish to have Whitmer record the history for posterity:

> . . .wherefore I, the Lord, will that my servant John Whitmer. . . shall continue in writing and making a history of all the important things which he shall observe and know concerning my church;

> . . .which shall be for the good of the church, and for the rising generations, that shall grow up on the land of Zion, to possess it from generation to generation, forever and ever.[17]

Yet by April of 1838 neither Smith nor Rigdon were satisfied with its content. Seemingly trumping God's commandment, Smith and Rigdon informed Whitmer that he was a poor historian and that they would prevent the publication of his chronicle unless certain "corrections" were made. The letter read simply:

> Mr. John Whitmer, sir: We were desirous of honoring you by giving publicity to your notes on the history of the Church of Latter-day Saints, after making such corrections as we thought would be necessary, knowing your incompetency as a historian, and that writings coming from your pen, could not be put to press without our correcting them, or else the Church must suffer reproach. Indeed, sir, we never supposed you capable of writing a history, but were willing to let it come out under your name, notwithstanding it would really not be yours but ours. We are still willing to honor you, if you can be made to know your own interest, and give up your notes, so that they can be corrected and made fit for press; but if not, we have all the materials for another, which we shall commence this week to write.[18]

---

14   Sidney Rigdon, "Prospectus," Messenger and Advocate, Vol. III, No. 2 (August, 1837), pp. 545-547. The article was re-run in Vol. III, No. 3 (September, 1837), pp. 571-574.

15   Joseph Smith, Doctrine and Covenants, Section 47: 1 (p. 114).

16   John Whitmer, Whitmer's History, Ch. VI, p. 4.

17   Joseph Smith, Doctrine and Covenants, Section 69: 1-2 (p. 162). This revelation is also reproduced on the front of Whitmer's history.

18   Whitmer, introductory page. A copy of the letter may also be found in Joseph Smith's History of the Church, Vol. III, pp. 15-16, and Faulring, p. 171. Whitmer retained his original manuscript and, years later, it came into possession of the R.L.D.S. church, which published all but the last three chapters in its 1908 Journal History (the last three chapters discuss polygamy and secret organizations within the church). See the reproduction of Whitmer's history by Jerald and Sandra Tanner for further explanation.

As early as the fall of 1836, according to Whitmer, Rigdon and Smith had, "by secret plots and midnight machinations," begun to form a covert society of men who would become the enforcement arm of their edicts and desires.[19] This secret brotherhood became known as "the Danites," a name chosen from Genesis 49: 16-17, in which the tribe of Dan was prophesied to "judge his people" and to "be a serpent in the way, a viper by the path, that bites the horse's heels, so that his rider falls backward [RSV]." Publicly Smith and Rigdon denied any direct connection with the group led by a man named Sampson Avard, but the society's constitution was said to be written by Rigdon himself.[20] In a portion of the secret oath later revealed by Avard, each inductee swore to "regard the First President of the Church of Jesus Christ of Latter Day Saints, as the supreme head of the Church on earth, and obey him the same as the supreme God," and to "always uphold the Presidency, right or wrong."[21]

Concern for such high handed and coercive tactics was expressed by Oliver Cowdery in February of 1838 in a letter to his brothers Warren and Lyman:

> The radical principles taught my Messrs. Smith and Rigdon here [are] subversion of the liberties of the whole church. . . . I told them if I had property, while I live and was sane, I would not be dictated, influenced, or controlled by any man or set of men, by no tribunal of ecclesiastical pretenses whatsoever. . . . My soul is sick of such scrambling for power and self-aggrandisement. . . . I came to this country to enjoy peace. If I cannot I shall go where I can.[22]

Mr. Van Wagoner, Rigdon's most recent and thorough biographer, concluded the following concerning the authoritarian pall that had descended upon the church by 1838: "During Mormonism's early years, when Cowdery was second elder, the church had been characterized by democratic vigor. In the turmoil of 1838, whatever egalitarian style existed was supplanted by a command-and-compliance culture."[23]

Division in the camp ripened into insubordination within the ranks. According to Lucy Mack Smith, Joseph had prophesied the coming of a

---

19 Whitmer, p. 24.

20 Van Wagoner, p. 217. See also McKiernan, p. 162. Credible witnesses counter Smith's and Rigdon's denial of involvement (see especially footnote 30).

21 Ibid., p. 224, footnote 26.

22 From the "Oliver Cowdery Letterbook," January 30, 1838, Huntington Library, San Marino, California; quoted in Van Wagoner, p. 215.

23 Van Wagoner, p. 215.

great apostasy.[24] Back in April of 1837, the Mormon leaders were indebted to non-Mormon individuals and businesses for an amount surpassing $150,000, an imposing sum in those days.[25] Smith addressed a church conference regarding the matter and uttered the following plea and promise: "our brethren abroad have only to come with their money, take these contracts, relieve their brethren from the pecuniary embarrassments under which they now labor, and procure for themselves a peaceable place of rest among us."[26] But the response was meager and unenthusiastic, and some began to desert the faith. Eventually, at least six of the twelve Apostles rebelled. Smith described the unraveling situation in his <u>History of the Church</u>:

> . . .evil surmisings, fault-finding, disunion, dissension, and apostasy followed in quick succession, and it seemed as though all the powers of earth and hell were combining their influence in an especial manner to overthrow the Church at once, and make a final end. . . .
>
> No quorum in the Church was entirely exempt from the influence of those false spirits who are striving against me for the mastery; even some of the Twelve were so far lost to their high and responsible calling, as to begin to take sides, secretly, with the enemy.[27]

Among those prominent in the rebellion were Frederick Williams, the First Counselor to Joseph Smith, and Warren Parrish, the bank teller who eventually became Smith's successor as cashier after "the Prophet's" resignation. Shortly after the inception of the bank, in the fall of 1836, Joseph allegedly discovered a large amount of money missing from the bank and petitioned Williams for a search warrant. For some reason Williams denied him the warrant, and was relieved of his position by Smith.[28] Later on, Warren Parrish was accused of embezzling twenty-five thousand dollars from the bank, after he had openly criticized Smith's banking procedures.[29] Parrish was furious, and on a Sunday when Joseph

---

24 Lucy Mack Smith, <u>History of Joseph Smith</u>, p. 241.

25 Brodie, p. 202.

26 Warren Cowdery, ed., quoting Joseph Smith in "Anniversary of The Church of The Latter-Day Saints," <u>The Messenger and Advocate</u>, Vol. III, No. 7 (April, 1837), p. 488.

27 Joseph Smith, <u>History of the Church</u>, Vol. II, pp. 487-488.

28 Lucy Mack Smith, pp. 240-241. Yet just three years earlier Smith had testified that "Brother Frederick G. Williams is one of those men in whom I place the greatest confidence and trust, for I have found him ever full of love and brotherly kindness. He is not a man of many words, but is ever winning, because of his constant mind. He shall ever have a place in my heart, and is ever entitled to my confidence. He is perfectly honest and upright, and seeks with all his heart to magnify his Presidency in the Church of Christ." [Joseph Smith, <u>History of The Church</u>, Vol. I, p. 444.].

29 Brodie, p. 198. Fawn Brodie astutely points out that if Parrish had in fact done so, he must have taken some virtually worthless bank notes; otherwise, that amount in the vault would have rescued the bank during Joseph Smith's tenure as cashier.

Jr. was absent and Joseph Sr. preached to the people, the latter made reference to the whole bank affair "reflecting somewhat sharply" on Parrish. According to the recollections of "the Prophet's" mother:

> Although the reflection was just, Parrish was highly incensed and made an attempt to drag him out of the stand. My husband appealed to Oliver Cowdery, who was justice of the peace, to have him brought to order, but Oliver never moved from his seat. William, seeing the abuse which his father was receiving, sprang forward and caught Parrish, and carried him in his arms nearly out of the house. At this John Boynton stepped forward, and drawing a sword from his cane, presented it to William's breast, and said, "if you advance one step further, I will run you through." Before William had time to turn himself several gathered around him, threatening to handle him severely, if he should lay the weight of his finger upon Parrish again. At this juncture of affairs, I left the house, not only terrified at the scene, but likewise sick at heart, to see that the apostasy of which Joseph had prophesied was so near at hand.[30]

In May and June of 1837 the disaffection increased. The apostates began to gather frequently in the temple [see Figure 9] to murmur against the prophet. On one of these occasions, when Smith was absent, Parrish vigorously slandered his character. In his attacks "he was warmly sustained by many of those present."[31] A proposal was actually made before the Council to have Joseph Smith deposed as First President and be replaced by

Figure 9.   The Kirtland Temple (Dedicated March 27, 1836) (From http://solo21.abac.com/frodsham.)

---

30   Lucy Mack Smith, p. 241. The scene is also described in Fielding, p. 250.

31   B.H. Roberts' notes, <u>History of The Church</u>, Vol. II, p. 489. See also an account in Fielding, p. 248.

David Whitmer. But a sterling rebuttal led by Brigham Young stifled the effort, and Smith retained his position.[32]

However such hostility needed to be deflected, and Smith was "led" to a clever solution. "In this state of things, and but a few weeks before the Twelve were expecting to meet in full quorum," he later recalled, "God revealed to me that something new must be done for the salvation of His Church." That "something" resulted from a suggestion by Heber C. Kimball, one of the Twelve Apostles, that a Latter-day Saint missionary enterprise be established in England. Kimball would preside over the effort and an entourage of Mormon leaders would accompany him. He was then given a formal blessing and ordained for the work by the First Presidency.[33]

Not only was much attention displaced to the new and ambitious effort, but Eva Pancoast has maintained that some of Smith's loudest opponents were intentionally sent away as missionaries as well.[34] On the day of their departure (June 13), Smith was too ill to be present for the send off.[35] But John F. Boynton, one of the disgruntled Saints, apparently saw the mission as a diversion for the resistance to "the Prophet" and chastised Kimball saying, "If you are such a d__d fool as to go to the call of the fallen Prophet, Joseph Smith, I will not help you a dime." Kimball, a supporter of Smith, seemed to confirm the widespread alienation of many Latter-day Saints when he declared that, at the time, there "were not twenty persons on the earth that would declare that Joseph Smith was a Prophet of God."[36]

On July 27, Smith—along with Sidney Rigdon and Thomas Marsh— left on a five-week missionary journey to Toronto, Canada, probably hoping that hostilities would subside by the time of his return.[37] But it would not be so. The spiritual ideals of restorationism were becoming buried in a mound of political intrigue and infighting. On one Sunday morning Parrish led a group of dissenters into the temple armed with pistols and Bowie knives. Eliza Snow gave an account of what eventuated:

> Soon after the usual opening services, one of the brethren on the west stand arose, and just after he commenced to speak, one on the east interrupted him. Father Smith, presiding, called to order—he told the

---

32 See Parkin, pp. 311-312. In a footnote (no. 74) Parkin speculates that the choice of David Whitmer as Smith's legitimate successor may have been made on the basis of his ordination by Smith in July of 1834 while in Missouri.

33 Joseph Smith, <u>History of The Church</u>, Vol. II, p. 489.

34 Pancoast, p. 191.

35 See Joseph Smith, <u>History of The Church</u>, Vol. II, pp. 492-493, for greater detail.

36 See quotes in Parkin, p. 312.

37 Fawn Brodie (p. 204) places the time of his departure as "mid-July," but Ivan Barrett (p. 350) lists the specific date as July 27, probably based upon the date given by Smith in his <u>History of The Church</u>, Vol. II, p. 502. I see no reason to doubt this date.

apostate brother that he should have all the time he wanted, but he must wait his turn—as the brother on the west took the floor and commenced to speak, he must not be interrupted. A fearful scene ensued—the apostate speaker became so clamorous, that Father Smith called for the police to take that man out of the house, when Parrish, John Boynton, and others, drew their pistols and bowie-knives, and rushed down from the stand into the congregation; J. Boynton saying he would blow out the brains of the first man who dared to lay hands on him. Many in the congregation, especially women and children, were terribly frightened—some tried to escape from the confusion by jumping out of the windows. Amid screams and shrieks, the policemen, in ejecting the belligerents, knocked down a stove-pipe, which fell helter-skelter among the people; but, although bowie-knives and pistols were wrested from their owners, and thrown hither and thither to prevent disastrous results, no one was hurt, and after a short, but terrible scene to be enacted in a Temple of God, order was restored, and the services of the day proceeded as usual.[38]

At the end of August, 1837, when Smith returned to Kirtland, he found a divided church. Even the three original witnesses to the authenticity of the Book of Mormon had revolted, deserting him to pledge allegiance to a new young prophetess who claimed that she could see the future through a black stone. Frederick Williams became her scribe, as she prophesied the demise of Smith due to his transgressions. Either Martin Harris or David Whitmer was to succeed him.[39]

Smith knew it was time for a critical confrontation. A conference was scheduled for September 3 to be held in the Temple. Before that Occasion David Whitmer and Oliver Cowdery were rehabilitated to the Mormon fold and, though only partially contrite and still somewhat suspicious, they were sent off to Missouri. Martin Harris was excommunicated.[40] Anticipating that the rest of the apostate party would attend in full force, Brigham Young rallied Smith's supporters earlier in the day. At the conclusion of the conference, Smith and Rigdon had been retained in their positions, and Frederick Williams was dismissed from his.

On September 27 Joseph once again felt secure enough to pay a return visit to the Saints in Missouri. But his sense of security proved to be an illusion. Once again apostasy revived, and this time the dissenters secured their power. With a new air of confidence and freedom came some radical reaction as well. At one of their gatherings, four men declared the Book of Mormon to be utter nonsense. One member of "the Parrish party" went so far as to declare that "Moses was a rascal, the Prophets were tyrants,

---

38　Parkin, pp. 315-316. Barrett also narrates the story on p. 351 of his book.

39　See Brodie, p. 205, and Lucy Mack Smith, pp. 241-242.

40　Brodie, p. 205.

Jesus Christ was a despot, Paul was a liar, and all religion was a fudge." Apparently Parrish admitted that he agreed with his friend "in principle."[41]

But most seemed more intent on a restoration of what they believed to be sound doctrine and practice. Warren Cowdery and Martin Harris joined a burgeoning group calling themselves "The Old Standard."[42] Their plea included a reiteration of the need for repentance and baptism for the forgiveness of sins, and a re-emphasis upon the unity of Christendom. However it excluded the authority of Joseph Smith and the Book of Mormon.[43]

On December 10 Smith once again arrived back in Kirtland, and called for a public trial. But this time things were different. The opposition party was now strong, having expelled many elders, including Brigham Young, from Kirtland. A sick Rigdon mustered his energy for an eloquent and emotional plea, but it proved to be of no avail. Smith had lost control, and when Grandison Newell had pursued an arrest warrant for him on charges of fraudulent banking, Smith and Rigdon fled Kirtland for the last time.[44] Smith recorded in his journal:

> January: 1838—a new year dawned upon the Church in Kirtland in all the bitterness of the spirit of apostate mobocracy; which continued to rage and grow hotter and hotter, until Elder Rigdon and myself were obliged to flee from its deadly influence, as did the Apostles and Prophets of old, and as Jesus said, "when they persecute in one city, flee to another."[45]

The toll exacted on Kirtland as a loyal stake for the new Zion was expensive. In the seven months following November of 1837 around three hundred Kirtland Mormons, constituting about fifteen percent of all the Latter-day Saints everywhere at the time, either left the Mormon church or were excommunicated. This number included almost one-third of the church leaders, all three witnesses to the Book of Mormon, four members of the Quorum of Twelve, three former and three current presidents of the Seventy, and Frederick Williams, a member of the First Presidency.[46]

PERSECUTIONS AND TURNCOATS AT FAR WEST (1838-1839)

Dissension followed Smith and Rigdon to Missouri. Rigdon's frustrations with persecution and sedition led him to become increasingly more violent

---

41 Barrett, p. 353.

42 Fielding, p. 279.

43 Barrett, p. 353.

44 Brodie, pp. 206-207. Three days after they fled, the Kirtland printing office burned to the ground. Parrish accused Smith of having it done in order to prevent opposition and fulfill a prophecy of destruction.

45 Quoted in Werner, p. 94.

46 Van Wagoner, p. 187.

in the years from 1838 to 1844. At first, according to Sidney Rigdon's sworn testimony, when he arrived at Far West in Caldwell County on April 4th, 1838, he enjoyed a few months of relative peace and quiet.[47] Yet the Mormons in Missouri had for some time already been undergoing persecutions, and Rigdon grew impatient to help them. In a revelation given back on February 24, 1834, the Lord had allegedly commanded Joseph Smith and the Mormons to "avenge me of mine enemies," and that "It is my will that my Servant Sidney Rigdon shall lift up his voice in the congregations. . . ."[48]

On June 17 or 19,[49] 1838, Rigdon delivered his now famous "Salt Sermon," based upon the text of Matthew 5:13: "Ye are the salt of the earth, but if the salt hath lost its savor, wherewith shall the earth be salted? It is hence forth good for nothing but to be cast out and trodden under the foot of man."

Both Smith and Rigdon had determined, due to much ill treatment received lately from dissenters and apostates, to eradicate heresy. As Sidney spoke he grew more and more infuriated, warning the dissenters that they "would eventually be trodden under foot until their bowels gushed out."[50] He even offered the crowd his assistance "to trample down or erect a gallows on the square of Far West and hang them up..."[51]

Joseph Smith followed Rigdon with a short speech of agreement saying that "any person who spoke or acted against the presidency or the church. . .should lose their heads." When George Harris, a member of the High Council tried to mollify Smith's harsh statement, and when Smith then agreed that he really meant "the heads of their influence," Rigdon repudiated the moderation and asserted that, "He [Smith] meant the ball on their shoulders, called the head."[52]

---

47 B.H. Roberts' inclusion, "Testimony of Sidney Rigdon," History of The Church, Vol. III, p. 449.

48 Joseph Smith, Doctrine and Covenants, Section 100: 5c and 6b (p. 245)

49 Fawn Brodie (p. 217) and Richard S. Van Wagoner (p. 217) have listed the earlier date for the occasion; while F. Mark McKiernan (p. 85), probably based upon John Whitmer's history (p. 22), prefers the date of June 19. William Brodie Crouch in his The Myth of Mormon Inspiration (p. 85), along with M.R. Werner (p. 101), both erroneously equate Rigdon's Salt Sermon with his Fourth of July Sermon, which was given the following month.

50 Newell Bringhurst, Brigham Young And The Expanding American Frontier, (Boston and Toronto: Little, Brown, and Company, 1986), p. 36.

51 Brodie, p. 218.

52 John Whitmer, sworn statement before Judge Austin King at Richmond, Missouri, in November, 1838; quoted in McKiernan, p. 86. See also Alexander Campbell's commentary on the event and statements made in his article entitled "Mormonism" in the Millennial Harbinger, Vol. VII, No. 1 (January, 1843), pp. 24-25.

Nevertheless, Cowdery, Phelps, and the Whitmers, who were some of the leading dissenters, stubbornly refused to depart. They remained in Missouri to plea their cause until Rigdon sent them a threatening letter signed by eighty-three prominent Mormons. It read in part:

> . . .Whereas the citizens of Caldwell County have born with the abuse received from you at different times, and on different occasions, until it is no longer to be endured. . .out of the county you shall go, and no power shall save you. And you shall have three days after you receive this communication, including twenty-four hours in each day, for you to depart with your families peaceable; which you may do undisturbed by any person; but in that time, if you do not depart, we will use the means in our power to cause you to depart, for go you shall. . . .[53]

Joseph Smith dramatized the results of the warning in two simple sentences: "These men took warning and soon they were seen bounding over the prairie like the scape Goat to carry of [f] their own sins. We have not seen them since."[54]

Almost three weeks later Rigdon was in even more of a fighting mood, but this time he was warning the mobs of anti-Mormons who kept raiding Mormon settlements. In the second of his famous speeches, known as his Fourth of July Sermon, he defined the contest:

> We take God and all the holy angels to witness this day, that we warn all men, in the name of Jesus Christ, to come on us no more forever. The man, or the set of men, who attempts it, does it at the expense of their lives. And that mob that comes to us to disturb us, it shall be between us and them a war of extermination; for we will follow them till the last drop of their blood is spilled, or else they will carry the seat of war to their own houses and their own families, and one party or another shall be utterly destroyed. Remember it, then, all men. . .We this day, then, proclaim ourselves free, with a purpose and a determination than can never be broken. No never! NO NEVER!! <u>NO NEVER!!!</u>[55]

Needless to say, such warnings do not usually bring about peace, but the "sword," in tense situations. The catalyst for armed conflict proved to

---

53 See Brodie, pp. 218-219.

54 Faulring, p. 187.

55 Extracts from a pamphlet entitled <u>Mormonism Exposed</u>, published in Alexander Campbell's <u>Millennial Harbinger</u>, Vol. VII, No. VII (July, 1843), pp. 296-297. For various reactions to his speech see Pratt's <u>Autobiography</u> (Ch. 21), Swartzell (pp. 16-17), Brodie (pp. 222-224), and Faulring (p. 186). Van Wagoner (p. 221) quotes Emily Austin as saying that, after that speech, "Rigdon's life could not have been insured for five coppers [pennies]." Rigdon's own son later admitted (typescript, p. 15): "This should not in my opinion have been said. It only excited the mind of the Mo. It was reprinted that he had threatened to commence a war of extermination against [the Missourians]."

be the August 6 election for Daviess County Sheriff. A mob was determined to prevent the Mormons from voting. Names and accusations were exchanged, brawls ensued, calls to arms were given, and "The Mormon War" began. Rigdon, in dramatic fashion grabbed a sword and shouted, *"we will bathe our swords in the vital blood of the Missourians or die in the attempt!"*[56] Some Mormons, seeing what was about to take place, abandoned what they believed to be a lost cause. William Swartzell wrote:

> My eyes were opened; the scales dropped off; and I began to view things more correctly than ever. I concluded that I had been fed on such stuff long enough; the idea of such a band attacking a State which could call to its aid twenty-five other free and independent sovereignties, more densely populated than itself, was preposterous. God (thought I) can have no dealings with this people, who have been led away by imposters; and I, for one, will leave them to their fate.[57]

By this time the Mormons had efficiently and secretly organized the Danites into a military defense force. For security reasons, no member was to reveal anything about the aims or make-up of this group. But such notable leaders as Thomas Marsh (at one time president of the Council of Twelve Apostles), Dr. Sampson Avard (a Mormon teacher), and William W. Phelps (editor and elder in charge of the Saints in Missouri) later revealed much about it.[58] Phelps testified that Rigdon was really the instigator of a strict policy that, should anyone find a deserter, he "should kill him, and haul him aside into the brush."[59]

Upon hearing of Mormon killings in a town called Gallatin, Rigdon accompanied a band of 150 armed men, including Joseph Smith and Sampson Avard, in a march to the county seat. There they attempted to coerce a judge and intimidate a sheriff for their cause, and they even captured a canon from the mob.[60] The mob soon retaliated:

> Men were shot down like wild beasts, or had their brains dashed out. Women were insulted and children were killed while pleading for their lives. . . .Men were caught, tied up, and whipped, until some died in their homes. Others had to tie handkerchiefs around their bodies to keep their bowels from falling out. Others were shot down, their wives and little ones driven out from their habitation, and this often in the night having nothing but

---

56   Swartzell, p. 29. Rigdon uttered these words as a vow, pointing his sword up toward Heaven as he said them.

57   Ibid., p. 33.

58   See John Ahmanson, Secret History-An Eyewitness Account of The Rise of Mormonism, trans. By Gleason Archer, (Chicago: Moody Press, 1984), Chapter 10.

59   McKiernan, pp. 95 and 97.

60   Ibid., pp. 89-90.

their night clothes on; their houses would be set on fire, and all consumed, leaving hundreds of women and little children. . .wandering barefooted and nearly naked in the darkness of the night and dead of winter in the fields and open prairies.

. . .Females in this heart-rending condition gave birth to children in the open air, and [were] exposed to the inclemencies of winter. The consequences were that many sickened and many died.[61]

When Rigdon and Smith appealed to Governor Lilburn Boggs for help, they found him unsympathetic. So they attempted to drive out the mobs themselves. Apostle David Patten led an attack on what he believed to be a gathered mob at Crooked River, only to find out that he had instead attacked some troopers of the state militia. That was all Boggs needed! On October 27, 1838, he issued the "Extermination Order," and on October 30 around 200 members of the Livingston County Militia perpetrated the Haun's Hill Massacre.

The Mormons were recent immigrants from Ohio, and Rigdon had personally known most of them. The militia fired on a flag of truce, killing seventeen and wounding fifteen. One of the militiamen, William Reynolds, found ten-year-old Sardius Smith hiding under the bellows of the blacksmith shop, and Reynolds shot the boy, explaining that little Mormons only grew up into big ones. He later bragged how the child kicked and squealed when the bullet blew off the top of his skull. Other militia looted the settlement, while a militiaman named Rogers hacked seventy-eight-year-old Thomas McBride to death with a corn knife as he lay wounded on the ground. The survivors of the massacre—three men and several women—buried the dead in an unfinished well.[62]

Another heart rending account involved a Mormon blacksmith:

He had 2 little boys. He took the boys and put them under the bellows and then took his gun and went out to see what could be done to defend the people. While out of the shop he got his death wound and came back to his shop and lay down near where his boys were in hiding and died. While Smith lay there dead two of the mob came in the shop and seeing Smith dead and seeing the boys one of them put the muzzle to his gun against the head of one of the boys and fired blowing the top of his head off and his brains were blown over the head of his brother. The other ruffin [sic] shot the other little boy in the hip and then went away.[63]

---

61 Letter from Sidney Rigdon to the Pennsylvania State Legislature, 1844, reprinted by permission as an Appendix to McKiernan's book.

62 John W. Rigdon, "Lecture On The Early Mormon Church," p. 20, as summarized in McKiernan, p. 93.

63 John W. Rigdon typescript, p. 18.

In late October the militia also surrounded Far West. Rigdon tried to rally the defenders, threatening that anyone refusing to fight should be "pitched upon their horses with pitchforks and bayonets, and forced into the front line of battle. . ."[64] When some defected anyway, he angrily mounted a stand in the schoolhouse and shouted:

> The last man has run away from Far West that is going to. The next man who starts shall be pursued and brought back, dead or alive. I move a resolution that if any man attempts to move out of this county, or even packs his things for that purpose, then any man in this house who sees it shall, without saying anything to any other person, kill and haul him aside into the brush. All the burial he shall have will be in a turkey buzzard's guts, and nothing will be left of him but his bones![65]

General Samuel Lucas ordered the town to surrender its leaders or face destruction. On October 31, 1838, Rigdon and the others surrendered in order to save the rest. Lucas then ordered General Doniphon to execute them, but Doniphon staunchly refused, bellowing, "It is cold-blooded murder. I will not obey your order. . . . If you execute these men, I will hold you responsible before an earthly tribunal, so help me God."[66]

Between November 13 and 24, Rigdon was chained together with fifty other church leaders in a courthouse whose unfinished roof allowed it to snow on the prisoners. He became ill, went out of his mind, and suffered fits of uncontrollable laughter which caused the guards to mock him.[67] By the time of his trial for treason in February of 1839, Rigdon's mind had recovered, but he was still sick and emaciated. He nonetheless pled his own case, and did so with such fervor that General Doniphon later wrote, "Such a burst of eloquence it was never my fortune to listen to, at its close there was not a dry eye in the room. . ."[68] He was acquitted. The audience raised $100 and gave it to him, and the sheriff gave him a horse, a pistol, and a guide to help him escape to Illinois, bidding him to fare well.[69]

---

64 Extracts from Mormonism Exposed, under the title "Mormonism," Millennial Harbinger, December, 1842, p. 541.

65 Quoted in Brodie, p. 232. Alexander Campbell, "Mormonism In An Agony," The Millennial Harbinger, Vol. VI, No. 8 (August, 1842), p. 362, moralizes in an interesting sharp reaction to these events and Rigdon's speech, as he quotes parts of it and comments.

66 Dean Hughes, p. 96.

67 Orson Pratt's History of The Late Persecutions (p. 27) as recounted in F. Mark McKiernan, p. 97

68 Van Wagoner, p. 254 quoting from Saints' Herald (August 2, 1884).

69 McKiernan, pp. 98-99, also quoting from the above article.

THE NAUVOO EPISODE AND THE DECLINE OF RIGDON'S INFLUENCE (1839-1844)

In February of 1839, Rigdon arrived in Nauvoo,[70] a town of about 12,000 on the east bank of the Mississippi River. It was at the time an important station for the underground railroad, helping slaves escape their masters, and feelings between the free state of Illinois and the slave state of Missouri were bitter. The people of Illinois had observed the Extermination Order and the Haun's Hill Massacre with horror, and when Rigdon and other Mormons escaped to Illinois, the residents took them in with pity and nursed them back to health. Another motivation for such a welcome reception, however, may have been the large state debt of over $14,000,000, and an increase in residents was seen as an expanded tax base.[71]

By April, Rigdon had created such sympathy for the Mormons and had verbally attacked Missouri Governor Boggs so viciously that Boggs issued a bench warrant for his re-arrest. But Governor Thomas Carlin of Illinois ignored his request and refused to extradite him. When Joseph Smith and the other Mormon leaders escaped imprisonment in Missouri on April 16 and joined Rigdon in Nauvoo, they began making plans to sue the state of Missouri for redress. Rigdon wanted to go further and petition the United States government to impeach the state of Missouri for unlawful government,[72] but Smith convinced him to settle for damages instead.

On October 29, 1839, Rigdon and Smith left for Washington D.C. to plea their cause, but Rigdon became ill and on November 29, was so sick that he could not be present with Smith for the meeting with President Martin Van Buren. So "The Prophet" had to make the case for the Mormon cause, and he failed dismally. Smith recorded Van Buren's reply as, "Gentlemen, your cause is just, but I can do nothing for you. If I take up for you I shall lose the vote of Missouri."[73] Smith also failed in a meeting with John C. Calhoun, and he later maintained that the absence of Rigdon led to the failure of the D.C. mission, believing that Sidney could have convinced them both.[74] For the next five years Rigdon's health was poor and his influence began to dwindle. Since the time before the Missouri persecutions until 1843, he had lost 47 pounds.[75] In 1840, John C. Bennett an ambitious and dynamic man,

---

70 From a Hebrew word meaning "beauty" and "rest."

71 Thomas Ford, <u>History of Illinois From Its Commencement As A State In 1818 to 1847</u>, (Chicago, 1854), p. 224.

72 Joseph Smith, <u>History of The Church</u>, Vol. IV, p. 75.

73 Ibid., p. 80.

74 Darryl Chase, <u>Sidney Rigdon - Early Mormon</u> (M.A. Thesis, University of Chicago, 1931), p. 216.

75 Isaac Errett, editorial, "<u>Pioneer Mormon Dead</u>," found in the <u>Christian Standard</u>, (August 5, 1876), p. 252.

replaced Rigdon as "The Prophet's" main counselor and spokesman. The passage of time would expose Bennett as a liar, a fraud, and a con man, but for the time being this worldly-wise man had everyone's admiration, including Sidney's.

From 1830 to 1844 Rigdon had been one of Smith's most devoted followers. He believed Smith to be a prophet, and he believed in the validity of the Book of Mormon and "The Prophet's" revelations—even apparently until his own death in 1876. But Rigdon's confidence in Smith's integrity and infallibility gradually eroded as those years progressed.

The first test of Rigdon's loyalty came early in their relationship. When Rigdon's communal experiment yielded a plethora of problems for the Saints, Smith terminated the effort with a revelation on February 9, 1831.[76] Since Sidney Rigdon had made a clean break with Alexander Campbell over this issue, as well as others, it seems reasonable to believe that he privately disagreed with the move, and may have even resented it. However his alternatives were few. As McKiernan expressed it, "Actually he had little choice; either he accepted Smith as a Prophet and obeyed the revelation, or he rejected both."[77] To openly oppose "the Prophet" would be tantamount to renouncing him, as he had done with Campbell earlier. Since Mormonism seemed to conform with more of his theology than any other church, Rigdon probably just suppressed or sublimated his frustration with the decision. Smith still represented "the fullness of the gospel" to Rigdon.

As for Smith's attitude toward Sidney, he early recognized his copious abilities and his widespread influence. His respect for Rigdon's commitment, intelligence, and powers of persuasion was readily evident. But, like Campbell, he never seems to have fully trusted Rigdon. On November 19, 1833, he confessed:

> Brother Sidney is a man whom I love, but he is not capable of that pure and steadfast love for those who are his benefactors that should characterize a President of the Church of Christ. This, with some other little things, such as selfishness and independence of mind, which too often manifested destroy the confidence of those who would lay down their lives for him— these are his faults.[78]

---

76 See Doctrine and Covenants, Section 42: 8-10. This revelation became known to Mormon history as "The Law of Consecration." Members dedicated their property to the church, which managed it for them and provided for their needs, but they retained actual ownership in case they left the church, etc.

77 McKiernan, p. 48.

78 Joseph Smith, History of The Church, Vol. I, p. 443. Also quoted in Faulring, p. 14, and Van Wagoner, p. 164.

Rigdon was also quite ascetic in lifestyle, whereas Smith was admittedly fond of worldly pleasures. In 1833 "the Prophet" dictated a revelation which came to be known as "The Word of Wisdom," *advising* members to abstain from such things as tobacco and alcohol. Yet he occasionally imbibed himself and, at times, was clearly drunk.[79] By December 4, 1836, Rigdon had managed to get the council to pass a decree mandating total abstinence, and Smith, surrendering to public opinion, acquiesced in the matter.[80] Thus a potential source for conflict between the two men was averted.

Then there were times of personal rebuke, and even public censure, which certainly must have grated on Rigdon's pride. On one Sunday in Far West in 1838, while solemnly awaiting a siege by the Missouri militia, Smith supposedly challenged his men to a wrestling match. After Smith left the ring and others continued to wrestle, Rigdon showed up, sword in hand, and excoriated them for "breaking the Sabbath." When the men appealed to "the Prophet" to intervene, he did so on their behalf. John D. Lee—later infamous for his part in the murder of overland tourists in the Mountain Meadows Massacre—recorded the proceedings:

> The Prophet walked into the ring and said, as he made a motion with his hand:
>
> "Brother Sidney, you had better get out of here and let the boys alone; they are amusing themselves according to my orders. You are an old man. You go and get ready for the meeting and let the boys alone." Just then catching Rigdon off his guard, as quick as a flash he knocked the sword from Rigdon's hand, then caught him by the shoulder, and said: "Now, old man, you must go out, or I will throw you down."
>
> Rigdon was as large a man as the Prophet, but not so tall. The prospect of a tussle between the Prophet and the mouthpiece of the Prophet was fun for all but Rigdon, who pulled back like a crawfish; but the resistance was useless, the Prophet dragged him from the ring, bareheaded, and tore Rigdon's fine pulpit coat from the collar to the waist; then he turned to the men and said:
>
> "Go on, boys, and have your fun. You shall never have it to say that I got you into any trouble that I did not get you out of."
>
> Rigdon complained about the loss of his hat and the tearing of his coat. The Prophet said to him:
>
> "You were out of your place. Always keep your place and you will not suffer: but you got a little out of your place and you have suffered for it. You have no one to blame but yourself."

---

79   Conkin, p. 182.

80   Brodie, p. 167.

After that Rigdon never countermanded the orders of the Prophet, to my knowledge; he knew who was boss.[81]

There were other occasions when Rigdon was publicly reprimanded, and briefly ostracized, by Smith and the Council. But probably the most significant tension between them involved the institution and practice of "plural marriage." Not only did Rigdon detest the practice as a Church leader, but he became personally involved as a father. Back on the Western Reserve, gossip connected Joseph Smith with Athalia and Nancy Rigdon, Sidney's sixteen and fifteen-year-old daughters. Clark Braden, who Van Wagoner identifies as once having been a "prominent RLDS Mormon" himself, reported that a bitter quarrel had broken out between Sidney and "the Prophet" shortly before they fled the Western Reserve, because Joseph Smith was insistent on having the teenage Nancy "sealed" to him.[82] Apparently "Rigdon viewed Spiritual wifery and the smokescreen that concealed it as reprehensible, less to do with God's work than the affairs of men."[83] Nonetheless the incident, for the time being, seems to have been buried.

However, in April of 1842, the problem resurrected again. Nancy Rigdon—who has been variously described as a "buxom," "winsome," and " beautiful," girl of "great moral excellence," and "superior intellectual endowments"[84]—was summoned by Smith to the printing office. Most accounts seem to agree that, upon her arrival, Smith ushered her into a private room, locked the door, and then expressed his romantic inclinations toward her, while at the same time trying to convince her that it was the Lord's will, and therefore no sin. Naive Nancy was surprised and shocked, then grew angry, threatening to scream so loud that the whole neighborhood would hear her if he did not immediately unlock the door. . .which he did.[85]

It seems reasonable to assume that the episode embarrassed and worried "the Prophet." According to John C. Bennett, Smith exposed his intentions to him by offering Bennett five hundred dollars in town lots on the main street of Nauvoo if he would help procure Nancy as part of Smith's harem.[86] Furthermore, a day or two after Smith's amorous

---

81   This statement was taken from John D. Lee's later work, The Mormon Menace, which is reproduced in Darryl Chase's Sidney Rigdon: Early Mormon as Appendix IV (pp. 210-211). The same account and quotes may be found in Brodie, pp. 235-236.

82   See Van Wagoner, p. 291, and The Braden-Kelly Debate, p. 202. Nancy later denied this occasion (see Van Wagoner, p. 303, footnote 12).

83   Van Wagoner, p. 369.

84   Ibid., pp. 306-7 (footnote 41).

85   Ibid., pp. 295 and 306 (footnote 40).

86   Werner, p. 144, quoting from Bennett's Mormonism Exposed, pp. 243-244. However it must be remembered that, before Bennett wrote his book, he himself had been accused of adultery and was excommunicated from the Mormon church. He certainly had ample motivation to implicate "the Prophet" in such misdeeds.

attempt, he wrote Nancy a letter, disguised as spiritual guidance, but with a hidden and suggestive double entendre to it. For example, parts of it read:

> Happiness is the object and design of our existence; and will be the end thereof, if we pursue the path that leads to it; . . . . That which is wrong under one circumstance, may be, and often is, right under another.

> . . .Everything that God gives us is lawful and right; and it is proper that we should enjoy His gifts and blessings whenever and wherever he is disposed to bestow; . . .Blessings offered, but rejected, are no longer blessings. . . .

> Our heavenly Father is more liberal in His views, and boundless in His mercies and blessings, than we are ready to believe or receive; . . . .[87]

Smith requested that Nancy burn the letter, but she instead showed it to her father. Rigdon was furious, and demanded that Smith come to see him. When he arrived, Mormon elder George Robinson was also present. Robinson later wrote to a friend that Smith, at first, denied having written such a letter; but when Rigdon then produced it and shoved it in his face, Smith confessed to it, but alibied that he had only done it to test Nancy's virtue.[88] The legacy of this occurrence caused Rigdon—not to question the Bible, the <u>Book of Mormon</u>, Mormonism itself, or the concept of restorationism—but to regard Joseph Smith as a fallen prophet, and therefore one who had lost his authority.

On July 20, 1842, a Mormon newspaper entitled <u>The Wasp</u> attempted to refute the growing number of assaults on "the Prophet's" integrity by printing a document signed by many prominent Nauvoo citizens attesting to Smith's "high moral character." Orson Pratt, George W. Robinson, and Sidney Rigdon refused to sign it, which infuriated Smith. In a special conference held on August 29, 1842, "the Prophet" referred to all three men by name and boasted, "I can kick them off my heels, as many as you can name; I know what will become of them."[89] Then, on August 31, he reassured the Female Relief Society:

> All the fuss, and all the stir, and all the charges got up against me are like the jack-a-lantern, which cannot be found.

---

87 This letter was eventually printed in the <u>History of The Church</u>, Vol. V, pp. 134-146, from which source I have quoted it. For a good explanation of its evolution to that source, see Van Wagoner, p. 307 (footnote 46).

88 Werner, p. 145; Brodie, pp. 310-311; and Bennett, p. 246.

89 Joseph Smith, "Minutes of A Special Conference Held At Nauvoo," <u>History of The Church</u>, Vol. V, p. 139.

Although I do wrong, I do not the wrongs that I am charged with doing; the wrong that I do is through the frailty of human nature, like other men. No man lives without fault.[90]

Publicly, Joseph Smith and the Quorum of the Twelve denied their practice of polygamy. But near the end of June, 1844, Smith and at least twenty-nine other men in Nauvoo, which included some of the Twelve, had collected a total of one hundred and fourteen wives.[91] Van Wagoner has rebuked this group as an "esoteric culture within a culture. . . where lying was permitted if it served a higher purpose."[92]

Although Rigdon could not condone such practices, he does not appear to have spoken out publicly to accuse "the Prophet" and others of adultery during these years. Perhaps he feared personal recriminations if he did so, or maybe he recognized the futility of fighting an uphill battle against the power structure. But Nancy Rigdon's son, a Mr. S. M. Ellis, wrote a letter on November 17, 1933, to a Mr. J.L. Nuffer, attributing to Sidney a more altruistic motive: "My grandfather knew of the secret conduct of the leaders of the church at that time, but for the welfare of the church he kept his mouth shut. . . ."[93]

The personal trust between Rigdon and "the Prophet" had been ruptured. In March of 1843, Rigdon was accused of being in league with John C. Bennett and George W. Robinson to undermine the influence and authority of Smith. In a meeting that took place on Thursday, April 6, 1843, Smith explained his purpose: "It is my object to ascertain the standing of the First Presidency. I present myself for trial. I shall next present my councillors for trial."[94] The first item concluded with Smith being unanimously retained as President of the Church. Smith then presented Rigdon for trial. Rigdon denied his supposed affiliation with Bennett, asserting, "My feelings concerning [John C.] Bennet[t] were always the same and [I] told my family to guard that fellow, for some time he will make a rupture among this people. [I] had so little confidence. I always felt myself at his difiance [sic]."[95] The assembly accepted his testimony and voted that Rigdon remain in his position as counselor to the President.[96]

---

90 Joseph Smith, "Minutes of The Female Relief Society's Meeting," History of The Church, Vol. V, p. 140.

91 Van Wagoner, p. 369.

92 Ibid.

93 This letter is quoted in Van Wagoner, p. 309 (footnote 73).

94 Faulring, The Diaries and Journals of Joseph Smith, p. 342.

95 Ibid., p. 343.

96 For a full account of this meeting see the History of The Church, Vol. V, pp. 327-329, and Faulring, pp. 337-344.

This new vote of confidence did not remain long for Rigdon, however, for in July someone charged him with conspiring with Illinois governor Thomas Carlin to surrender Smith to an extradition request from Missouri governor Lilburn Boggs. In a diary entry dated July 17, Smith wrote: "Sidney Rigdon, I most solemnly proclaim the withdrawal of my fellowship from this man on the condition that the Judging be true and let the Saints proclaim it abroad that he may no longer be acknowledged as my counselor. . . ." This time a unanimous vote of the Council disfellowshipped Rigdon and demanded his preaching license.[97]

Rigdon was befuddled and dismayed. First, he denied the charge to his peers, maintaining, "[I] never [saw] Gov[ernor] Carlin but three times [and] never exchanged a word with any man living on this subject. I ask [your] pardon for having done anything which should give a reason to make you think so."[98] He then wrote a letter to Governor Carlin asking him to help exonerate him of the charge, and on August 18, 1843, Carlin responded with a letter which seems to have been intended to be read aloud to the Mormon Council. It read in part:

> Now, Sir, it gives me pleasure to be perfectly able to disabuse you. I have not seen you to my recollection, nor had any correspondence with you until the present, since 1839 and in all the intercourse I have had with you, I have always looked upon you as one of the most devoted followers of Joseph Smith and one of the pillars of the Church of Latter-day Saints. I never sought through the aid of any person to entrap Joseph Smith.[99]

Smith was not satisfied with these responses, however, believing that there was still a conspiracy to deliver him into the hands of the Missourians. He responded to Governor Carlin's epistle by saying, "The letter is one of the most evasive things, and carries with it a design to hide the truth."[100] When Rigdon was restored to his position as Counselor in the First Presidency in a special conference on Friday, October 6, Smith objected and protested, "I have thrown him off my shoulders, and you have again put him on me. You may carry him, but I will not."[101]

Oddly enough, despite the open rupture in their relationship, Smith and Rigdon were to be paired one more time in 1844. On January 29, during a local political caucus, Mormon frustrations with Henry Clay and John C. Calhoun led to Smith being nominated as a candidate in the next

---

97   Faulring, p. 406.

98   Ibid., p. 410.

99   Inclusion by B.H. Roberts in his <u>History of The Church</u>, Vol V, pp. 553-554. This letter may also be found in Faulring, p. 411.

100 Ibid., p. 554.

101 Joseph Smith, <u>History of The Church</u>, Vol. VI, p. 49. This quote may be found in many other sources, including Barrett (p. 545), McKiernan (p. 124), and Van Wagoner (p. 324).

presidential election.[102] Incredibly, Rigdon was chosen to be his running mate as Vice President.[103] The prospects of these two men winning the election were extremely remote, but equally frightening. Not only were they at odds with one another, but there are indications that Rigdon began to see himself as a competitor to Smith. Even earlier in their relationship Rigdon had said, "the Lord suffers me to be afflicted because I aspire to get ahead of Br. Joseph, thinking myself more capable to lead the Church than he is. But the Lord don't think so."[104] Then too, both Smith and Rigdon had somewhat of a divine-right monarchy in mind. Openly proclaiming his disdain for the authority of the laws of secular society, Rigdon crowed:

> Mankind have labored under one universal mistake, that salvation was distinct from government. . . .When God sets up his kingdom, he will sustain it above all laws & kingdoms of the world & the world has no power over the kingdom of God. . . .I will live above them, ... I have a right to proclaim myself a king and a priest unto the most high God.[105]

But Smith and Rigdon would never get their chance. On June 27, 1844—after another confrontation with the authorities resulting in the voluntary surrender of Smith and other Mormon leaders in order to avoid a slaughter—a mob broke into the Carthage, Illinois, jail and murdered the Mormon prophet and his brother. According to Dallin Oaks, "The murder of Joseph and Hyrum Smith at Carthage, Illinois, was not a spontaneous, impulsive act by a few personal enemies of the Mormon leaders, but a deliberate political assassination, committed or condoned by some of the leading citizens in Hancock County.[106]

During the years from 1838 to 1844, much of the focus on restorationism blurred in the gloom of the power struggles that ensued . In the years that followed, egotism and legalism helped fracture the internal unity of both restoration movements.

---

102 Pancoast, p. 141.

103 There is some disagreement as to when Rigdon was nominated. Werner (p. 161) lists his selection on the same day, January 29. But Van Wagoner (p. 332) claims that Rigdon was not chosen until May 6, after two other candidates—James A. Bennett and Solomon Copeland—were eliminated. Brodie then adds that the party platform was constructed on May 17. For a more detailed account of these electoral proceedings, see Brodie, chapter 25, or Van Wagoner, chapter 23.

104 Jedediah M. Grant, <u>A Collection of Facts Relative To the Cause Taken by Elder Sidney Rigdon in the States of Ohio, Missouri, Illinois and Pennsylvania</u> (Philadelphia: Brown, Bicking, and Guilbert, 1844),   p. 14.

105 Van Wagoner, p. 333, quoting from <u>Wilford Woodruff's Journal</u>. See p. 346 (footnote 20) for more bibliographic information.

106 Dallin H. Oaks, <u>Carthage Conspiracy: The Trial of The Accused Assassins of Joseph Smith</u> (Urbana, Illinois: University of Illinois Press, 1975), p. 6. Read chapter one for a detailed account of those events surrounding the end of Smith's life.

Chapter
—14—

DISSIPATING RESTORATIONISM: DIVISIONS AND SUBDIVISIONS

When Smith was martyred, Rigdon was in Pittsburgh. Back on June 18 the entire Rigdon family had begun the trip to Pennsylvania on the steamship Osprey, ostensibly having been ordered to do so by "the Prophet," who feared for Sidney's personal safety.[1] Rigdon learned of Smith's death on July 6, and almost immediately sent notes for the other church leaders to meet him in Pittsburgh. But the others preferred to quorum at Nauvoo, and Rigdon, who resisted returning at first, repented when he thought he heard the ghost of Joseph Smith exhorting him, "You must not stay, you must go."[2]

The stake at Nauvoo found itself, for the moment, virtually without leaders. Many of Smith's early associates had denounced him and left the church during "The Great Apostasy" of 1837-1838. Others, still loyal to him, were scattered as far as Boston and Philadelphia and even overseas. But as each learned of Smith's death, they began the journey back to Nauvoo. Brigham Young learned of Smith's murder on July 9, and he and Orson Pratt left immediately from New Hampshire.[3]

Rigdon arrived in Nauvoo on Saturday, August 3. Before leaving Pittsburgh he had confided to Jedediah M. Grant "in the presence of several

---

1 Van Wagoner, pp. 335 and 347 (footnote 47). Van Wagoner was able to view Smith's diary in the Lee Library at Provo, Utah, in which (June 22, 1844) he confessed that he feared his own death, and therefore sent Rigdon away in order to keep him alive in order "to avenge my Blood."

2 Ibid., p. 336. Van Wagoner here quotes a selection from Andrew F. Ehat, "Joseph Smith's Introduction of Temple Ordinances and The 1844 Mormon Succession Question" (Master's thesis, Brigham Young University, 1982), p. 197. Ehat's original source, according to Van Wagoner (p. 348) was the diary of either Willard Richards or William Clayton, neither of which is apparently any longer available to researchers.

3 Barrett, p. 624.

others, that he should now take his place, at the head of the church. . . ."[4]
The next morning he spoke at the 10 a.m. worship service and informed the audience that he had received a vision while he was in Pittsburgh. He described seeing Joseph Smith at the right hand of Jesus, and asserted that no man on Earth could ever take his place as prophet and revelator. However, Rigdon claimed that it was the Lord's desire that the Latter-day Saints have a spokesman for "the Prophet" and a guardian for the Church, and he professed to be that divinely-appointed man, especially based upon his long-time role as Smith's spokesman while he was alive. He followed this allegation with a rather bizarre prophecy, notifying the Saints that Armageddon was near and that very soon they "would see one hundred tons of metal per second thrown at the enemies of God." He then continued:

> I am going to fight a real bloody battle with sword and with gun. . . . I will fight the battles of the Lord. I will also cross the Atlantic, encounter the queen's forces, and overcome them — plant the American standard on English ground, and then march to the palace of her majesty, and demand a portion of her riches and dominions, which if she refuse, I will take the little madam by the nose and lead her out, and she shall have no power to help herself. IF I DO NOT DO THIS, THE LORD NEVER SPAKE BY MORTAL. [my bold][5]

Brigham Young and some of the other leaders arrived in Nauvoo on the following Tuesday, August 6.[6] The official History of The Church recorded that Rigdon met with the Twelve Apostles, the High Council, and the high priests at four p.m. on August 7, and virtually repeated the vision and claims he had made on Sunday. Young, a bit skeptical, responded to the group assembled:

> I do not care who leads the church, even though it were Ann Lee; but one thing I must know, and that is what God says about it. I have the keys and the means of obtaining the mind of God on the subject.

He then proposed that they resume deliberation the next day at ten a.m., and his suggestion carried unanimously.[7]

---

4   Jedediah M. Grant, A Collection of Facts Relative To The Course Taken by Elder Sidney Rigdon in The States of Ohio, Missouri, Illinois and Pennsylvania (Philadelphia: Brown, Bicking, Guilbert, Printers, 1844), p. 44.

5   See B. H. Roberts, History of The Church, Vol. VII, pp. 224-225. See also Van Wagoner, pp. 336-337, who quotes Orson Hyde, Speech of Elder Orson Hyde, Delivered Before the High Priest's Quorum, in Nauvoo, April 27th, 1845, Upon the Course and Conduct of Mr. Sidney Rigdon, and Upon the Merits of His Claims to the Presidency of the Church of Jesus Christ of Latter-day Saints (Liverpool: James and Woodburn, 1845), p. 16

6   Dean Hughes, p. 129. Both Ivan Barrett (p. 625) and Max Werner (p. 189) claim that Rigdon had originally scheduled a conference for this date, but Stake President William Marks postponed it until August 8 in order to allow a majority of The Twelve to arrive.

7   See the narrative of the events as well as the quotation in B.H. Roberts, History of The Church, Vol. VII, pp. 229-230.

On Thursday, August 8, between five and ten thousand saints[8] gathered in a spacious, open-air grove overlooking the Mississippi River. Rigdon began to speak, but a strong wind muted his voice and his audience had difficulty hearing him speak. There was a short pause until a wagon platform could be placed in a location of acoustical advantage, and then he continued on. Some authors believe his hearers were apparently unimpressed with his plea. One said, "He was nervous and embarrassed, for the unexpected return of the Apostles had disconcerted him. For an hour and a half he spoke, but his oratory was not up to his usual standard, and the people showed evident signs of restlessness.[9] B. H. Roberts, in a seemingly derisive tone, wrote that Rigdon "*harangued* [italics mine] the saints for about one and a half hours. . . ."[10] Yet Orson Hyde, one of Rigdon's foes, reported that Rigdon urgently advocated his case "with all the eloquence and power that he was master of."[11]

Whether or not Rigdon's eloquence had inspired support for him at the conclusion of his plea will never be known. Brigham Young, in a cunning maneuver, mounted the platform just as Rigdon was about to call for a response from the people, and adjourned the meeting until two p.m., at which time they would again reconvene. This shrewd ploy had the effect of defusing any momentum Rigdon had aggregated. Van Wagoner's evaluation of the two contenders for influence seems most accurate: "Rigdon was without question Young's oratorical superior, but Young, never a passive observer, was more clever, ambitious, and politically astute."[12]

At two p.m. Brigham Young then addressed the assembly. Many later claimed that as he proceeded his effect grew and became "magnetic," and that he spoke in such a way as he had never been able to before. He rebutted Sidney's arguments, contending that the legitimate power in the Church should reside with the Twelve Apostles, and not in the hands of one man:

> Here is President Rigdon, who was counselor to Joseph. I ask, where are Joseph and Hyrum? They are gone beyond the veil; and if Elder Rigdon wants to act as his counselor, he must go beyond the veil where he is.

> There has been much said about President Rigdon being President of the Church, and leading the people, being the head, etc. Brother Rigdon has come 1,600 miles to tell you what he wants to do for you. If the people want President Rigdon to lead them they may have him; but I say unto

---

8   See variations in, Barrett, p. 626, and Van Wagoner, p. 339.

9   Werner, p. 189.

10   B. H. Roberts, <u>History of The Church</u>, Vol. VII, p. 231.

11   Van Wagoner, p. 339, again quoting Hyde.

12   Ibid., p. 338.

you that the quorum of the Twelve have the keys of the kingdom of God in all the world.

The Twelve are appointed by the finger of God. . . .

. . .You must not appoint any man at our head; if you should, the Twelve must ordain him. You cannot appoint a man at our head; but if you do want any other man or men to lead you, take them and we will go our way to build up the kingdom in all the world.

I know who are Joseph's friends and who are his enemies. I know where the keys of the kingdom are, and where they will eternally be.[13]

The more he spoke, the more his words crescendoed until many onlookers claimed that his voice, features, gestures, and even posture, seemed to somehow miraculously transform into those of "the Prophet" himself. In an indirect reference to Rigdon's occasional questionable loyalty to Joseph Smith, Young prodded his listeners, "Here is Brigham, have his knees ever faltered? Have his lips ever quivered?" He then boldly expressed his own personal concern that implied the possibility of some devious shenanigans, and must have implanted worrisome doubts among the crowd, when he accused, "I tell you there is an overanxiety to hurry matters here."[14]

When a final vote was procured, the overwhelming majority supported Young's position, with only a few brave souls dissenting.[15] The authority of the Church was placed into the keeping of the Twelve, and ultimately, since he was their leader, into the hands of Brigham Young. This ostensibly overt rejection of Rigdon hurt him deeply, since he believed he had done more to establish the Church than any one else, and the wounds engendered on this occasion he would nurture the rest of his life.

However, the years that followed seemed to substantiate that the choice was a right one for the Mormons. Whereas Ridgon was a powerful evangelist, he had questionable organizational leadership skills. In Brigham Young this proved to be a strength. Even Sidney's own son, looking back upon the event, felt compelled to admit [errors not mine]:

I do not think the Church made any mistake in placing leadership on Brigham Young he in my opinion was best man for place the Church could

---

13   B. H. Roberts, <u>History of The Church</u>, Vol. VII, p. 233.

14   Ibid.

15   See Werner, p. 192, for example. Jedediah Grant, p. 18, claims that the two votes in each case (i.e. *against* a guardian, and then *for* The Twelve) were unanimous, but this is hard to believe, first, because Grant's style is almost constantly and unrealistically filled with superlatives, and second, because Rigdon <u>did</u> have a few outspoken and powerful supporters, as history soon demonstrated.

have selected. Sidney Rigdon had no excutive ability, was broken down with sickness, and could not have taken charge of the Church at that time.[16]

Rigdon, of course, was disgruntled with the results of the proceeding. While at first making a public show of support for the Twelve, he nonetheless began working behind the scenes to undermine their authority. The perceptive Brigham Young had been suspicious of Rigdon's ambitions and maneuvers all along, remarking that it was curious that Rigdon had attempted to expedite a decision on August 6—before a majority of the Twelve had arrived—because "He represented to the congregation that it was necessary that he should return home immediately on account of the situation of his family," and yet "since that action was taken Elder Rigdon has shown no more anxiety to return to Pittsburgh."[17] M. R. Werner has asserted that the postponement of the meeting until August 8:

> . . .was fatal to Sidney Rigdon's plans, for Brigham Young and the Apostles reached Nauvoo at 8 o'clock in the evening of August 6. If the conference had taken place that day, Sidney Rigdon would have been by virtue of his oratory president of the Church, and Brigham Young would have been in the strategically disadvantageous position of the leader of a schism.[18]

Young's first problem as head of the Church, by virtue of his leadership of the Twelve Apostles, was to secure his own position while at the same time negating the influence of his rivals, of whom Rigdon was the first and foremost. Yet events had already begun flowing in Young's favor. Rigdon, it seems, had been discrediting his own influence for the past five years or so (1839-1844). Jedediah Grant recalled, "If Mr. Rigdon's inexplicable course at Nauvoo, was not a transgression, I confess myself unable to give it a name," claiming that he had gradually "disrobed" from the "mantle" of leadership in recent years.[19] And Heber C. Kimball expressed his opinion that "Elder Rigdon is a man I have always respected as a man, but I have not respected his course for more than five years past."[20] Even more recently Grant had observed "that Mr. R's mental economy has become greatly impaired, is evident from the many contradictory statements he has made within the last six months."[21]

On Sunday September 8, Rigdon had stirred up enough mischief that he was brought to trial in front of the High Council. There were multiple charges expressed by the various speakers. Other than having become

---

16 John Wickliffe Rigdon typescript, p. 25.

17 Grant, p. 22

18 Werner, p. 189.

19 Grant, p. 45.

20 Heber C. Kimball as quoted in Grant, p. 34.

21 Grant, p. 46.

incompetent to retain his leadership position, some expressed concern about his integrity. Referring to Rigdon's initial public assembly when he arrived at Nauvoo in August, Grant maintained that "Elder Rigdon promised that the meeting should be turned into a prayer meeting, but not long after he rescinded his promise to Elder P. and told the people it was a business meeting."[22]

Young and others also charged him with propagating false revelations, holding secret meetings in which he ordained men of his own volition and on his own authority, and of "trying to divide the Church by speaking against the living and the dead [i.e. Joseph Smith]."[23] Brigham Young lamented that "Elder Rigdon is now going to work to make a division, and yet he said on the stand, he did not want to make a division."[24] Rigdon had denounced Joseph Smith in a public gathering on an earlier occasion: "Oh Joseph! thou wicked servant, thou hast fallen because of thy transgression! Thou hadst the promise that thou shouldst live if thou wert faithful. . . ."[25]

One other charge with which he was confronted, was threatening to demean (or expose the indiscretions of, depending upon one's perspective) many of the Mormon leaders. On one occasion Rigdon apparently threatened, "if you oppose me, I will expose all your secret wickedness, I will expose all your iniquity."[26]

Rigdon was not present to answer the charges at his trial, having sent word through Elder Marks that he was sick. However, this seems to have been an excuse, as he was extended what appears to be ample opportunities to respond if he so chose. Orson Hyde claimed that he could prove Rigdon wasn't sick. And Jedediah Grant was puzzled by his absence:

> . . .he was invited so to do. He could have sounded his defense in the ears of more than six thousand people, in the very place where his grievances should have been redressed. Is he not a man of sense? Does he not possess a flow of language and eloquence not often surpassed? Yes he does.[27]

The authoritative eloquence of Brigham Young convinced almost everyone that Rigdon ought to be disfellowshipped. At one point in the trial, Young recalled, "Brother Joseph has said at different times, that if Elder Rigdon was to lead the Church twelve months, he would lead them to the devil."[28] Later on he asserted his personal convictions about Sidney:

---

22   Ibid., p. 17. See support for this charge on p. 26.

23   See multiple testimonials in Grant, pp. 18-45.

24   Ibid., p. 23.

25   Ibid., p. 40.

26   Ibid., p. 24. See reiteration on p. 28 also.

27   Ibid., p. 39.

28   Ibid., p. 30

I never had any confidence in Brother Sidney as a revelator, and why? Because I have so repeatedly heard Brother Joseph rebuke him for speaking in the name of the Lord, what was not so. . . . I feel that Brother Rigdon came here with a bad spirit, and has delivered a revelation. If such things as are contained in his revelation, have been revealed to him, it is from a source with which we want nothing to do. When he first came here I thought he was deceived, but since last Tuesday evening I have been convinced that he is dishonest. . . . I believe he is an evil designing man.[29]

The History of The Church simply states that, at the conclusion of the September 8 trial, W.W. Phelps moved that Rigdon "be cut off from the Church, and delivered over to the buffetings of satan [sic] until he repent." When Newell K. Whitney presented the motion to the High Council, the vote was unanimous. Then, when Phelps proposed the same motion to the whole Church the vote was nearly unanimous, with only ten supporting Rigdon.[30]

When Sidney learned of his excommunication by the High Council, and by the whole Church as well, he was, as might be expected, deeply hurt. He reacted to his rejection with words quite similar to those he used when he left the Campbellite movement. In retrospect, his son Wickliffe remembered that "He said he had done more to establish the Chruch [sic] than any member of it."[31] He then proceeded to curse all who had condemned him, exonerating only those who would leave Nauvoo with him and re-establish the true Church back in Pittsburgh.[32] An interesting declaratory document was drawn up by those loyal to him [see the following page], and on September 10, Rigdon left Nauvoo for the last time.

Rigdon had become disenchanted with both restoration movements—first the Stone-Campbell movement, and now the Latter-day Saints. He still believed in restorationism, but not in the leaders of the two movements. Sidney also continued to believe in the Book of Mormon, but saw Joseph as a fallen prophet. Rigdon eulogized, "Joseph Smith departed from the Living God and like David and Solomon he contracted a whoring spirit and the Lord smote him for this thing, and cut him off from the earth."[33]

At first his congregation had used the name Church of Jesus Christ of Latter-day Saints, and began a publication on October 15, 1844, entitled

---

29 Ibid., p. 36. Another copy of this speech may be found in the Times and Seasons (Nauvoo, Illinois), Vol. V, No. 19 (October 15, 1844).

30 B. H. Roberts, History of The Church, Vol. VII, pp. 268-269.

31 John Wickliffe Rigdon typescript, p. 25.

32 Grant, p. 37.

33 The Latter-day Saints' Messenger and Advocate (January 1, 1845), p. 75, as quoted in R.C. Evans, Forty Years In The Mormon Church And Why I Left It, p. 90.

THE

MILLENNIAL HARBINGER.

Vol. I.   BETHANY, VA. DECEMBER, 1844.   No. XII.

MORMON CHURCH EXTINCT.

The melancholy catastrophe of the murder of Joseph Smith, the presiding President, and Hyrum his brother, resulted in leaving one individual only known to the church as pointed out by repeated revelations, as Prophet, Seer, and Revelator for the Church -- viz. Sidney Rigdon.

President Rigdon, who was then in Pittsburg, received instruction from the Lord to repair to this place, and present himself to the church for their acceptance or rejection; which actually did result in his rejection, and the appointment of the Twelve (by a large majority of the church) to the presidency of the whole church and its entire control.

Verily believing as we do, that this was a vital departure from the order of Heaven, and a rejection of the only man who sustained the legal relation of a Revelator to the Church, and who was competent to reorganize the first Presidency, we dissented and lifted our voices against such proceedings, and manifested our adherence to President Rigdon.

In consequence of this rejection, President Rigdon has received a commandment to reorganize the church; and for this reason the Twelve and their adherents have assiduously studied and striven to misrepresent the character and designs of President Rigdon and his friends, and have not scrupled to ascribe to them motives and designs the most base and dishonorable.

We do declare that President Rigdon is above all malevolent aspersions of his reputation, and is known to us as a worthy law-abiding citizen, and a gentleman of unblemished character.

We do, moreover, declare our sincere conviction, that, in rejecting Sidney Rigdon, the Church of Jesus Christ of Latter Day Saints does no longer exist, except in connexion with him; and that God has given no authority for an organization of the church, differing from that contained in the Book of Doctrine and Covenants.

Heretofore the accused has had the privilege of a trial and an opportunity to reply to the charges brought against them; but on the memorable 8th of September, 1844, this privilege was denied in open and flagrant violation of all the laws and rules of the church; thus manifesting clearly that the course they pursued towards us is one unsanctioned by law and unallowed by justice.

Samuel James,	William Richards,
Leonard Soby,	George Soby,
J. B. Bosworth,	Samuel Bennett,
George W. Crouse,	J. A. Forgeous,
Lewis James,	G. Bentley,
G. W. Robinson,	William Coltien,
J. H. Newton,	T. J. Lanyon,
Briggs Aldcn,	David Scott,
Elijah Reed,	Thomas Crompton,
John Evans,	J. Hatch, and many others.

NAUVOO, September 8, 1844.

Figure 10. Found in The Millennial Harbinger, Alexander Campbell, ed., 3rd Series, Vol. 1, December, 1844, pp. 618-619. (from http://www.sidneyrigdon.com/dbroadhu/VA/harb1844.htm.)

<u>The Latter-day Saints' Messenger and Advocate</u>. But on April 6, 1845, the remnant in Pennsylvania formerly changed the Church name to simply *Church Of Christ* and affirmed Sidney Rigdon as its president.

> Unlike typical visionaries, though, Rigdon no longer drew strength from the future, divining from tomorrow's promise a new order. Recasting his religious iron in Pittsburgh, he looked back to Kirtland, Ohio, when the old faith had been untainted by "strange doctrines which have crept in unawares." It was his intention "to contend for the same doctrines, order of church government and discipline, maintained. . . in Kirtland."[34]

Rigdon continued his verbal assault for awhile on the waywardness of his former brethren, especially in the abomination of their polygamy. The March 15, 1845, issue of the Church newspaper had clearly stated the church's position toward the Utah Saints:

> Whereas, in consequence of the rejection by that people, of what we undoubtedly deem to be the order of the Church and kingdom of God, and the introduction of doctrines and practices clearly inimical to the law of God, and altogether subversive of the laws of the land, abrogating the marriage contract, and substituting under the professed sanction of heaven, a system of extreme licentiousness, [and]. . .

> Whereas, the better to conceal the justly odious system [in which] polygamy, duplicity, hypocrisy, and falsehood are inculcated as virtues, . . .

> Resolved, that we hold no fellowship with the people calling themselves the Church of Jesus Christ of Latter-day Saints, and can have no communion with them, unless they repent and obey the principles of righteousness and truth.

> Resolved, that *we* [italics mine] maintain the truth and the truth only, . . .[35]

However the congregation of one hundred and fifty failed to grow and Rigdon grew discouraged. Years of personal and spiritual frustrations gradually eroded and soured his disposition, as often happens to make negative and bitter old men out of some of us. The patience of youth began to give way to the impetuosity of redeeming the time, and Sidney Rigdon became even more intolerant of variant opinions than he was before. In the fall of 1846, his group began to disintegrate during a conference at which Rigdon apparently taught doctrines that many members found to be against their beliefs. By January of the new year, "the church was virtually extinct," except for a few scattered branches and

---

34   Van Wagoner, p. 367. His quote segments are taken from the <u>Latter Day Saints'</u> <u>Messenger and Advocate</u> (October 15, 1844), p. 16. See also McKiernan, p. 134.

35   Quoted in Steven L. Shields, <u>Divergent Paths of Restorationism: A History of The Latter Day Saint Movement</u> (Los Angeles: Restoration Research, 1990), p. 37.

individuals here and there.[36] Wickliffe Rigdon later wrote [errors not mine]:

> The little church that was there concluded to follow him but [he] was so extreme in his ideas that they left him. He was at times [so] perfectly wild [that] he could not control himself. . . . His daughter Eliza about nineteen years old died in Pittsburgh that effected him very much and he never was the man he once was.[37]

Sidney Rigdon lived the last thirty years of his life in relatively quiet obscurity, especially when compared with his previous twenty-five or so. He did make one more serious attempt to "gather" the Saints at a new "Zion," this time in Antrim township in Franklin County, Pennsylvania. In May of 1846 the Rigdon family, along with some of his followers, left Pittsburgh to establish "Adventure Farm" near Greencastle, accompanied by Rigdon's visionary apocalyptic promises. But when "Christ delayed his coming," Rigdon's few followers became discouraged, his church dissolved, and the farm property was foreclosed upon because the balance could not be paid to it's creditor.[38]

The Rigdons were now without home or substance. George W. Robinson, Sidney's son-in-law and loyal companion in his religious ventures, invited the family to join them at their new farm on Jackson Hill, near Cuba, New York, *provided* that he "never open his mouth about religion again."[39] Rigdon's fanatical preaching and excessive claims no longer yielded anything but trouble. Wickliffe remembered that "He seemed sane upon every other subject except religion," and that "He never preached after he came to Alle. Co. [because] his family would not let him."[40]

Late in 1850 George Robinson sold his farm and again invited Sidney and his family to move in with them at a nearby town called Friendship, where Robinson was prospering in the mercantile business,[41] and where Rigdon would remain for the rest of his life. During the late 1850's and 1860's, a man named Stephen Post attempted another Mormon restoration movement on Sidney's behalf, but it was never really successful. And in

---

36   Shields, p. 38.

37   John Wickliffe Rigdon typescript, p. 26.

38   See Van Wagoner, Chapter 26, for more detail on the Antrim experiment. Van Wagoner (p. 392) dates the seizure of "Adventure Farm" on April 7, 1847, but gives no source for his information. McKiernan (p. 143) postulates a foreclosure date in August of 1847, listing as his reference Jacob F. Richard, History of Franklin County, Pennsylvania (Chicago, 1887), pp. 564-565.

39   Ibid., p. 399. Here Van Wagoner quotes the Journal History (April 6, 1848), p. 4.

40   John Wickliffe Rigdon typescript, p. 26.

41   For more details see Van Wagoner, p. 400.

1863, Brigham Young extended an invitation for Sidney and Phebe Rigdon to join them in Utah and be cared for by the Saints there.[42] Sidney, however, turned down the offer.

As Sidney grew older, his private religious statements and beliefs became more and more bizarre. In a January 25, 1864, revelation Rigdon was, through the auspices of God, self-congratulatory: "And I the Lord say to you that no man that ever stood before me had a greater trial of his faith than this was. No, Noah, Daniel nor Job, Abraham, Moses nor Samuel."[43] In 1869, in an interview with former Rigdonite A.W. Cowles, he began to exhibit some of the symptoms of megalomania when he boasted, "Yes, if I were only young again I could sweep away all your religions from under the whole heaven!"[44] And in 1871, when Sidney was seventy-eight, he "had come to view himself without peer in the annals of human kind," promising that "nothing can prevail against [the Rigdons] to hinder them from doing the work [to] which they are ordained. Old age with its infirmities shall give place to the vigor of early maturity; . . . ."[45] Near the end of November in 1872, Rigdon had a stroke "so severe that newspapers around the country carried notice of his death." By January he was able to write Stephen Post and inform him that, not only was he well, but also his physicians who had "supposed that restoration was out of the question," were now claiming that his recovery was "unparalleled in the history of the disease. . . ." This experience bequeathed to Sidney and Phebe the belief that they would never die.[46]

But on July 14, 1876, Rigdon finally succumbed to successive strokes, dying in Friendship, New York, while Phebe agonized over his final days on Earth. He left little in the way of personal memoirs; his library was small and he had persistently resisted interviews or photographs.[47] McKiernan has written that when he died his relatives burned a manuscript numbering over fifteen hundred pages, but he did not disclose his source of information.[48] The Masonic fraternity conducted the services over his lifeless body, and he was buried in the Friendship Village graveyard. . . **in an unmarked grave!**[49]

---

42   John Wickliffe Rigdon typescript, p. 27.

43   This is a small excerpt from a larger quote in Van Wagoner (p. 414), who gained access to Lee Library's Stephen Post correspondence, et. al., in the Special Collections section at Brigham Young University in Provo, Utah.

44   Ibid., pp. 420-421.

45   Ibid., p. 416 and 444.

46   Ibid., p. 443.

47   Isaac Errett, editorial, "Death of Sidney Rigdon," found in The Christian Standard (Cincinnati: The Standard Publishing Co.), Vol. XI, No. 31 (July 29, 1876), p. 245.

48   McKiernan, "Bibliographical Essay," p. 171.

49   Isaac Errett, editorial, "Pioneer Mormon Dead," The Christian Standard, Vol. XI, No. 32 (August 5, 1876), p. 252.

I. OTHER MORMON DIVISIONS AND SUBDIVISIONS

Stephen L. Shields has recently (1975) repined: "For some reason as yet unexplored and unexplained, the Restoration Movement has shown a schismatic tendency from its very first."[50] This author will attempt to offer some possible explanations for that dilemma in the second half of my conclusion. One answer proposed by Robert K. Fielding—who obviously had little affinity for the Mormon church—was that:

> The tendency to schism was more or less endemic in the Church, owing to the erratic cranks on religion's "lunatic fringe" who were attracted to the new movement either as truth seekers or as searchers for disciples for their own religious views.[51]

Sidney Rigdon was not the only member of the Latter-day Saints to split off and form a new church. After the death of "the Prophet," "it seemed that schisms would disintegrate the church"—as Lyman Wight headed for Texas; Charles Thompson migrated to St. Louis; James J. Strang settled on Beaver Island in Michigan; and Lucy and William Smith, Joseph's mother and brother, eventually relocated to Independence, Missouri.[52]

The latter formed what is now known as the *Reorganized* Church of Jesus Christ of Latter-day Saints in 1852, with Joseph Smith, Jr. taking his place as the head of the Church in 1860. Denying that his father ever preached or practiced polygamy,[53] Joseph Smith, Jr. declared on December 23, 1879:

> I am now pretty widely recognized as the leader of that wing of the Mormon Church declaring *primitive* [italics mine] Mormonism, but denying and opposing polygamy and Utah Mormonism. . . . We hope they [the Utah Mormons] are waning in power. We are maintaining an active ministry in Utah, striving to show the people there their errors. . . .[54]

Shortly after "the Prophet's" murder, another man, James J. Strang, claimed to be the legitimate leader of the Church. He produced a letter dated June 18, 1844, in which Joseph Smith supposedly chose him as his successor. Jedediah Grant took note of his claim with disdain:

> Here is a revelation come from Michigan, which points out a Mr. Strang as the one to take the lead of this people. So Brother Sidney is not the only man who proposes to have been appointed to lead this Church. The devil

---

50   Shields, "Introduction To The First Edition," p. 15.

51   Fielding, p. 255.

52   Brodie, p. 398.

53   Werner, p. 195.

54   Mather, p. 210.

seems to have set a good many hooks and baited them very nice, that some may be sure to catch.[55]

Commanding the Twelve Apostles to recognize his mantle of authority and to relocate the "gathering" headquarters to Voree (Burlington), Wisconsin, Strang was rebuffed and excommunicated on August 26, 1844. By 1850 most of his followers had settled on Beaver Island in Northern Lake Michigan, where he was actually crowned king in an elaborate ceremony.[56] His community there thrived for a short while, and at one time Strang's following rivaled even that of Brigham Young.[57] But on June 16, 1856, two men killed him, to the delight or relief of his adversaries, and around two thousand of his followers were evicted from the island by residents hostile to Mormonism. No strong leader emerged to take his place, and the church dwindled.

Other groups fractured from the Mormon majority and formed their own factions. Alphes Cutler organized a small communal group in 1853, and William Bickerton organized another group (from Rigdon's followers) in 1862. Schisms proliferated within the Latter-day Saints communion, and at least six main divisions remain active today.[58]

II. DISSENSION AND DIVISION WITHIN THE STONE-CAMPBELL MOVEMENT

The Church of Jesus Christ of the Latter-day Saints was not the only restoration movement to realize such cleavage. The Disciples of Christ also experienced some disagreements, which evolved into dissensions after Alexander Campbell's death,[59] and ripened into major fractures in the twentieth century. The Stone-Campbell Restoration Movement did not result in a unity of all denominations, as was hoped. Instead, the Disciples of Christ in many ways became a new denomination unto itself.

---

55 Grant, p. 29.

56 Shields, p. 41.

57 Ibid., p. 42.

58 Ibid., p. 11. Shields (pp. 3-9) lists 184 subdivisions or splinter groups comprising these six divisions in 1990. Paul Conkin (p. 209) claimed that there were "nearly fifty Mormon or Mormon-related denominations" in 1997.

59 The proximity of Alexander Campbell's death (1866) with the end of the Civil War (1865) causes one to wonder which event might really have been more significant in releasing the forces of division. The A Capella Church of Christ, for example, which eventually split off from the main body, was concentrated heavily in the South. For the traditional position *supporting* the view that the Civil War did not bring about the splits, see Garrison and DeGroot, The Disciples of Christ: A History, Ch. XV. For a rather convincing argument *against* the traditional perspective, read the transcript of Henry Webb's workshop at "Restoration Unity Forum VI," held in Cuyahoga Falls, Ohio, on November 1-3, 1988, which was published by the College Press Publishing Co. of Joplin, Missouri, in 1988.

W.E. Garrison has written that, when Alexander Campbell died in 1866, "His death apparently released the forces of reaction."[60] But the roots of these Stone-Campbell divisions may be discerned as far back as the inception of the movement, when the twin goals of restorationism and unity were established. It was advocated then that a basic restoration of the New Testament Church would trivialize differences and reunite the denominations. In fact, however, restorationism and unity proved to be incompatible bedfellows.

Through the auspices of The Christian Baptist, Alexander Campbell had argued for "The Restoration of The Ancient Order of Things." This required a study and definition of what the "Ancient Order of Things" was, and led to the attempt to establish a "pattern" by which one could measure a legitimate restoration. The creation of such a template tended to yield a legalistic—and in some people, exclusivistic—mindset which then, of course, worked in opposition to ecumenism. Barton Stone realized this back in 1827 when—remembering the eventual sectarian competition and squabbles of the Presbyterians, Baptists, and Methodists, at Cane Ridge in 1802—he asked, "What but this [sectarian spirit] terminated the revival of religion in Kentucky and the west, twenty five years ago?"[61]

Many accused Campbell of such an attitude, while others blamed some of his followers for not comprehending his truly ecumenical perspective.[62] Errett Gates, for instance, blamed "the literalist, the extremist," as being "the inevitable phenomena connected with an earnest effort to restore the primitive faith and practice."[63] Allen and Hughes marveled, "That this spirit of exclusivism and even coercion surfaced so soon is deeply ironic when one considers that the Churches of Christ were born of a passion for freedom and that their earliest leaders drank deeply of the spirit of the American Revolution."[64]

The unity-minded Stone worried about one example of this "patternism" in the insistence of many Campbellites that baptism is "essential" to salvation. An early Disciple slogan had been, "In essentials unity, in non-essentials liberty, and in all things love." The original "essentials" revolved around the facts of the Gospel—Christ's death, burial

---

60   W.E. Garrison, Religion Follows The Frontier, p. 228.

61   Barton Stone as quoted (with no reference note) by Richard Hughes in his Reviving The Ancient Faith, p. 104.

62   For examples of the former, see Baptist bishop R.B. Semple's letters in The Christian Baptist and The Millennial Harbinger, as well as those of Andrew Broaddus. For the latter perspective see, for example, Hughes (pp. 17-21); Garrison and DeGroot, The Disciples of Christ, A History (pp. 340-341); and J.D. Murch, Christians Only (pp. 158-163).

63   Gates, pp. 74-75.

64   Allen and Hughes, Illusions of Innocence, p. 103.

and resurrection for our salvation. Now, the adult immersion of believers was becoming, to many, also an essential, and the unimmersed were not to be admitted into the fellowship of "true believers."

When Alexander Campbell discerned a drift toward exclusivism within his own ranks, he began to moderate his attacks on the denominations. When The Christian Baptist gave way to The Millennial Harbinger in 1830, his aggressive tendencies mellowed. Observing the chauvinism of legalists like John Howard, Arthur Crihfield, and Tolbert Fanning, he reacted strongly:

> This plan of making our own nest, and fluttering over our own brood; of building our own tent, and of confining all goodness and grace to our noble selves and the "elect few" who are like us, is the quintessence of sublimated phariseeism. . . . To lock ourselves up in the bandbox of our own little circle; to associate with the few units, tens, or hundreds, as the pure church, as the elect, is real Protestant monkery, it is evangelical nunnery.[65]

By 1833 those legalists who continued to attack other sects "were acting out a script that Campbell himself had abandoned."[66] Campbell now tried to counterbalance the growing influence of those who promoted the primitive church "not as an ecumenical ark for all Christians but as the one true church in a sea of false and apostate denominations."[67] In 1837 Arthur Crihfield began publishing a journal entitled The Heretic Detector, with the obvious purpose of exposing apostasy wherever he believed it to be. In that same year Campbell received a letter from a lady living in Lunenburg, Virginia, asking, "who is a Christian?" He responded, "I answer, Everyone that believes in his heart that Jesus of Nazareth is the Messiah, the Son of God; repents of his sins, and obeys him in all things according to his measure of knowledge of his will."[68]

Other voices of moderation attempted to reenforce Campbell's struggle against exclusivism, and mourned its disastrous results. When Alexander was away in 1835, his father Thomas wrote an article in The Millennial Harbinger, expressing "a feeling of deep regret, that a reformation. . . for the express purpose of putting an end to religious controversy among christians, should appear to take the unhappy turn, to which, with painful anxiety, we have seen it verging for the last ten years." He then continued:

---

65 Alexander Campbell, as quoted (with no footnote reference) in Allen and Hughes, Illusions of Innocence, pp. 180-181.

66 Hughes, Reviving The Ancient Faith, p. 27.

67 Ibid., p. 54.

68 Alexander Campbell, "Any Christian Among Protestants Parties?", The Millennial Harbinger, Vol. I, [New Series], No. 9 (September, 1837), p. 411.

But, alas! how have we wandered from our divine premises! We have forsaken terra firma, and are again out to sea, amidst the rocks and vortices, that have absorbed every adventurer from Arius to the present day. And, indeed, if we are to calculate the future by the past, especially for the last ten years, we might live to see an exhibition of all the curious questions and perplexing controversies of the last fifteen centuries, upon the face of the periodicals professedly in favor of the proposed reformation [restoration].[69]

Also in 1835, Barton Stone, responded to an "exclusivist" in his Christian Messenger, with a strongly-worded statement implying that the writer was attempting to make an "essential" doctrine out of a "non-essential" one:

Your *opinion*, deduced from this truth [that baptism is essential to salvation], is, that no unimmersed person, however penitent or believing, can be saved, or have his sins remitted, or can receive the gift of the Holy Spirit. . . .

These are your opinions—*opinions*, I call them, and am happy in the thought that they are not Bible-truth. You have indeed carried the doctrine to the extreme. . . . I dissent from your opinion. Did I believe as you do, then I must of necessity conclude that my former experience was a delusion—That I never was pardoned, or had my sins remitted—that I never received the Spirit—That I never loved God, his service, nor his people. Were I convinced of this, I should be shut up in desperation, for I have received nothing new in experimental religion since I was immersed, unless it be the satisfaction received since I complied with what I was convinced was my duty. . . .

Another reason for rejecting your opinion, is, because they who profess this doctrine are no better than those condemned by them. We see no more fruits of the Spirit in them— no more holiness in their lives—no more humility, and self-denial [than in the unimmersed]. . . . Do we not see as much conformity to the world manifested—as much pride—as much injustice—as much avarice? . . . Talk no more of being washed from your sins by immersion, when we see you living in sin; and many of you living on the gains of oppressing the poor African.[70]

On August 4, 1840, Walter Scott, responding to a letter from Philip Fall—a Church of Christ preacher in Nashville—regretfully bemoaned:

When you express your doubts of the matters connected with the recent reformation I sympathize with you, for the thing has not been what I hoped it would be by a thousand miles. We are indeed "a sect" differing

---

69 Thomas Campbell, commentary addended to "M. Winans to Elder Henry Grew," The Millennial Harbinger, Vol. VI, No. 6 (June, 1835), p. 272.

70 Barton Stone, "Reply to Brother Gooch," The Christian Messenger (Jacksonville, Ill.), Vol. IX, No. 10 (October, 1835), pp. 221 and 223.

but little, of anything that is good, from the parties around us. Alas! My soul is grieved every day.[71]

But the "literalists," "legalists," or "exclusivists," did not see themselves in the same light as their correctors. Instead they were being "faithful" where others were not; they were being "obedient" when others were seeking their own way. Boldly, Moses E. Lard, editor of Lard's Quarterly, begun for the purpose of defending "the true faith" asserted in 1863:

> The Bible does not recognize the unimmersed as Christians; . . .
>
> I recognize no human being as a Christian who is not immersed. . . .
>
> What! will retort the astounded opponent, utterly shocked and scandalized at the boldness of what is here said, do you mean to say that the Martin Luther was not a Christian? I mean to say distinctly and emphatically that Martin Luther, if not immersed, was not a Christian. . . . If a man can be a Christian without immersion, let the fact be shown; or if a man can or may commune without being a Christian, let the fact be shown. I deny both. Immovably I stand here. But I shall be told that this is Phariseeism, that it is exclusivism. Be it so; if it be true, and this is the only question with me respecting it, then am I so far the defendant of Phariseeism and exclusivism.[72]

Isaac Errett, the irenic and moderate editor of The Christian Standard inaugurated only three years later, responded to such inflexible exclusivism by contending that "It has now become a question, growing out of the peculiar logic employed by these brethren, *whether we shall have any religious fellowship whatever with any outside of our own churches?*" He continued on to muse "whether we shall not outvie the Old Landmark Baptists themselves in exclusiveness and make ourselves ridiculous before the whole religious world by the monstrous extravagance of our assumptions." Referring to the men of the Reformation as those who have come out of Babylon [a common metaphor in those days for those leaving the Roman Catholic Church], Errett refused to condemn them for infidelity, as some of the more rigid restorationists were doing. Instead he asserted:

> They talked much and suffered much for the name of Christ. We inherit the blessed fruits of their labors. We follow them through the scenes of their superhuman toil, to the dungeons where they suffered, and to the stakes where they won the glories of martyrdom, . . . we ask not whether these lofty heros of the church militant, to whom we owe *our* heritage of spiritual freedom, may commune with us—but rather, if we are at all worthy

---

71   Philip S. Fall correspondence (in the library of the Kentucky Historical Society), quoted in Dwight Stevenson, Walter Scott: The Voice of The Golden Oracle, p. 179.

72   Moses E. Lard, "Do the Unimmersed Commune?", Lard's Quarterly, Vol. I, No. 1 (September, 1863), pp. 44-49.

to commune with them! We feel honored in being permitted to call them *brethren. Our reformation movement is the legitimate offspring of theirs.*

. . .has it, we ask, come to this, that such as these, in whose presence many of us are dwarfed almost to nothingness, must hear our feeble and unworthy lips saying unto them, "Stand by thyself; come not near to me; for I am holier than thou"? . . .

Bro. Franklin counsels us not to weaken the hands of those who are laboring to restore primitive Christianity, by too wide a stretch of Christian charity. We thank him for his counsel. . . . In return, we trust Bro. F. will allow us to counsel him not to damage this great plea for Christian union by a spirit of exclusiveness. . . , which refuses to recognize as Christians all the unimmersed, and claims for ourselves to be Christians *par excellence,* because of a bit of accuracy on the question of baptism;—lest it should place us in a position so ridiculous or so odious, as to close the avenues of approach to multitudes of godly people—our equals in faith, our superiors in piety and humanity—whom we wish to enlighten on the evils of sectarianism. A denominationalism more intense and more intolerant it would be difficult to conceive, than that in which we must land, if this kind of argument is to prevail among us.[73]

The tension between those who tended to emphasize restoration and those whose primary goal was unity began to increase as the century progressed. Men like Benjamin Franklin [**not** of American Revolutionary renown], Moses Lard, Tolbert Fanning, and David Lipscomb, continued to fellowship with the rest of "The Brotherhood," but were at odds with many on numerous issues. Lard eventually advocated disassociation over the organ controversy. Paul Conkin summarized the situation as follows:

The two goals—New Testament purity and Christian unity—did not easily cohere. Stone had epitomized the goal of unity and had compromised almost all doctrines in behalf of this goal. Thomas Campbell leaned toward this position. Alexander Campbell, in his Reformed Baptist years, had moved far toward a separatist and purist stand but after 1832 had adopted a moderate or middle position that maintained some tension between the two goals. Benjamin Franklin first and best reflected the purist bent and thus wanted to exclude from membership and communion those who did not in every respect duplicate the New Testament Church.[74]

---

73   Isaac Errett, "The Limits of Religious Fellowship," The Millennial Harbinger, Vol. V [Fifth Series], No. 3 (March, 1862), pp. 126-131. Errett's allusion to "Bro. Franklin" in the quote was in reference to Benjamin Franklin, the rather legalistic editor of a journal entitled The American Christian Review from 1856 to 1878.

74   Conkin, p. 37. This author believes, however, that Moses Lard or Daniel Sommer better represent the uncompromising "purist bent" than Franklin, who was not as ambitious to disfellowship as they were.

Divisions among the Disciples of Christ focused, in the main, around four major issues. The first of these had to do with the organization of missionary societies. The practical-minded concluded that individual churches by themselves could have no significant impact on the mission fields, but that a joint effort in the form of a society sponsored by the churches and with such a specific focus, could have a much greater effect. To that end the American Christian Missionary Society was created in 1849, with Alexander Campbell as its first president. Here again was a moderation of Campbell's position, for he had earlier opposed them as being for sectarian purposes.[75]

Yet it was not long until the Society met strong opposition. Benjamin Franklin, who at first favored its creation, became a bitter opponent of it in his American Christian Review, believing that such an agency could become a source of control (via its large budget) over the Brotherhood. Jacob Creath could not understand Campbell's change of position, maintaining: "If you were right in the Christian Baptist, you are wrong now. If you are right now, you were wrong then. If you were right in the Christian Baptist, we are right now, in opposing conventions. . . . If we are wrong, Bro. Campbell taught us the wrong."[76]

And Tolbert Fanning saw such a "compromise" as a symptom of infidelity. In the creation of the missionary societies he later saw the seeds of liberalism, "for they *began* by setting aside the word. How else could they *end?*" As Earl West later warned:

> Their very existence was a reflection upon the wisdom of God, the adequacy of the church, and the Bible as a necessary guide. Their origin came, not from divine revelation, but from human planning; therefore, there was a subtle implication that the Bible was not a sufficient guide, but that something beyond it was needed.[77]

Going "beyond" the Bible for purposes of organization or creed was exactly what the Restoration Movement had opposed in the first place. Furthermore, David Lipscomb, whose Gospel Advocate became the southern rival of Isaac Errett's The Christian Standard in the 1860's, accused the society of being a promotional tool for his competition. Frustrated with their developing adversarial relationship, Isaac Errett proclaimed, "We are done with David Lipscomb," and another source of alienation between the two poles of the Disciples Brotherhood was manifested.[78]

---

75 See Richardson, Vol. II, p. 57. See also some of Campbell's responses, such as "To Mr. Robert Cautious," The Christian Baptist, Vol. I, No. 8 (March 1, 1824), pp. 157-158, etc.

76 Jacob Creath, "Conventions - No. V," The Millennial Harbinger, Vol. VII [Third Series], No. 11 (November, 1850), p. 54.

77 Earl West, The Search For The Ancient Order: A History of The Restoration Movement, 1800-1865, Vol. I (Germantown, Tennessee: Religious Book Service, 1990), pp. 342-343.

78 W. E. Garrison, Religion Follows The Frontier, p. 266.

The second divisive issue concerned the use of mechanical instruments in the worship service. In 1849 L.L. Pinkerton introduced the use of a melodian into his worship service in Midway, Kentucky, because "The singing was so deplorable that it scared the rats away!"[79] He was accused of being a liberal and introducing "worldly" [i.e. from the saloons, etc.] "innovations" into the Church. Alexander Campbell even deprecated its use for "all spiritually-minded Christians" as a sort of spiritual crutch that sounded like "a cow-bell in a concert."[80]

Nonetheless almost no leader of the early years, other than Moses Lard, was willing to make this issue a condition for fellowship. Lard felt that, since the New Testament *Koinonia* did not use instruments in the worship service, neither should any restoration church. Also, since the New Testament did not *authorize* their use, they were not to be used.[81]

In his Quarterly for March of 1864, Lard referred to anyone who would introduce a musical instrument into the worship service as "an insulter of the authority of Christ," and as "a defiant and impious innovator on the simplicity and purity of the ancient worship." He then pronounced, "The day on which a church sets up an organ in its house, is the day on which it reaches the first station on the road to apostasy," and issued the stern injunction: "Let no brother who takes a letter from one church ever unite with another using an organ. Rather let him live out of a church than go into such a den." He then proceeded on to prophesy and pass judgment on them:

> Thus these organ-grinding churches will in the lapse of time be broken down, or wholly apostatize, and the sooner they are in fragments the better for the cause of Christ. I have no sympathy with them, no fellowship for them, and so help me God never intend knowingly to put my foot into one of them.[82]

A third source of division among the Campbellites was the issue of slavery, as well as the Civil War itself. Ironically, it was Moses Lard who contended that, because the issue of slavery was not an "essential" to salvation, but rather a matter of personal opinion, "we can never divide!"[83]

---

79 Quoted in Leroy Garrett's The Stone-Campbell Movement, p. 310, without footnote reference.

80 Richardson, Vol. II, p. 366. For verification see Alexander Campbell, "Instrumental Music," The Millennial Harbinger, Vol. I, [Series Four], No. 10 (October, 1851), p. 582.

81 Another traditional "Brotherhood" slogan was "Where the Bible speaks, we speak; where the Bible is silent, we are silent." Most restorationists considered the latter half to refer to matters of opinion. But a few, like Lard, Franklin, Fanning, Lipscomb, and J.W. McGarvey believed in a hermeneutical "Law of Exclusion," meaning that whatever is not specified for use in the worship service, is prohibited.

82 Moses E. Lard, "Instrumental Music In Churches And Dancing," Lard's Quarterly (Lexington, Kentucky), Vol. I, No. 3 (March, 1864), pp. 331-333.

83 Moses E. Lard, "Can We Divide?", Lard's Quarterly, Vol. III, No. 3 (April, 1866), p. 336.

Yet the majority agreed with his viewpoint that, no matter how emotional the issue was, the Bible had no clear "yea or nay" on the subject.

Thomas Campbell's travels to Kentucky left him with a bad impression of slave owners. Barton Stone freed the slaves he inherited. And Alexander Campbell had a deep-seated distaste for the institution. Occasionally addressing the subject, he was definitely in favor of emancipation:

> *Slavery*, that largest and blackest blot upon our national escutcheon, that many-headed monster, that Pandora's box, that bitter root, that blighting and blasting curse under which so fair and so large a portion of our beloved country groans—that deadly Upas, whose breath pollutes and poisons everything within its influence—is now evoking the attention of this ancient and venerable commonwealth in a manner as unexpected as it is irresistible and cheering to every philanthropist—to everyone who has a heart to feel, a tear to shed over human wretchedness, or a tongue to speak for degraded humanity. . . .[84]

At the same time, however—both because he lived in Virginia and because he too believed the issue to be one of *political* opinion—he tried to steer a middle course. "I have always been anti-slavery," he wrote, "but never an abolitionist."[85] Walter Scott echoed the same sentiments:

> I am no friend to slavery, I deprecate its commencement, I deplore its continuance, and tremble for its issue; but I am silent because I think to speak would be folly. What ought to be said I can not say, and what ought not to be said, I will not say.[86]

Until recent times traditional Disciple historiography had promoted the belief that the Civil War was not a major factor in Disciple division. There was no discernable rift at the war's conclusion, and there were no presbyteries or synods which could be split anyhow. The pacifist stance of *most*[87] Disciple leaders, coupled with their views that the slave issue was a matter of opinion, also helped maintain the unity that was their original reason for existing. Also, the Stone-Campbell movement had developed in the border-state region, where there were fewer Yankee abolitionists and Dixie "fire eaters" than in New England or the Deep South. They had learned to tolerate each other to some extent.[88]

---

84   Richardson, Vol. II, p. 367.

85   Ibid., p. 533. For corroboration see Alexander Campbell, "American Slavery," The Millennial Harbinger, Vol. II [Third Series], No. 8 (August, 1845), p. 358.

86   Quoted in William Baxter, The Life of Elder Walter Scott, p. 360, without footnote reference.

87   James A. Garfield, for example, was one who was definitely not a pacifist.

88   This opinion is represented, for example, by Garrison and DeGroot, pp. 330-337.

However, the seeds, if not the stalk, of division were present back in 1863, for instance, when "Northern radicals" voted an allegiance resolution into the articles of the American Christian Missionary Society. In essence the resolution expressed support for the Union soldiers "who are defending us from the attempts of armed traitors to overthrow the Government."[89] The Southern Disciple leaders, who were prevented by the war from attending the conference in Cincinnati, were embittered, especially against Isaac Errett, the soon-to-be editor of The Christian Standard, who had a major part in their adoption. David Lipscomb's The Gospel Advocate became the standard-bearer for the southern contingent of Disciples of Christ.

Martin Marty has astutely observed that, with the constant posture of defending slavery against a disapproving world, southern churchmen became more and more resistant to political or religious change. This calcification led to more literalism toward the Bible, and since the Scriptures did not openly condemn slavery, but rather even seemed to acknowledge it, opposition was rejected as illegitimate.[90] Dean Walker agreed with this perspective, adding:

> Most of all, the passions of war and the "subjugation" of the South by the post-war military *regime* created a state of mind in the South which was not favourable to the catholic nature of the Restoration Movement. It was futile to talk of any union, even Christian union, when men were being coerced into political union by the Federal Army.[91]

In a paper presented by Henry Webb at a 1988 Restoration Forum near Akron, Ohio, convincing statistics revealed that the Restoration Movement **did**, for the most part, eventually split along lines correspondent to those of the Civil War. While the impasse of the first major division seemed to revolve around the instrumental question, the underlying cause was the resentment between the two regions. Focusing specifically on the state of Tennessee, for example, Webb noted that the mountainous and non-slave eastern portion was heavily pro-union, both politically and religiously. Whereas the middle and western pro-slave sections contained an overwhelming number of churches that eventually disfellowshipped the main body in 1906, the eastern portion contained an equally lopsided number of churches that remained *with* the original movement.[92] Dennis W. Meinig has suggested another possible influential factor as well: East Tennessee had geographical and economic connections with Baltimore and Philadelphia through the Great

---

89   David E. Harrell, Jr., "The Sectional Origins of The Churches of Christ," The Journal of Southern History, Vol. 30 (1964), p. 268; quoted in Tristano, p. 135.

90   Marty, Righteous Empire, p. 64.

91   Walker, Adventuring For Christian Unity, p. 42.

92   See Henry Webb, "Post-Civil War Tennessee: A Study In The Dynamics of Division," Restoration Forum VI (Joplin, Missouri: College Press, 1988), pp. 128-143. See also Webb's new history, In Search of Christian Unity (Cincinnati: Standard Publishing, 1990), Chapter 8.

Valley; whereas middle and western Tennessee focused on the Mississippi River and New Orleans for their markets.[93]

The fourth impetus for division in the Stone-Campbell Movement, as well as in other denominational structures, was liberalism. In the first half of the nineteenth century, this generally meant a situation in which one was willing to compromise with the society around him and adopted "innovations" such as musical instruments or missionary societies. The Campbellian mindset was somewhat susceptible to new ideas anyway, because its philosophical taproot grew out of the Enlightenment emphasis upon reason as the final arbiter of truth. Some began to adjust their concept of the primitive church as being "not the one true and perfect order of things, but rather an example of how the church adapted itself to the particular environment of the first century and the Roman Empire. Thus the church "ceases to be *normative* [italics mine] and becomes instead merely a particular and transitory manifestation of church."[94]

Reactions to this kind of perspective quickly emerged. Tolbert Fanning criticized Robert Richardson for allowing the Bible to be adjusted to the "learned theology and philosophy of the times." Ben Franklin saw the creation of the American Christian Missionary Society as a subtle, but fatal, step in this wrong direction. As Earl West, one of Franklin's direct spiritual descendants, expressed it: "Unknowingly, the Trojan horse had been rolled into the mighty fortress, and now Zion was beginning to boil with internal dissension."[95]

Near the end of the nineteenth century the word *liberalism* came to be associated with the philosophical approach of *Modernism*. The rise of Biblical textual criticism was countered by an emotional apologetic for the divine authority and infallibility of the Bible. Men who were identified with the "liberal" side of the instrument and missionary society issues now found themselves allied with the "conservatives" against what was perceived to be a thrust at the very heart of the standard of Christian truth. Those who still exalted unity as their pre-eminent purpose were caught in the quandary of trying to restore the original pattern of New Testament Christianity, and yet retain, let alone *promote*, catholicity.

There were, however, others who simply gave up this ecumenical spirit, and dug in for a fight. One of these men was Daniel Sommer, who became the editor of Franklin's_American Christian Review. Through this newspaper he issued a call to arms for the faithful to summon the "So-called Christian Church" for judgment. Meeting in convention at Sand Creek, Illinois, in August of 1889, Sommer read his "Address and Declaration" [an obvious parody of Thomas Campbell's work] calling for

93 Meinig, p. 278.

94 Tristano, pp. 9-10.

95 West, p. 345.

the six thousand assembled conservatives to join him in declaring to the rest of the Brotherhood that "if they do not turn away from such abominations, that we can not and will not regard them as brethren." A few years later he was confident that a new church would be created:

> The Sand Creek Declaration is being adopted, and those who will not do right are purged out as old leaven. In [the] course of a few years the Church of Christ will be entirely separated from the Christian Church. Then there will be no more fellowship between them as there now is between the Church of Christ and any other branch of sectarianism. Hallelujah.[96]

He was right! In 1906 the more literalistic adherents of the Disciples of Christ officially ruptured from the rest, and were listed ever afterward simply as the Church of Christ. Later in the century a second major excision happened, when the more moderate Disciples "withdrew" their churches from the Disciples of Christ Yearbook listings in protest of the liberal "Restructure" that formalized the Disciples into a denomination with an ecclesiastical headquarters in Indianapolis, Indiana.

There are now three main divisions descendent from the Stone-Campbell Restoration Movement: 1) the Church of Christ ("Non-Instrumental") or ("A Cappella"); 2) The Church of Christ/Christian Church ("Independent"); 3) the Christian Church (Disciples of Christ). Within the first group, there have been many *subdivisions* over such issues as the validity of the Sunday School, the use of multiple communion cups, the legitimacy of extra congregational agencies, etc. As of 1990, as many as twenty-seven discernable factions could be evidenced within the Stone-Campbell Movement.[97]

Mark Noll wrote a suitable eulogy for the noble ideal originally propounded by this Restoration Movement: "They took as their name simply 'Christians' or Disciples of Christ in the hopes of uniting all believers in a commonsense, democratic form of the faith. Over time, the inevitable happened, and this anti-denominational movement developed a vigorous denominational tradition."[98] And William Warren Sweet composed an appropriate epitaph: "Thus the movement which had begun as a protest against the numerous sects of Christians, instead of uniting them, had only succeeded in adding one [three?] more to the number."[99]

---

96   Daniel Sommer, quoted in Leroy Garrett's <u>The Stone-Campbell Movement</u>, p. 392.

97   Garrett, p. 433.

98   Noll, p. 237.

99   Sweet, p. 237.

Chapter
—15—

CONCLUSION

In this study I have attempted to follow two parallel topics—Rigdon and Restorationism. Both, in their youth, were naturally idealistic, hopeful, and energetic. But both, in their maturity, adjusted to the realities around them, redefined their priorities somewhat, and became contentious. I will now conclude this study with some observations about each topic separately.

I. AN EVALUATION OF RIGDON

Post mortem assessments of Rigdon typically featured a broad interpretation of the man. William Linn referred to Rigdon's obituary, which read: "It can only be said that he was a compound of ability, versatility, honesty, duplicity, and mystery."[1] Daryl Chase, in his 1931 Master's Thesis for the University of Chicago, which was entitled <u>Sidney Rigdon—Early Mormon</u>, offered his perspective that, "Judged by the general standards of intellectual and character measurements, Sidney Rigdon was not a great man," though he hastens to add that "for years he was considered a man of importance by many people."[2] Joseph Smith, Rigdon's close colleague from 1830 to 1844, somewhat prematurely eulogized, "Truth was his pursuit, and for truth he was prepared to make every sacrifice in his power."[3]

Many Campbellite authors chose to moralize about him in terms of the human weaknesses that can destroy a man. "Discontent follows ambition like a shadow," Henry Haskins once said,[4] and numerous

---

1   William Linn, <u>The Story of The Mormons</u> (New York: N.P., 1902), pp. 319-320.

2   Chase, p. 1.

3   Joseph Smith, <u>The Journal History</u>, Vol. III, No. 1, pp. 7-8, as quoted in McKiernan, p. 13.

4   Quote from <u>A Little Book of Aphorisms</u>, ed. by Frederick B. Wilcox (New York: Charles Scribners Sons. 1947), p. 7.

Disciples were quick to blame Rigdon's ambition for his defection to the Mormons, as well as his eventual frustrations in life. Henry Shaw sermonized:

> His ambition to be a religious leader, coupled with a jealous attitude toward those who had already succeeded, prevented him from attaining the very thing he desired most; first from the Baptists, next from the Disciples, and finally from the Mormons.[5]

Isaac Errett put it more succinctly:

> He was wrecked through an insane ambition. Let all self-seekers take notice![6]

So how are we to interpret Rigdon, and his enthusiasm for, and commitment to, restorationism? Was he typical or atypical of others on the early nineteenth century frontier, especially in the Western Reserve? Despite his personality quirks, he certainly *was* typical in his thirst for a religious faith that was both primitive and personal. Mark McKiernan, one of his two main biographers, has argued:

> Rigdon was a refraction of the religious tendencies held by millions of early nineteenth-century Americans who were greatly concerned about the fate of their eternal souls and joined one religious denomination after another.[7]

Sidney, in a sense, was a "seeker" his whole life—first as a Baptist, then as a Campbellite, next as a Mormon, and finally at the head of his own church. His deep-seated frustrations never seemed to have been totally abated. Despite the progression (or digression, depending upon one's point-of-view) of one form of Christianity for another, Rigdon never seemed to find the peace of mind he obviously craved.

There were, of course, those who evaluated Rigdon as a crackpot. James Adams, the nephew to Stephen Post (who attempted to lead Rigdon's church in his final years), wrote to his uncle claiming that Rigdon's revelations were "just the imaginations of a man's mind."[8] And Richard Van Wagoner, Rigdon's other significant biographer, depicted Sidney as the man with "a pathological kind of religiosity," and continued on to moralize that, "Madmen claiming to speak for God can infect others with their madness."[9]

---

5   Henry K. Shaw, <u>Buckeye Disciples: A History of The Disciples of Christ In Ohio</u> (St. Louis: Christian Board of Publication, 1952), p. 246.

6   Isaac Errett, "Death of Sidney Rigdon," p. 245.

7   McKiernan, p. 12.

8   Letter from Adams to Post, September 3, 1876, quoted in Van Wagoner, p. 454.

9   Van Wagoner, p. 457.

This writer will grant that Rigdon had some "spells" during which he apparently was completely disconnected with reality. And I am also willing to confess that, measuring by my own set of values, I find Rigdon to be an extremist in many of his actions. But the title of Mr. Van Wagoner's book, <u>Sidney Rigdon—A Portrait of Religious Excess</u>, suggests something far different. The subtitle of his thorough and scholarly work clearly implies that Rigdon had the problem of being *too religious*. Yet even Van Wagoner himself admits early in his book that "One cannot fully penetrate Rigdon's soul without understanding how the restoration of Christian Primitivism effected his thinking."[10]

Rigdon was deeply committed, definitely narrow-minded, and even perhaps compellingly "driven." He did not regard "religion" as many do today—as simply one facet of life to be balanced among the rest. But this author contends that Mr. Van Wagoner apparently fails to understand that the term "religious excess" is an oxymoron. In other words, he either does not realize, or does not admit, the *ultimate* nature of faith. Paul Tillich, one of America's foremost theologians of a couple generations ago, identified faith as "the state of being concerned with the ultimate," and has purported that just as it "demands total surrender," it also "promises ultimate fulfillment."[11]

Rigdon would have been very familiar with Biblical injunctions like, "Go and sell *all* that you possess, and you will have treasure in Heaven." [Matthew 19: 21]; or "Seek *first* His Kingdom and His righteousness, and *all* these things shall be yours as well." [Matthew 6: 33]; or "You shall love the Lord your God with *all* your heart and with *all* your soul and with *all* your might," [Deuteronomy 6: 5] and that if you do you might gain "the peace that passes *all* understanding" [Philippians 4: 7], and you "will *never* thirst again." [John 4: 14 and 6: 35]. The very essence of the Christian faith does not permit it to be merely a category of life, but rather an all-pervading world view through which virtually every decision or activity should be filtered and interpreted.

Any religion necessarily postulates a basic metaphysical and cosmological understanding of the nature of existence. The implications that follow from the premises proported by that world view dictate courses of action. In one sense, if a person is not "excessive," it may be because he has not fully committed himself to the precepts or demands mandated by that perspective, or perhaps lacks the courage to do so. What may seem excessive to one man is to another the most logical way of behaving, depending upon what premises each one accepts. Martyrdom seems a bit fanatical to most people, but to Sir Thomas More, who believed he was

---

10   Ibid., pp. 18-19.

11   Paul Tillich, <u>Dynamics of Faith</u> (New York: Harper & Row, 1957), pp. 1-2.

earning an infinitely longer and better life than was his on Earth, it was his only reasonable alternative.

Rigdon doggedly pursued a "personal relationship with God" because he shared the psychological hunger of many frontiersmen at that time for an "assurance of salvation." And he was willing to forgo what he regarded as less important desires in order to accomplish this perceived greater object. Hence, in early 1830 when Rigdon was offered a spacious farm and a secure salary by his Mentor congregation, he spurned their generous overture in pursuit of "the true church." As McKiernan has said, "His quest for the fullness of the gospel compelled him to abandon positions of prestige, power, and financial security."[12]

A Wesleyan man recently asked me, "Was Sidney Rigdon a restorationist who strayed?" It is my considered opinion that, if Rigdon could answer that question, he would adamantly insist that *he* never strayed, but that Alexander Campbell would not venture far enough toward *complete* restorationism, and that Joseph Smith and Brigham Young were the ones who strayed from the true path.

Rigdon typified a pattern of restoration development in that he began optimistically with the naive conviction that Christian unity could be achieved through restorationism. As time passed, however, strong disagreements developed as to what the New Testament pattern of doctrine and practice was. He spent his last years shorn of his youthful idealism, discouraged and disillusioned, with all his hopes for a restored and united Church dashed. The concept of restorationism had not lived up to its promise.

II. AN EVALUATION OF RESTORATIONISM

Of all the works done on the Christian restoration movements in America, perhaps the most philosophically perceptive is <u>Illusions of Innocence</u>, co-authored by Leonard Allen and Richard Hughes. Oddly enough—since both men hail from the rather legalistic A Cappella tradition—it is also one of the most critical of the pitfalls of restorationist doctrine. Recognizing that, in the first half of the nineteenth century, the impetus for restorationism was interconnected with the hope of millennialism, Allen and Hughes connect this restorationist desire with the psychological need to return to an age of innocence and simplicity in a world that many perceive to be growing more self-indulgent and complex. While the millennium was the exit, the restoration of the primordium was the entrance.

Of course, the themes of origin and end are deeply interrelated: last things often involve a return to first things; primordium becomes millennium

---

12   McKiernan, p. 13.

when the end of times is heralded by "the restoration of all things." Yet in our most future-oriented of cultures it is instructive to see how often we have hankered for an earlier time when all was well, when we had not fallen into the guilt of history, when we experienced the innocence that is our birthright as Americans.[13]

It is not unique to restorationists—unless we can admit that in many ways we are all restorationists of one sort or another—to live with the impression that, if we could just return to the pristine, we would eliminate most of the problems caused by the corruptions of modern civilization. The recently romanticized concepts of American Indian village life—eating only fruits, nuts, and berries, or wild game, yielding good health; living at peace with nature and neighbors, and being in touch with ancestral spirits, yielding happiness; and using herbs, roots, and incantations to cure whatever ails us—are just a few examples of this deep psychological desire.

Clearly the restoration ideal has not been the exclusive property of a few eccentric Christian sects. It has informed the fundamental outlook of preachers and presidents, of soldiers and scholars. Indeed, the restoration perspective has been a central feature of American life and thought from the earliest Puritan settlements, and now continues to exercise a profound influence on the thinking and behavior of the American people.[14]

In the case of the Stone-Campbell Restoration Movement, author Leroy Garrett has argued that the original focus was on unity, and more on reformation than restoration, a view for which he has been censured by numerous critics. In his diagnosis as to why the Stone-Campbell movement failed in its aim to unite American Christendom, Garrett blamed the intrusion of an emphasis upon restorationism, contending that **"restorationism by its very nature has been divisive throughout the history of the church** [my bold], spawning scores of sects, and was a major cause in dividing the Stone-Campbell movement. . . ."[15] Paul Conkin has supported this perspective, when he wrote, "Such fragmentation seems endemic in all restorationist and congregational forms of Christianity. . . ."[16]

But Dr. Garrett has, I fear, yielded to the same temptation that many other religious historians have who are frustrated or embarrassed by the failure of their respective denominations to live up to their own ideals or attain their own objectives. They strive for a sort of theological or sociological catharsis by finding a rather simplistic explanation for complex problems. Some questions must be asked of Dr. Garrett. If restorationism is by nature divisive, how can one explain the 1832 union of Stone's

---

13   Hughes and Allen, <u>Illusions of Innocence</u>, p. IX.

14   Ibid., p. 24.

15   Garrett, p. 7.

16   Conkin, p. 42.

"Christian Churches" with Campbell's "Disciples of Christ," especially when one group had its roots in American revivalism and the other grew out of European Enlightenment rationalism? Also, how can one account for the rapid growth of both major indigenous restoration movements, the Disciples and the Mormons, during the whole of the nineteenth century? Statistics show, for example, that the Disciples of Christ virtually doubled every ten years from 1832 to 1875 (from 25,000 to 400,000 members), and then tripled from 1875 to 1900 (from 400,000 to 1,120,000 thousand members).[17]

Initially the Stone-Campbell Restoration Movement kept the goal of unity elevated among its priorities, and the "essentials" for restorationism were few. The founders stressed toleration in matters of opinion. Barton Stone and Thomas Campbell were somewhat pacific in nature and amenable in persuasion when compared to some of their spiritual descendants. As long as the unity movement centered its test of fellowship around the widely accepted facts of the Gospel, unity was retained and the movement grew. But when what earlier had been termed "opinions" evolved and became "essentials," the movement stagnated and began to split.

In many ways restoration movements, like most religious reform movements, go through a sort of biological life cycle. They are born with a great deal of exuberance and commitment from those directly involved. Their infancy often renders them vulnerable, pliable, and open to the influence of more dynamic forces around them. Their adolescence, a time of development and definition, disturbs others when the onset of idealism and muscle-flexing begins to challenge the comfort zones of those around them. Then follows a period of adjustment and assimilation into the community as an equal (denomination)[18], or an experience of rejection as a rabble-rousing outcast (sect).

But such movements tend to grow older in much the same way as people do. They lose the fervor and vitality of their original purpose, and begin to calcify, becoming brittle, defensive, and introverted, focusing on perpetuating their own structures and forms. As A.T. DeGroot expressed it in The Restoration Principle:

17　See Garrison and DeGroot, The Disciples of Christ: A History, pp. 324-329; and Murch, Christians Only, p. 193. For possible variations on these figures see Garrett, p. 197. Specific numbers for these early years are inaccurate and vary widely, but a figure of 25,000 in 1832 is generally accepted, and a total of 200,000 is listed in the US census of 1860, though even this count has been challenged by some.

18　Nathan Hatch, in The Democratization of Christianity (pp. 15 and 16) described this phase when he wrote, "Yet the white-hot intensity of early Disciples, Methodists, Baptists, and Mormons grew cooler over time. Cultural alienation gave way to a pilgrimage toward respectability."

When a culture is young and full of sap, like a fresh green shoot, it is more concerned with questions of *ends and meanings* than with questions of *ways and means*. The *means* which it uses to solve the inevitable problems of food, shelter, transportation, etc., are always kept subordinate to the intrinsic *ends* of life which it envisages with deep, worshipful appreciation in its art and literature as well as in its religion. But when a culture grows old, the symptom of its incipient decay is to be seen in the thickening of its woody stalk, the growing predominance of externals and mechanisms in its life, the loss of its vital upward urge toward intrinsic and enduring values.[19]

This author would then qualify Garrett's thesis. Restorationism is divisive *when it becomes intolerant*. The slogan "In essentials unity; in non-essentials liberty; in all things love;" seems very catholic at face value. But what *are* the essentials? With Thomas Campbell the essentials were few, basically just revolving around the central belief of the Gospel that Jesus was the resurrected Christ, and the Son of the living God. Alexander Campbell, along with Walter Scott, eventually pushed those essentials further with a formula for salvation that mandated a fivefold process: faith, repentance, baptism, forgiveness of sins, and the gift of the Holy Spirit. Sidney Rigdon then added to the evolution of these necessities by expanding on and delineating the manifestations which prove the gift of the Holy Spirit. Often referred to as the *gifts* of the Holy Spirit, these included such supernatural actions as the gift of prophesy, speaking in tongues, faith healing, and even the ability to do miracles. A true restoration movement, Rigdon believed, would include the restoration of these first-century church phenomena as well as its forms. But with each multiplication of essentials for salvation (and therefore fellowship) came the potential for division, since each new doctrine itself could be controversial and divisive. Hence the *aktionsart* of restorationism being a unity movement gave way to the concept of restorationism as a *purity* movement with all the "correct" doctrines being defended by guardians of "the True Faith."

Therefore it seems logical to assert that restorationism is divisive in proportion to the delineation and definition of its "essentials" for fellowship. The more essentials there are, the smaller the template and the fewer who qualify for membership or inclusion. Thus the hope for unity is inversely proportionate to the number of defined requirements or developed mandates of restorationism. Tolerant restorationism united people; intolerant restorationism isolated and divided them.

Of course the real question then becomes, how much can we tolerate and not adulterate God's message, for which there is no easy answer. It is very natural to seek for a solution to this dilemma by researching the tenets held by the founder of a movement. Yet such

---

19   DeGroot, The Restoration Principle, p. 169.

research can easily lead to conflicting opinions. For example, was Alexander Campbell more of a tolerant catholic or a truth-seeking restorationist in emphasis? Or, did he always have the same priorities, or did they change as he got older? DeGroot has concluded, "Unfortunately for the peace and unity of religious faith, the understanding of *what* the Founder wanted to be kept fresh, to be made central in his way of living, has been as varied as the personalities of the restoration leaders themselves."[20]

Allen and Hughes have suggested that the Campbells tended to share the common perspective of many of their contemporaries [including Joseph Smith] that the Bible was fundamentally a legal document.[21] Lester McAllister notes that a legalistic approach does not naturally tend toward unity:

> Again Campbell, in his idealism, sees all Christians united if only they will conform to a clear pattern supposedly presented in the New Testament. He forgets that there are many ways of interpreting the Scriptures and that what appears plain to one is obscure to another. The vision is a worthy one, but the bringing of it to reality has been exceedingly difficult and has been attended, not by unity, but by actual further division within the church.[22]

Another question poses itself. If restorationism is unitive—and therefore we all return to the model of the New Testament church and have unity in Christendom—what caused the original church to fracture in the first place? The easy answer offered by the guardians of orthodoxy is, of course, infidelity. The old Landmark Baptists believed that the Bible provided a blueprint of the primitive church, from which a church could not deviate and still be a "true church." They also believed that they *alone* represented the true doctrine of that church.[23]

The Disciples of Christ also held "the central conviction that there was a divine *pattern* [italics mine] of apostolic Christianity and that the answer to the problems of contemporary Protestantism was to return to these Biblical standards."[24] That word "pattern" is very redundant in Church of Christ literature especially, and implies that there is an exact theological paradigm which must be re-established in order for the church to be what God intended for it to be. The central problem of Christian restorationism is, and always has been, finding agreement on what the original pattern of

---

20   Ibid., p. 133.

21   Hughes and Allen, <u>Illusions of Innocence</u>, p. 116.

22   McAllister, p. 24.

23   See Allen and Hughes, <u>Discovering Our Roots</u>, pp. 69 ff., for more description.

24   Harrell, <u>The Quest For A Christian America</u>, p. 27

doctrine and practice of the New Testament church was! John Owsten concurs:

> . . .both Disciples and Baptists have inherited Glasite practice: our propensity to divide into other parties when we cannot agree. This, I believe, is an inherent danger in any "restoration" or "back to the Bible" movement. We cannot often agree on what needs to be restored from the original church.[25]

But disagreement itself is not the problem. As Leroy Garrett has written, "Restorationists or primitivists who find in Scripture a fixed pattern for the church are tempted to impose their interpretation of 'the true church' upon others."[26] That is where the exclusiveness causes division. Jim North, a highly respected contemporary Stone-Campbell movement author, contends that "various evangelical churches are 'wrong' on a number of points of doctrine and practice," and that "If *all* professed Christians will observe *all* that the Scriptures plainly commands, there will be unity on this score [italics mine]."[27] But William Whitsitt, a professor at Southern Baptist Seminary, took issue with such face-value simplicity. When the Campbells proposed that "Where the Scriptures speak we speak, and where the Scriptures are silent we are silent," he retorted:

> Here was, beyond dispute, an excellent ideal; but, in point of fact, it could hardly ever amount to anything more than an ideal. Neither Thomas Campbell, nor Alexander, nor any of their supporters has ever possessed wit enough to give effect to it by making out just where the Scriptures do speak. . . . What is the profit of professing to speak where the Scriptures speak, without more power than these gentlemen had to determine where the Scriptures speak or where they are silent?[28]

Perhaps the Achilles heel of restorationist dogma has been its inability to be convincing to many that the New Testament Church is so easily identified. Harold Bloom has noted that "One of the grand myths of the American Religion is the restoration of the Primitive Church, which probably never existed."[29] Even A.T. DeGroot, a Disciple historian, has been willing to admit, "In the last analysis, there never was a one-and-only primitive Christian church."[30] W. E. Garrison, another Disciple historian, has seconded that observation:

---

25   John Owston, " The Scotch Baptist Influence On The Disciples of Christ," <u>Leaven</u> (Malibu: Pepperdine U., Winter quarter, 1997), p. 39

26   Garrett, p. 349.

27   North, <u>Union In Truth</u>, pp. 364 and 91.

28   Whitsitt, pp. 67-68.

29   Bloom, <u>The American Religion: The Emergence of The Post-Christian Nation</u>, p. 40.

30   DeGroot, <u>The Restoration Principle</u>, p. 182.

The most important discovery that one makes about primitive Christianity is that it never existed—if one means by "primitive Christianity" a definite set of teaching and practice embodied in one uniform and unified institution showing no influence from its environment or from the cultural heritage of the people of whom it was composed and the leaders by which it was guided.[31]

DeGroot did concede, however, that "There were numerous primitive Christian churches, with greater and lesser degrees of common practice and belief, the inclusive, distinguishing feature of which was the will to do the will of Christ."[32]

Richard Hughes has interpreted and criticized Alexander Campbell for "sketching out for his followers what seemed to him the clear, self-evident essentials of the true Church of Christ," and for then launching "a devastating attack on everything and everyone who did not agree with his vision of the ancient Christian faith."[33] Whether this is an accurate or unfair portrayal of him will continue to be debated by many. But there is little doubt that many of his followers came to reflect this spirit. Earl West, a prolific A Cappella Church of Christ author, exhibited this attitude when he wrote:

> For the most part the churches of Christ down through the years have maintained that immersion is essential to being a Christian. They have refused to try to substitute opinions for this plain declaration of scriptures. Let this be called "exclusiveness," "phariseeism," "literalism," and an "extreme" or come what may; still, it is loyalty to God's word, and shows a respect for the revealed will, and that's what counts.[34]

Yet Church of Christ leaders and members today reject such labels as denomination or sect in reference to their own identity, even though, as Hughes himself admits, "Their denial of these categories flies in the face of social reality."[35] DeGroot described the Stone-Campbell Restoration Movement as a free fellowship seeking Biblical direction which evolved into "a more or less rigidly described group of those who had found 'the truth' about organization, work, and worship," adding that, "Protestantism then discovered that it had gained another fragment, much akin to the others."[36] Conkin points out the eventual irony connected with the restoration movement's unity emphasis:

---

31 W.E. Garrison, <u>Religion Follows the Frontier</u>, p. 11.

32 DeGroot, p. 182.

33 Hughes, <u>Reviving the Ancient Faith</u>, pp. 27 and 22.

34 West, <u>The Search For The Ancient Order</u>, Vol. I, p. 350.

35 Hughes, p. 2.

36 DeGroot, pp. 150-151.

But as events as well as careful scholarship soon attested, the New Testament did not provide an unambiguous model, and thus those reformers who placed most emphasis on a return to the ancient order were soon the ones who most sharply disagreed over doctrine, polity, and worship. In other words, restorers turned out to be the prototypal sectaries, however earnestly they hoped that a return to an early model would end sectarian strife.[37]

There is another weakness inherent in the restoration hope, and that is the assumption that if correct doctrine and polity were restored, the church would be one. Yet others have seen that this central concern of the Disciple and Mormon movements was not always the same concern of other Christian groups. Henry Webb notes that:

> . . . the serious challenge to the ideal of restoration is encountered at the point of defining exactly what is to be restored. A brief glance at the many books and pamphlets appealing for some type of restoration discloses the fact that there is a bewildering variety of understanding of precisely what should be restored. Some have focused their concern for restoration on the church as an institution. Others have emphasized doctrines and sacraments while some others, more influenced by Pietism, see the need for individual holiness as the focus of restoration.[38]

Continuing on to recognize that the Disciples of Christ movement had its roots in enlightenment rationalism,[39] Webb expresses his opinion that:

> The plea that lies at the heart of the Restoration Movement is addressed primarily to the mind, and the tendency to understand faith as belief of testimony is primarily an intellectual approach to religion. Here again, a widening gap with the culture is encountered. The society at large seems to be in search of religious values that address deep personal anxieties and minister to alienation and insecurities that beset individuals. . . . The result of these conditions is widespread social and individual frustration and

---

37 Conkin, p. 2.

38 Henry Webb, <u>In Search of Christian Unity</u>, p. 37.

39 Henry May has written: "At times the effort to simplify Christianity made by men like Barton Stone or particularly Thomas and Alexander Campbell, by returning to the words of Christ as their sole authority, can sound somewhat like Enlightenment attempts (for instance Jefferson's) to separate the teachings of Jesus from the distortions of the priests. This similarity is pointed out by Sidney Mead, who has argued powerfully that pietism and rationalism have much in common. . . .Mead, of course, is not unaware of the differences between these two movements, especially in their epistemology. From my present perspective the differences are more important than the similarities: People whose ultimate authority is either scripture or faith do not belong in the Enlightenment. The Campbellites made the New Testament their authority, and did not approach it selectively as Jefferson did. Their Jesus is a divine figure and not, like Jefferson's, a secular moralist. Henry May, <u>The Enlightenment In America</u>, p. 402, footnote 29.

anxiety, and those religious bodies that seem to speak more effectively to individual needs are growing. Such bodies tend to sublimate doctrine to personal satisfaction and emotional expression, a tendency that is clearly seen in the phenomenal expansion of Pentecostal-type denominations and also in the charismatic subgroups that can be found in virtually all of the older denominations. The trend is discernable also in the extent to which psychology has replaced theology in contemporary preaching. . . .[40]

The recent success of the Holiness and Pentecostal movements seem to attest to this thesis. The Mormon church has also ridden this wave, through its personal and charismatic aspects. Even many of the more mainstream denominations have realized a swing in the more emotive "signs and wonders" direction.[41]

It would be quite inaccurate to assume that all the descendants of Alexander Campbell were narrow legalists. The Christian Church/Church of Christ has tried to steer a moderate course and continues to believe that unity can still be accomplished through restoration. The Christian Church (Disciples of Christ) has been even more aggressive in the last half century in ecumenical movements, being willing to de-emphasize, or at least re-interpret, the focus on restorationism for the sake of Christian unity.

Robert Richardson, often referred to as Alexander Campbell's "alter ego", maintained that Christian unity can be achieved only if the core beliefs of Christianity are emphasized, and not the particulars. He maintained that the early Christians did not unite upon the basis of Bible, for they did not even have the Bible, but instead they found unity in the Gospel, the belief that Jesus was the Christ, the son of the living God. He asserted:

> Let the Bible be our spiritual library; but let the Gospel be our standard of orthodoxy. Let the Bible be our test of Christian character and perfection, but let the Christian confession be our formula of Christian adoption and of Christian union. In a word, let the Bible be to us every thing designed by its Author, but let "Christ crucified" be not only our peace with God, but our peace with one another.[42]

Isaac Errett, the editorial leader of the Stone-Campbell brotherhood in the "second generation," as Alexander Campbell was in the first, virtually echoed those same sentiments when he wrote, "Let the bond of union among the Baptized be *Christian character* in place of *orthodoxy*—right

---

40   Webb, pp. 417-418.

41   For further discussion on this subject, see Discovering Our Roots, Chapter 12, and Garry D. Nation's article, "The Restoration Movement," in Christianity Today (May 18, 1992), pp. 27-31.

42   Robert Richardson, "Reformation - No. IV.," The Millennial Harbinger (Series III), Vol. IV, No. 9 (September, 1847), p. 509.

doing in place of *exact thinking*; and outside of plain precepts, let all acknowledge the liberty of all, nor seek to impose limitations on their brethren, other then those of the law of love."[43]

This author believes—based upon over thirty years of service in restoration churches and a restoration college—that the present era is exhibiting a cross-denominational desire for restorationism, at least among evangelical churches, unequaled since the nineteenth century. Leroy Garrett has described restorationism only within the context of a spiritual movement. But there are significant psychological and social realities to it as well. Restorationism is a reaction to the stress between the complexities of life and the psychological desire for simplicity. A multiplicity of societal and denominational "truth claims" have yielded a legacy of confusion, and many display a hunger for a simple and "real" (personal) faith that offers a basic, black-and-white interpretation of the world in juxtaposition to the complex conditions around us.

It has been inherent in the nature of restoration movements to offer moral absolutes, to be both appealing and yet divisive. Restoration movements have appeared in most every era of American history, and often in European history as well. Hence the future portends that Restoration movements will almost continuously be with us, and also probably continually fragmenting. One author has observed, "Historically, however, restoration fervor has tended to be a one-generation phenomenon. Later generations establish denominational institutions, become sectarian, or disperse."[44]

The loss of restoration momentum and the appearance of introverted subdivision at the end of the nineteenth century suggests that another factor may have intruded at this time—the rise of Darwinian optimism. As Fundamentalism resisted the inroads of Modernism, so also restorationism struggled with progressivism, and later, relativism. The crux of the contest revolves around the age-old tension of objectivism versus subjectivism, or essentialism versus existentialism. The former advocates a belief in one eternal set of truths to be discovered or ascertained, and then obeyed. The latter tends to recognize this world to be a multiversity of relativistic truths, apprehended by different individuals in different ways. One author has maintained that herein was the trouble with Campbell's movement—that retrograde restorationism and the forward-looking post millennialism were incompatible:

> The problem, which Campbell failed to see at the time but which became abundantly apparent as the years went by, was that primitivism and post

---

43   Isaac Errett, "The True Basis of Union," <u>The Christian Standard</u>, Vol. III, No. 125 (June 20, 1868), p. 196. This quote may also be found in Garrison and DeGroot, p. 358, and Garrett, p. 325.

44   Garry D. Nation, "The Restoration Movement," p. 31.

millennialism, as Campbell employed those concepts, pointed in two fundamentally opposite directions. Primitivism pointed backward, not forward. It was a tool for regression, not for progression. It prized the past, not the future. Primitivism, as Campbell defined the concept (though he never used the term), stood fundamentally opposed to human progress as progress generally was understood in the eighteenth and nineteenth centuries in Europe and America.[45]

Restorationism need not be viewed in such a negative light, however. While looking backward for a source or plan, as one might do in an effort to restore a historical mansion, it is also forward-looking in that restorationism is essentially an effort at regeneration. Campbell, as a postmillennialist, *was* an optimist, and did not resist the achievements of modern science but welcomed them.

Allen and Hughes have contributed another interesting postulate. They contend that the recent remarkable success of Allan Bloom's The Closing Of The American Mind was a reflection of the reservoir of restorationist sentiment present in the United States today:

> Bloom's book was fundamentally a restorationist treatise, tapping deeply into the bountiful wellspring of American restorationist ideology. Like the early "Christians in the West," Bloom began with an impassioned appeal for the freedom to inquire and to search, contending that true liberal education requires "that no previous attachment be immune to examination and hence re-evaluation." Like so many Americans before him, he legitimated both the freedom and importance of inquiry with appeals to the primordium of nature. . . .

> For Bloom, appreciation for "cultures," ethnic festivals, and the women's movement had no place in the American Eden. Such things found a place only after the fall. . . .

> The fact that Bloom cast the book in the time-honored tradition of restoration rhetoric and the fact that the public response was so positive suggests that the restoration ideal continues to exert considerable sway in American public life.[46]

Perhaps the most perceptive and astute observation concerning the restoration movement has been offered by a scholar who has no connection with restorationism. Richard M. Tristano, a Roman Catholic and "outsider," has suggested that "we can learn more from the ideals expressed by the founding fathers of American Restorationism than from the failures of those ideals as they came into contact with the reality of a hostile world."[47] He then concluded:

---

45   Hughes, Reviving The Ancient Faith, p. 29.

46   Hughes and Allen, Illusions of Innocence, pp. 226-229.

47   Tristano, The Origins of The Restoration Movement, p. 10.

American Christianity has flourished in a political and social environment which is probably the freest in the history of Western civilization. Human imagination, private opinion, socioeconomic factors, and ethnic, regional, and linguistic differences have helped to produce a plethora of Christian groups. None of these elements is scriptural, but all of them are deeply rooted in the American experience. The need which the Restoration Movement perceived was how to balance the human liberty which Americans cherished, with the message of the Gospel, which after all is not about the diversity but the unity of humanity. How can we balance the human need for pluralism and authority, individual conscience and community, toleration and religious certitude? These are questions for our own age.[48]

In their slogan, "In essentials unity; in opinions liberty; and in all things love," the Disciples of Christ attempted to allow for diversity in a pluralistic society. The Mormon response to pluralism was, however, "much sharper than anything experienced by the Campbellites."[49] The Mormon restoration movement was not that concerned about—or perhaps recognized the futility of—trying to unite the denominations; the Latter-day Saints were more focused upon gathering the loyal saints for the end. In this sense then, the Stone-Campbell movement was more of a failure, because it advocated a unity which did not occur, and then subdivided within itself. Thomas Campbell's plea to outsiders in The Declaration And Address of 1809 ironically mirrors back on the movement today:

> Alas! poor people! how do our divisions and corruptions stand in your way? What a pity that you find us not upon original ground, such as the Apostles left the primitive churches? Had we but exhibited to you their unity and charity; their humble, honest, and affectionate deportment towards each other and towards all men: you would not have had those evil and shameful things to object to our holy religion, and to prejudice your minds against it. But your conversion, it seems, awaits our reformation—awaits our return to primitive unity and love. To this may the God of mercy speedily restore us, both for your sakes and our own.[50]

---

48   Ibid., p. 154.

49   Marvin S. Hill, The Role of Christian Primitivism In The Origin And Development of The Mormon Kingdom (Ph.D. dissertation for the University of Chicago, 1968), p. 78.

50   Thomas Campbell, The Declaration And Address (1809), p. 54.

Addendum

ON ALEXANDER CAMPBELL

Until recently Alexander Campbell was either ignored or granted scant attention in the major histories of American religion. Yet a good portion of this work involves Alexander Campbell. Someone may ask, "Who is Alexander Campbell, and is he significant enough to justify so much attention?" My reply to the first question is that Alexander Campbell is considered to be the most prominent founder and ideologist of the Disciples of Christ, just as Joseph Smith is in relation to the Mormons, though without the status of being regarded as a prophet or revelator.

Most everyone today knows something about Joseph Smith; but very few, even within his own movement today, know anything about Alexander Campbell. Yet he was an important man in his own era. In 1858 the editor of the Louisville Journal wrote that "Alexander Campbell is unquestionably one of the most extraordinary men of our time."[1] Paul Conkin has referred to him as "one of the most distinguished men of western Virginia," and alluded to his popularity as a lecturer and debater on a wide range of topics.[2] Baptist bishop R.B. Semple, one of Alexander Campbell's contemporaries and theological opponents, once remarked, "he is so much of a champion that to be beaten by him would not be so discreditable as it might be with some other antagonists."[3]

Campbell also had the respect of important men. He was chosen as a delegate to the Virginia Constitutional Convention in 1829. In 1857, he was invited by the governor of Louisiana to be a guest in his home, and they spent three days together.[4] Ex-president James Madison once commented, "It was my pleasure to hear him very often as a preacher of the gospel, and I regard him as the ablest and most original expounder of the Scriptures I have ever heard."[5] Robert E. Lee regarded Campbell to be "a man in whom were illustriously combined all the qualities that could adorn or elevate the nature to which he belonged," as well as "A man who if he had been delegated as the representative of his species to one of the superior worlds, would have suggested a grand idea of the human race."[6] And Henry Clay

1   Robert Richardson, Memoirs of Alexander Campbell, Vol. II, p. 639.

2   Paul Conkin, American Originals: Homemade Varieties of Christianity, p. 18.

3   R.B. Semple, correspondance from College Hill, D.C., Sept. 26, 1827; reprinted in The Christian Baptist, Vol. V, No. 4 (November, 1827), p. 399 (original p. 45); also printed in Richardson, Vol. II, p. 160.

4   Richardson, Vol. II, p. 626.

5   Ibid., Vol. II, p. 313.

6   Earl West, The Search For The Ancient Order, Vol. I, p. 37.

once wrote these words of commendation to the English Parliament on Campbell's behalf:

> . . .I take great satisfaction in strongly recommending him to the kind offices of and friendly reception and treatment of all persons with whom he may meet and wherever he may go. Dr. Campbell is among the most eminent citizens of the United States, distinguished for his great learning ability, for his successful devotion to the education of youth, for his piety and as the head and founder of one of the most important and respectable religious communities in the United States.[7]

Furthermore Campbell was often in demand as a speaker for important assemblies. At Indianapolis, the governor and members of the State Constitutional Convention attended one of his public meetings, and then invited him to open their official session the next morning.[8] The Missouri legislature extended him an invitation to address them at Jefferson City, which he did twice on a Sunday, and then delivered a lecture on education on Monday morning for which the legislature postponed its morning session until after noon.[9] And in late May, 1850, while in Baltimore, Campbell was invited by both Houses of Congress to address them in the Capitol in Washington on June 2. He spoke for an hour and a half using John 3:17 as his text.[10]

---

7   Richardson, Vol. II, p. 548.

8   Ibid., Vol. II, p. 589.

9   Ibid., Vol. II, p. 597.

10 Ibid., Vol. II, pp. 587-588.

Bibliography

I. Background Readings

Ahlstrom, Sydney E. A Religious History of The American People. 2 Vols. Garden City, New York: Doubleday and Company, 1975.

Allen, C. Leonard and Richard T. Hughes. Discovering Our Roots: The Ancestry of Churches of Christ. Abilene, Texas: Abilene Christian University Press, 1988.

Bailey, Thomas A., David Kennedy, and Lizabeth Cohen. The American Pageant: A History of the Republic. ed. 11. Lexington, Massachusetts: D. C. Heath, 1998.

Bainton, Roland H. Here I Stand: A Life of Martin Luther. New York: New American Library, 1950.

Boles, John B. The Great Revival: Beginnings of the Bible Belt. Lexington: The University of Kentucky Press, 1996.

Butler, Jon. Awash in A Sea of Faith: Christianizing The American People. Cambridge: Harvard University Press, 1990.

Cherry, P. P. The Western Reserve and Early Ohio. Akron: R. L. Fouse, 1921.

Conkin, Paul K. American Originals: Homemade Varieties of Christianity. Chapel Hill: The University of North Carolina Press, 1997.

Cross, Whitney. The Burned-Over District: The Social and Intellectual History of Enthusiastic Religion In Western New York, 1800-1850. Ithaca, New York: Cornell University Press, 1950.

Durant, Will. The Story of Civilization. Vol. 6, The Reformation: A History of European Civilization from Wycliff to Calvin: 1300-1564. New York: Simon and Schuster, 1957.

Erasmus, Desiderius. Praise of Folly and Letter to Martin Dorp, 1515. Trans. Betty Radice. Baltimore: Penguin Books, 1971.

Gilpin, W. Clark. "Did Religion Follow the Frontier?" Discipliana. (Nashville: Disciples of Christ Historical Society) Vol. 58, No. 2 (Summer, 1998), pp. 35-44.

Hall, David D. Worlds of Wonder, Days of Judgment: Popular Religious Belief in Early New England. Cambridge: Harvard University Press, 1989.

Hatch, Nathan O. The Democratization of American Christianity. New Haven: Yale University Press, 1989.

Herbert, Lord (Edward) of Cherbury. De Veritate. Trans. Meyrick H. Carre. Bristol, England: Published for the University of Bristol by J.W. Arrowsmith LTD., 1937.

Hudson, Winthrop S . Religion In America: An Historical Account of the Development of American Religious Life. New York: Charles Scribner's Sons, 1981.

Hurt, R. Douglas. The Ohio Frontier: Crucible of the Old Northwest, 1720-1830. Bloomington: Indiana University Press, 1996.

Isaac, Rhys. The Transformation of Virginia, 1740-1790. New York: W.W. Norton and Co., 1982.

Jefferson, Thomas. Letter to Timothy Pickering. Monticello, February 27, 1821. Found in The Writings of Thomas Jefferson. Vol. XV, ed. Andrew A. Lipscomb. Washington D.C.: The Thomas Jefferson Memorial Association, 1904.

Jefferson, Thomas. Letter to William Short. Monticello, August 4, 1820. Found in Thomas Jefferson: Writings. Vol. 15, Library of America Series, ed. Merrill D. Peterson. New York: Library of America, 1984.

Lake County History. Published by the Lake County Historical Society and the Board of
    Lake County Commissioners as a Contribution to the Bicentennial of The United
    States of America. Painesville, Ohio: The Painesville Publishing Company, 1976.

Locke, John. A Letter Concerning Toleration. Found in Great Books of the Western World.
    ed. Robert Maynard Hutchins. Chicago: Encyclopedia Britannica, 1952.

Luphold, Harry F. "Origin of Mentor Township." The Historical Society Quarterly. (of Lake
    County, Ohio), August, 1975.

Luphold, Harry F. The Latch String Is Out—A Pioneer History of Lake County, Ohio.
    Mentor, Ohio: Lakeland Community College Press, 1974.

Luther, Martin. Transcript from the trial at the Diet of Worms. Documents of the Christian
    Church. ed. Henry Bettensen, Second Edition. London: Oxford University Press, 1963,
    pp. 279-283.

Marty, Martin C. Righteous Empire: The Protestant Experience In America. A
    Bicentennial Series: Two Centuries of American Life, ed. Harold Hyman and Leonard
    Levy. New York: The Dial Press, 1970.

May, Henry F. The Enlightenment In America. Oxford: Oxford University Press, 1976.

McCoy, Drew R. The Elusive Republic: Political Economy In Jeffersonian America. New
    York: W.W. Norton, 1980.

Mead, Sidney E. The Lively Experiment: The Shaping of Christianity in America. New
    York: Harper and Row, 1963.

Meinig, D.W. The Shaping of America. Vol. 2. Continental America, 1800-1867. New
    Haven: Yale University Press, 1993.

Melish, John . "The Western Reserve." An Ohio Reader: 1750 To The Civil War. ed.
    Thomas Smith (Director of the Ohio Historical Society). Grand Rapids: Eerdmans
    Publishing Company, 1975.

Miller, John C. The First Frontier: Life in Colonial America. New York: Dell Publishing Co.,
    1966.

Miller, Perry. Roger Williams: His Contribution to the American Tradition. New York:
    Atheneum, 1962.

Miller, Perry. Errand Into The Wilderness. Cambridge: Harvard University Press, 1984.

Miller, Perry. The New England Mind: From Colony To Province. Cambridge: Harvard
    University Press, 1953.

Morgan, Edmund S. The Puritan Dilemma: The Story of John Winthrop. The Library of
    American Biography, ed. Oscar Handlin. Boston: Little, Brown and Company, 1958.

Noll, Mark A. A History of Christianity in the United States and Canada. Grand Rapids:
    William B. Eerdmans Publishing Co., 1992.

Owston, John. "The Scotch Baptist Influence on the Disciples of Christ." Leaven. Malibu,
    California: Pepperdine University ("A Publication of Ministry For Churches of the
    Restoration Heritage") Winter quarter, 1997, pp. 38-43.

Pioneer and General History of Geauga County, Ohio—With Sketches of Some of the
    Pioneers and Prominent Men. Burton, Ohio: The Historical Society of Geauga Co.,
    1880; reprinted in Mt. Vernon, Indiana: Windmill Publishers, 1990.

Reid, Thomas. An Inquiry Into the Human Mind on the Principles of Common Sense. ed.
    Derek R. Brookes. University Park, Pennsylvania: Penn State University Press, 1997.

Robertson, Edwin. John Wycliffe: Morning Star of the Reformation. Hants, U. K.: Marshall
    Morgan and Scott, 1984.

Savonorola, Girolamo. "A Preacher of Reform." The Portable Renaissance Reader. ed.
    James B. Ross and Mary M. McLaughlin. New York: Viking Press, 1968, pp. 645-646.

Shepard, Paula (compiler). The Kirtland Heritage index. Chardon, Ohio: Printing
    Associates Co., 1984.

Smith, Elias, ed. "Address To The Public." Herald of Gospel Liberty. Vol. 1, No. 1
     (September 1, 1808), pp. 1-2.

Sweet, William Warren. The Story of Religion in America. New York: Harper and
     Brothers, 1950.

Wallace, Ronald S. Calvin, Geneva, and the Reformation. Grand Rapids: Baker Book
     House, 1988.

Weisenburger, Francis P. The Passing of the Frontier, 1825-1850. Vol. 3 of The History of
     the State of Ohio. ed. Carl Wittke. Columbus: Ohio State Archeological and
     Historical Society, 1941.

Wesley, John. Letter to "Our Brethren in America," Sept. 10, 1784; Reprinted in John
     Wesley. ed. Albert C. Outler, Library of Protestant Thought series. New York: Oxford
     University Press, 1964.

Wesley, John. "The Character of a Methodist." The Works of John Wesley. (Third Edition),
     Vol. 8. Grand Rapids: Baker Book House, 1991.

Wood, Gordon S. The Creation of the American Republic, 1776-1787. New York: W. W.
     Norton and Co., 1969.

Woodbridge, John D., Mark Noll, and Nathan Hatch. The Gospel In America: Themes in
     the Story of America's Evangelicals. Grand Rapids: Zondervan, 1979.

II. Readings on the Concept of Restoration

Campbell, Alexander. Christianity Restored. Bethany, Virginia: Printed by the author,
     1835. Reprinted in Rosemead, California: the Old Paths Book Club, 1959.

**Campbell, Alexander. "A Restoration of the Ancient Order of Things." A Series of 32 articles
     found in The Christian Baptist. D. S. Burnet Edition, 1835; compiled by Gary L. Lee as
     "Seven Volumes In One." Joplin, Missouri: College Press, 1983.**

Campbell, Alexander. The Christian System: in Reference to the Union of Christians, and
     a Restoration of Primitive Christianity, As Plead in the Current Reformation. Bethany
     Virginia: Published by Himself, 1835. Reprinted in Nashville: The Gospel Advocate
     Company, 1970.

DeGroot, Alfred T. The Restoration Principle. St. Louis: The Bethany Press, 1960.

Hughes, Richard T. And C. Leonard Allen. Illusions of Innocence: Protestant Primitivism in
     America, 1630-1875. Chicago: The University of Chicago Press, 1988.

Kershner, Frederick D. The Restoration Handbook: Studies in The History and Principles
     of The Movement to Restore New Testament Christianity. Series I. Cincinnati:
     Standard Publishing Company, 1918; reprinted in Dallas: Dallas Christian College,
     1960.

Nation, Garry D. "The Restoration Movement." Christianity Today. Vol. 36, No. 6 (May 18,
     1992), pp. 27-31.

Scott, Walter. The Gospel Restored. Cincinnati: Printed by O.H. Donogh, 1836.

Tristano, Richard M . The Origins of the Restoration Movement: An Intellectual History.
     Atlanta: The Glenmary Research Center, 1988.

III. Readings on The Stone-Campbell Movement

Baxter, William. Life of Elder Walter Scott: with Sketches of His Fellow Laborers, William
     Hayden, Adamson Bentley, John Henry, and others. Cincinnati: Bosworth, Chase and
     Hall, 1874.

**Campbell, Alexander, ed. The Christian Baptist. 7 Vols. Bethany, Virginia: Published by
     Himself, 1823-1830.**

Campbell, Alexander, et. al., eds. The Millennial Harbinger. 41 Vols. Bethany, Virginia (West
  Virginia): Published by Himself (until 1866), 1830-1870.

Campbell, Alexander. Memoirs of Elder Thomas Campbell, Together with a Brief Memoir
  of Mrs. Jane Campbell. Cincinnati: H.S. Bosworth, 1861.

Campbell, Thomas. The Declaration and Address of the Christian Association of
  Washington. Washington, Pennsylvania: Brown and Sample, 1809; reprinted in
  Coraopolis, Pennsylvania: Record Publishing Co., 1909.

DeWelt, Don and Bill Humble. Our Restoration Vision. 112 Min. Joplin: College Press,
  1988. Videocassette.

Garrett, Leroy. The Stone-Campbell Movement: The Story of An American Restoration
  Movement. Joplin, Missouri.: College Press, 1994.

Garrison, Winfred Ernest. Religion Follows The Frontier: A History of The Disciples of
  Christ. New York: Harper and Brothers, 1931.

Garrison, Winfred Ernest and Alfred T. DeGroot. The Disciples of Christ: A History. St.
  Louis: The Bethany Press, 1958.

Gates, Errett. The Early Relation and Separation of Baptist and Disciples. Chicago: The
  Christian Century Co., 1904.

Harrell, David Edwin, Jr. A Social History of The Disciples of Christ. Vol. 1, Quest For A
  Christian America: The Disciples of Christ and American Society To 1866. Nashville:
  The Disciples of Christ Historical Society, 1966.

Hayden, A.S. Early History of The Disciples in the Western Reserve, Ohio; with
  Biographical Sketches of the Principal Agents in their Religious Movement. Cincinnati:
  Chase and Hall, 1875.

Hill, Samuel S. "Campbell-Stone On the Frontier: The Only Ones Weren't the Only Ones."
  Lectures In Honor of the Alexander Campbell Bicentennial, 1788-1988. Nashville: The
  Disciples of Christ Historical Society, 1988.

Hinsdale, B.A. A History of the Disciples in Hiram, Portage County, O[hio]. Cleveland:
  Robison, Savage, and Co., 1876.

Hughes, Richard T. Reviving the Ancient Faith: The Story of Churches of Christ in
  America. Grand Rapids: William B. Eerdmans Publishing Company, 1996.

Humble, Bill J. Light From Above: The Life of Alexander Campbell. Arranged and edited
  by Les Gleaves. 60 Min. Nashville: Gospel Advocate Co., 1988. Videocassette.

Lard, Moses E., ed. Lard's Quarterly. (Georgetown, Kentucky). Vol. I (1863).

Mathes, James M. [The] Works of Elder B.W. Stone, Vol. 1. Cincinnati: Moore, Wilstach,
  Keys and Co., 1859; reprinted in Rosemead, California: The Old Paths Book Club, 1953.

McAllister, Lester G. Thomas Campbell: Man of the Book. St. Louis: The Bethany Press,
  1954.

"Minutes of the Mahoning Baptist Association." 1821-1829. Typescript. Located in
  Cleveland, Ohio: The Western Reserve Historical Society, Manuscripts Collection.

Murch, James DeForest. Christians Only: A History of The Restoration Movement.
  Cincinnati: The Standard Publishing Company, 1962.

Neth, John W. Walter Scott Speaks. Berne, Indiana: Economy Printing Concern, 1967.

North, James B. Union In Truth: An Interpretive History of the Restoration Movement.
  Cincinnati: The Standard Publishing Company, 1994.

Powell, J.M. The Cause We Plead: A Story of the Restoration Movement. Nashville: 20th
  Century Christian, 1987.

Richardson, Robert. Memoirs of Alexander Campbell, Embracing A View of the Origin,
  Progress and Principles of The Religious Reformation Which He Advocated. 2 Vols.
  Philadelphia: J.B. Lippincott, 1868; reprinted in Germantown, Tennessee by Religious
  Book Service, n.d.

Rogers, John. The Biography of Elder Barton Warren Stone, Written By Himself: With Additions and Reflections. Cincinnati: American Christian Publication Society, 1853.

Scott, Walter, ed. The Evangelist. 10 Vols. Cincinnati, then Carthage, Ohio: published by the editor, 1832-1842.

Shaw, Henry K. Buckeye Disciples: A History of The Disciples of Christ in Ohio. (A Centennial Publication of the Ohio Christian Missionary Society) St. Louis: Christian Board of Publication, 1952.

Smith, Mary Agnes Monroe. "A History of the Mahoning Baptist Association." M.A. Thesis, West Virginia University (Morgantown), 1943.

Stevensen, Dwight E. Walter Scott: Voice of the Golden Oracle. St. Louis: Christian Board of Publication, 1946.

Stone, Barton W. and John T. Johnson. The Christian Messenger. (Georgetown, Kentucky). Vols. I and VI (1826 and 1832).

Tyler, B.B. Concerning The Disciples of Christ. Handbook Series For The Bethany C.E. Reading Courses, ed. F.D. Power, Vol. 2. Cleveland: The Bethany C.E. Company, 1897.

Walker, Dean E. Adventuring For Christian Unity: A Survey of the History of Churches of Christ (Disciples). Cincinnati: The Standard Publishing Company, 1935.

Webb, Henry E. In Search of Christian Unity: A History of the Restoration Movement. Cincinnati: The Standard Publishing Company, 1990.

West, Earl Irvin. The Search For The Ancient Order. Vol. 1, A History of The Restoration Movement, 1800-1865. Germantown, Tennessee: Religious Book Service, 1990.

West, William Garrett. Barton Warren Stone: Early American Advocate of Christian Unity. Nashville: The Disciples of Christ Historical Society, 1954.

Whitsitt, William H. Origin of the Disciples of Christ (Campbellites). New York: A.C. Armstrong and Son, 1888.

Wilcox, Alanson. A History of The Disciples of Christ in Ohio. Cincinnati: The Standard Publishing Co., 1909.

IV. Readings on Mormonism

Backman, Milton V., Jr. "The Quest for a Restoration: The Birth of Mormonism in Ohio." BYU Studies, Vol. 12, No. 4 (Summer, 1972), pp. 356-364.

Barlow, Philip L. Mormons and The Bible: The Place of the Latter-day Saints in American Religion. Religion in America Series, ed. Harry S. Stout. New York: Oxford University Press, 1991.

Barrett, Ivan J. Joseph Smith and the Restoration: A History of the Church to 1846. Provo, Utah: Brigham Young University Press, 1973.

Bergera, Gary James, ed. The Autobiography of B.H. Roberts. Salt Lake City: Signature Books, 1990.

Booth, Ezra. "Mormonism." A series of nine letters written to Reverend Ira Eddy of Nelson, Portage County, Ohio. Published in Ravenna, Ohio, by The Ohio Star from October 13 through December 9, 1831; and also in Painesville, Ohio, by The Painesville Telegraph from October 25 through December 27, 1831.

Bringhurst, Newell G. Brigham Young and The Expanding American Frontier. Publication of the Library of American Biography, ed. Oscar Handlin. Boston: Little, Brown and Company, 1986.

Brodie, Fawn M. No Man Knows My History: The Life of Joseph Smith, the Mormon Prophet. New York: Alfred A. Knopf, 1960.

Bushman, Richard L. Joseph Smith and the Beginnings of Mormonism. Urbana and Chicago: University of Illinois Press, 1984.

Campbell, Alexander. "Delusions." The Millennial Harbinger (Bethany, Virginia). Vol. 2, No. 2 (February 15, 1831).

Corrill, John. A Brief History of the Church of Christ of Latter Day Saints, (Commonly Called Mormons;) Including an Account of Their Doctrine and Discipline with the Reasons of the Author For Leaving The Church. St. Louis: N. P., 1839.

Faulring, Scott H., ed. An American Prophet's Record: The Diaries and Journals of Joseph Smith. Salt Lake City: Signature Books, 1989.

Fielding, Robert Kent. "The Growth of the Mormon Church in Kirtland, Ohio." Ph.D. Dissertation, Indiana University, 1957.

Hill, Marvin S. "The Role of Christian Primitivism in the Origin and Development of the Mormon Kingdom, 1830-1844." Ph.D. Dissertation, The University of Chicago, 1968.

Howe, Eber D. Mormonism Unvailed . . .. Painesville, Ohio: Printed and Published by the author, 1834; reprinted in Salt Lake City: Utah Lighthouse Ministry, n.d.

Howe, Eber D. "Mormonism." The Painesville Telegraph (Painesville, Ohio). Vol. II, No. 35 (February 15, 1831).

Hughes, Dean. The Mormon Church: A Basic History. Salt Lake City: The Deseret Book Company, 1986.

Kennedy, J. H. Early Days of Mormonism. London: Reeves and Turner, 1888.

Kidder, D.P. Mormonism and The Mormons. New York: G. Lane and C.P. Trippett for the Methodist Episcopal Church, 1844.

Ludlow, Daniel H., ed. Encyclopedia of Mormonism: The History, Scripture, Doctrine, and Procedure of the Church of Jesus Christ of Latter-day Saints. New York: Macmillan Publishing Company, 1992.

Mather, Frederic G. "The Early Days of Mormonism." Lippincott's Magazine of Popular Literature and Science, Philadelphia: J.B. Lippincott & Co., (December, 1880), pp. 198-211.

Mathes, James M., ed. "Mormonism In Kirtland." The Christian Record, Vol. 3, No. 5 (May, 1884), pp. 143-150.

Millet, Robert L. ed. Joseph Smith: Selected Sermons and Writings. Sources of American Spirituality Series, ed. John Farina. New York: Paulist Press, 1989.

Oaks, Dallin H. Carthage Conspiracy: The Trial of The Accused Assassins of Joseph Smith. Urbana: University of Illinois Press, 1977.

Pancoast, Eva L. "Mormons At Kirtland." M.A. Thesis, Western Reserve University (Cleveland, Ohio), 1929.

Parkin, Max H. "Conflict At Kirtland: A Study of the Nature and Causes of External And Internal Conflict of the Mormons." M.A. Thesis, Brigham Young University, 1966.

Phillips, A.B. The Restoration Movement and The Latter-Day Saints. Independence, Missouri: Herald Publishing House, 1929.

Pratt, Parley Parker. The Autobiography of Parley Parker Pratt. Chicago: Law, King, and Law, 1888.

Shields, Steven L. Divergent Paths of The Restoration: A History of The Latter Day Saint Movement. Los Angeles: Restoration Research, 1990.

Shipps, Jan. Mormonism: The Story of a New Religious Tradition. Urbana and Chicago: The University of Illinois Press, 1985

Shook, Charles A. The True Origin of The Book Of Mormon. Cincinnati: The Standard Publishing Company, 1914.

Smith, Lucy Mack. History of Joseph Smith. Salt Lake City: Bookcraft, 1979.

Smith, Joseph, Jr. The Book of Mormon: An Account Written by The Hand of Mormon Upon Plates Taken From The Plates of Nephi. Salt Lake City: The Church of Jesus Christ of Latter-day Saints, 1950.

Smith, Joseph. History of The Church. 7 Volumes. Salt Lake City: The Deseret Book Company, 1978.

Smith, Joseph. Book of Doctrine And Covenants. Printed by the Reorganized Church of Jesus Christ of Latter-day Saints. Independence, Missouri: Herald Publishing House, 1958.

Snowdon, James H. The Truth About Mormonism. New York: George Doran Co., 1926.

Swartzell, William. Mormonism Exposed, Being a Journal of a Residence in Missouri from the 28th of May to the 20th of August, 1838. Pekin, Ohio: Published by the author, 1840; reprinted in Salt Lake City: Utah Lighthouse Ministries, n.d.

Tanner, Jerald and Sandra. Did Spalding Write The Book of Mormon? Salt Lake City: Utah Lighthouse Ministries, 1977.

Werner, M.R. Brigham Young. New York: Harcourt, Brace and Company, 1925.

Whitmer, John. "The Book of John Whitmer Kept By Commandment." Unpublished manuscript kept in the archives of the Church of Jesus Christ of Latter-day Saints, Salt Lake City, Utah: printed and published as John Whitmer's History in Salt Lake City by Utah Lighthouse Ministries, n.d.

V. Readings On Sidney Rigdon

Campbell, Alexander, ed. The Millennial Harbinger. Bethany, Virginia: Published by himself, years 1830 to 1849 inclusive:

Editorial. "Beaver Anathema, Mr. Winter, and The Star." April, 1830, p. 175.

"Francis." "Traveller's Reply." October, 1830, p. 449.

Campbell, Alexander. Sidney Rigdon." February, 1831, pp. 100-101.

Campbell, Alexander. "Mormonism." July, 1831, pp. 331-332.

Editorial [No Title]. December, 1837, p. 578.

Davison, Matilda. "The Mormon Bible." June, 1839, pp 265-267.

Campbell, Alexander. "Mormonism in an Agony." August, 1842, pp. 358-362.

Bentley, Adamson. "Mistakes Touching the Book of Mormon." January, 1844 pp. 38-39.

Document. "Mormon Church Extinct." December , 1844, pp. 618-619.

Campbell, Alexander. "Anecdotes, Incidents, and Facts." October, 1848, pp. 552-557.

Chase, Daryl. "Sidney Rigdon—Early Mormon." M.A. Thesis, The University of Chicago, 1931.

Cowdery, Oliver, ed. The Messenger And Advocate. Kirtland, Ohio: Published by The Church of Jesus Christ of Latter Day Saints, 1834-1836; Reproduced in Salt Lake City by Utah Lighthouse Ministries, n.d.:

Rigdon, Sidney. "The Ancient Order of Things." September 1835, pp. 182-185.

Rigdon, Sidney. Letter to "Brother Whitmer." January, 1836, pp. 241-245.

Rigdon, Sidney. Letter exchange with Olion Barr. February, 1836, pp. 257-263.

Rigdon, Sidney. Letter exchange with Olion Barr. March, 1836 pp. 272-274.

Rigdon, Sidney. Letter to "Brother O. Cowdery." April, 1836, pp. 297-299.

Rigdon, Sidney. Letter exchange with Oliver Barr. June, 1836, pp 321-329.

Rigdon, Sidney. Letter to "Brother O. Cowdery, June, 1836, pp. 334-335.

Rigdon, Sidney. "The Latter Day Glory." November, 1836, pp. 401-404.

Rigdon, Sidney. The Saints and The World." December, 1836, pp. 417-423.

Rigdon, Sidney. "Persecution." January, 1837, pp. 436-439.

Rigdon, Sidney. "Persecution." March, 1837, pp. 477-479.

Rigdon, Sidney. Prospectus." August, 1837, pp. 545-547; repeated September, 1837, pp. 571-574.

Errett, Isaac, ed. "Death of Sidney Rigdon." Christian Standard (Cincinnati, Ohio). July 29, 1876, p. 245.

Errett, Isaac, ed. "Pioneer Mormon Dead." Christian Standard. August 5, 1876, p. 252.

Goldsmith, Lucia A. Manuscript. "Sidney Rigdon, The First Mormon Elder." Located in Cleveland, Ohio: The Western Reserve Historical Society, Manuscripts Collection.

Grant, Jedediah M. A Collection of Facts Relative to the Course Taken by Elder Sidney Rigdon, in the States of Ohio, Missouri, Illinois and Pennsylvania. Philadelphia: Brown, Bicking and Guilbert, Printers, 1844.

McKiernan, F. Mark. The Voice of One Crying in the Wilderness: Sidney Rigdon, Religious Reformer, 1793-1876. Lawrence, Kansas: Coronado Press, 1971.

Rigdon, John W. Typescript. "Lecture Written By John M. [sic] Rigdon On The Early History of The Mormon Church." Located in Provo, Utah: Harold B. Lee Library of Brigham Young University, Special Collections.

Rigdon, John Wickliffe. "Sidney Rigdon and the Early History of the Mormon Church." The Sesqui-Centennial Times. Friendship, New York (July 25-31, 1965), pp. 1-2.

Rigdon, Sidney. Letter to Don C. Smith, October 13, 1837. The Elders' Journal, ed. Joseph Smith (Kirtland, Ohio). Vol I, No.1 (October, 1837), pp. 7-8. Reproduced in Salt Lake City by Utah Lighthouse Ministries, n.d.

Rigdon, Sidney. "To The Saints Abroad." The Elders' Journal, ed. Joseph Smith (Far West, Missouri). Vol. I, No. 4 (August, 1838), pp. 53-54.

Rollman, Hans. "The Early Baptist Career of Sidney Rigdon in Warren, Ohio." BYU Studies, Vol. 21, No. 1 (Winter, 1981), pp. 37-50.

Van Wagoner, Richard S. Sidney Rigdon: A Portrait of Religious Excess. Salt Lake City: Signature Books, 1994.

Whitsitt, William H. Sidney Rigdon, the Real Founder of Mormonism. Salt Lake City: Special Collection of Marriott Library at the University of Utah, 1885.

VI. Other Works Cited

Austin, Norman. The Greek Historians. New York: Van Nostrand Reinhold, Co., 1969.

Bloom, Harold. The American Religion: The Emergence of the Post-Christian Nation. New York: Simon and Schuster, 1992.

Bradley, Martin B., et. al. Churches and Church Membership in the United States 1990. Atlanta: Glenmary Research Center, 1992.

Calvin, John. Institutes of the Christian Religion. Reprinted as Calvin's Institutes in Grand Rapids: Associated Publishers and Authors, Inc., n.d.

Cose, Ellis. "Promise Keepers: Here to Pray for the Nation." Newsweek, Vol. 130, No. 15 (October 13, 1997), pp. 28-31.

Debate. Evidences of Christianity—A Debate Between Robert Owen and Alexander Campbell, Held in Cincinnati, Ohio, in April 1829. St. Louis: Christian Publishing Company, 1900.

Debate. Public Discussion of the Issues Between The Reorganized Church of Jesus Christ of Latter Day Saints and The Church of Christ [Disciples] Held in Kirtland, Ohio, Beginning February 12, and Closing March 8, 1884, Between E.L.Kelley, of the Reorganized Church of Jesus Christ of Latter Day Saints and Clark Braden, of the Church of Christ. Reproduced in Rosemead, California: The Old Paths Book Club, 1955.

Divine, Robert A., et.al. <u>America: Past and Present</u>. Ed. 5. New York: Addison Wesley Longman, 1999.

Fife, Robert O. "Evangelism or Unity—Which?" <u>The Lamp</u>. (Los Angeles: The Westwood Christian Foundation), Vol. 8, No. 5 (May, 1984), pp. 1-2.

Livius, Titus. <u>The Early History of Rome</u>. Book I, trans. by Aubrey D. Selincourt. Baltimore: Penguin Books, 1960.

Pendleton, Thorn and James Tallman. <u>The History of Central Christian Church, Warren, Ohio, 1803-1988</u>. Warren, Ohio: the Central Christian Church, 1988.

Rokove, Jack N. <u>The Beginning of National Politics: An Interpretive History of The Continental Congress</u>. New York: Alfred A. Knopf, 1979.

Scott, Thomas Lee, Jr. "Apostasy On The Western Reserve: Selected Disciples of Christ Experiences In The 1830's" (a Research paper presented to the Disciples of Christ Historical Society in Nashville, Tennessee). Done for Phillips University in Enid, Oklahoma, 1978.

Shantz, Daniel. <u>Walter Scott: God's Pied Piper</u>. Cincinnati: The Standard Publishing Company, 1984.

Sharn, Lori, "Churches Offering Worship Without Labels." <u>USA Today</u>. January 27, 1997, p. 4a.

<u>The Mentor Christian Church Scrapbook</u>. Mentor, Ohio: Published by the church, 1978.

<u>The Holy Bible</u>. [Revised Standard Version] Cleveland and New York: The World Publishing Company, 1962.

Tillich, Paul. <u>Dynamics of Faith</u>. New York: Harper and Row, 1957.

Webb, Henry. "Writing Denominational History." <u>Discipliana</u>. (The Quarterly Historical Journal of The Disciples of Christ Historical Society) Vol. 58, No. 1 (Spring, 1998), pp. 3-12.

Webb, Henry. "Post Civil War Tennessee: A Study In The Dynamics of Division." Workshop held November 2, 1988, in Cuyahoga Falls, Ohio, at "The Church in The Falls." Transcript published in Joplin, Missouri: College Press, 1988.

White, Richard. <u>The Middle Ground: Indians, Empires, and Republics In The Great Lakes Region 1650-1815</u>. New York: Cambridge University Press, 1991.

Wildmon, Donald E. "Christ's Church Will Survive Our Church." <u>The American Family Assocation Journal</u>. (Tupelo, Mississippi). September, 1988, p.2.

Winter, Ralph D. And Steven C. Hawthorne. <u>Perspectives On The World Christian Movement</u>. Pasadena: William Carey Library, 1992.